BIOLOGICAL ORGANISATION

CELLULAR AND SUB-CELLULAR

1 Lehmann
2 Pfau
3 Brenner
4 Waddington
5 Wilde
6 Guy

7 Perar
8 Busch
9 Callas
15 Pontecorvo
20 Gustafson
21 Dean
22 Pollock
23 Beale
24 Feldman

1 Lehmann	7 Pavan	13 Weiss	19 Beermann
2 Plaut	8 Rusch	14 Perkowska	20 Gustafson
3 Brenner	9 Callan	15 Pontecorvo	21 Dean
4 Waddington	10 Brachet	16 Nieuwkoop	22 Pollock
5 Wilde	11 Sirlin	17 Holtzer	23 Beale
6 Gay	12 Zwilling	18 Berenblum	24 Feldman

BIOLOGICAL ORGANISATION

CELLULAR AND SUB-CELLULAR

Proceedings of a Symposium
organised on behalf of
UNESCO

by

C. H. WADDINGTON

held at the
UNIVERSITY OF EDINBURGH, SCOTLAND
September, 1957

SYMPOSIUM PUBLICATIONS DIVISION

PERGAMON PRESS

NEW YORK · LONDON · PARIS · LOS ANGELES

1959

PERGAMON PRESS, INC.
122 E. 55th Street, New York 22
P.O. Box 47715, Los Angeles, California

PERGAMON PRESS LTD.
4 & 5 Fitzroy Square, London W.1

PERGAMON PRESS, S.A.R.L.
24 Rue des Écoles, Paris Ve

FIRST PUBLISHED 1959

Library of Congress No. 59–12063

PRINTED IN GREAT BRITAIN
Set by Santype Ltd., Salisbury and printed by Adlard & Son Ltd.,
Dorking and London

LIST OF CONTENTS

		PAGE
Preface		vii
List of Participants		ix
Introduction; The Preliminary Plan of the Symposium		xi
Chapter	I. The Nature of Biological Organisation	1
	II. Organisation at the Gene Level	22
	III. Organisation of the Chromosome	42
	IV. Functional Interactions of Nucleus and Cytoplasm	88
	V. Morphological Organisation of Nucleus and Cytoplasm	110
	VI. Activities of the Cytoplasm	136
	VII. The Chemical Organisation of the Cell	161
	VIII. Tissue Interactions : Embryonic Induction	193
	IX. The Organisation of Tissues into Organs	238
	X. The Organisation of Growth Processes	263
	XI. Cell Division	282
Index of Speakers		318
Index of Subjects		320
Index of Authors		325

Preface

AT THE Ninth General Conference of the United Nations Educational, Scientific and Cultural Organisation (UNESCO), held at New Delhi in 1956, it was decided to organise a Cell Biology Symposium. It was agreed that the topic of the symposium should be "Patterns of Cellular and Subcellular Organisation". Following this decision, the Department of Natural Sciences of UNESCO invited me to organise such a symposium, to be held in Edinburgh at a time related to that of the IXth International Congress for Cell Biology, which was arranged to take place in St. Andrews, Scotland, during the late summer of 1957. The UNESCO Symposium eventually met during the period September 6th to 10th of that year. Its proceedings are recorded in this volume.

The symposium was preceded by considerable preparatory work. In the first place a very general outline of the topics to be covered was drawn up and circulated to possible participants. On the basis of their replies, and some indication of who would actually be able to attend, a rather more detailed plan of the discussions was made, and again circulated to those whom it was hoped to invite; this document is reproduced here as the Introduction to the Symposium. The participants were asked to send to me short accounts of any new factual data which they felt they would wish to refer to, and also to give references to recent publications which they felt relevant; and as far as possible they were asked to circulate copies of their reprints to the other members of the group. The comments and bibliographies received in Edinburgh were duplicated and circulated a month or two before the meeting. In this way, all the participants were able to acquaint themselves in some detail with the special interests of each member of the group. The discussions could therefore concern themselves mainly with the general significance of various modern experimental and theoretical approaches, without wasting too much time on recapitulating detailed factual information which is already available in the literature. It was hoped in this way to make possible a really valuable exchange of views between workers in different, though related, disciplines. How far we were successful in this aim must be left to the judgment of the reader.

At the Symposium, no prepared papers were read. The proceedings were entirely informal. A tape recording was taken of the whole symposium. When this had been transcribed, it was submitted to the participants, who were asked to turn their remarks into comprehensible prose, but to retain the character of the spoken, rather than the written, word. The reader should remember that he is, as it were, listening in to spontaneous and off-the-record discussion, which in some cases may not be as cautiously and circumspectly expressed as would be the case in formally written papers. The problems which we discussed are among the most important in biology, and although it is obvious that no final answers could be given to them, it is hoped that other biologists will find something of interest in the views expressed.

Discussions such as these may, perhaps, be of particular value for the informal seminar teaching which is the most crucial phase in the final conversion of a post-graduate student into an independent scientist. Knowlege is, as Sir Eric Ashby has put it, an open system, and not a mere collection of ascertained facts. There are few better opportunities to convey to a student a real sense of what this means, and to give him an appreciation of the fascination and challenge which arise from the coming together of different viewpoints and fields of experience, than to allow him to overhear, and criticise, such informal discussions between active workers as those recorded here.

C. H. WADDINGTON

University of Edinburgh,
Scotland.

LIST OF PARTICIPANTS

Dr. G. H. BEALE,
Institute of Animal Genetics
University of Edinburgh.

Dr. W. BEERMANN,
Zoologisches Institut der Universität,
Marburg an der Lahn, Germany

Professor I. BERENBLUM,
Weizmann Institute of Science,
Rehovoth, Israel.

Professor J. BRACHET,
Université Libre de Bruxelles,
Auderghem, Belgium.

Dr. S. BRENNER,
Cavendish Laboratory,
Cambridge.

Professor H. G. CALLAN,
Department of Natural History,
St. Andrews University.

Dr. K. DAN,
Department of Zoology,
Tokyo Metropolitan University.

Dr. A. C. R. DEAN,
Physical Chemistry Laboratory,
Oxford.

Dr. J. GALL,
University of Minnesota.

Dr. Helen GAY,
Carnegie Institution of Washington,
Cold Spring Harbor, Long Island,
New York.

Dr. J. GUSTAFSON,
Werner-Grens Institut,
Stockholm.

Dr. H. HOLTZER,
Department of Anatomy,
University of Pennsylvania.

Professor F. E. LEHMANN,
University of Pennsylvania,
Zoologisches Institut,
University of Bern.

Dr. M. MITCHISON,
Department of Zoology,
University of Edinburgh.

Dr. P. D. NIEUWKOOP,
l'Institut International d'Embryologie, Utrecht, Holland.

Dr. C. PAVAN,
Departamento de Biologia, Geral,
Universidade de S. Paulo, Brazil.

Dr. W. PLAUT,
Department of Botany,
University of Wisconsin.

Dr. M. R. POLLOCK,
National Institute for Medical
Research, London.

Professor G. PONTECORVO,
Department of Genetics,
University of Glasgow.

Dr. H. RIS,
Department of Zoology,
University of Wisconsin.

Dr. H. P. RUSCH,
McArdle Memorial Laboratory,
University of Wisconsin.

Dr. F. S. SJÖSTRAND,
Department of Anatomy,
Karolinska Institutet, Stockholm.

Professor S. TOIVONEN,
Zoological Laboratory,
Helsinki University.

Professor C. H. WADDINGTON,
  Institute of Animal Genetics,
  University of Edinburgh.

Dr. P. WEISS,
  The Rockefeller Institute,
  New York.

Dr. C. E. WILDE,
  School of Dentistry,
  University of Pennsylvania.

Dr. E. ZWILLING,
  National Science Foundation,
  Washington, D.C.

In attendance

Dr. C. AUERBACH	Great Britain
Dr. S. BRAHMA	India
Dr. R. M. CLAYTON	Great Britain
Dr. A. EL WAHAB	Egypt
Dr. M. FELDMAN	Israel
Dr. H. KACSER	Great Britain
Dr. T. S. OKADA	Japan
Dr. E. M. PANTELOURIS	Cyprus
Dr. E. PERKOWSKA	Poland
Dr. S. RANZI	Italy
Dr. N. SHINKE	Japan
Dr. J. L. SIRLIN	Argentina

Introduction

A FEW months before the Symposium took place, the notes which appear below were circulated to the participants in order to provide a framework within which the discussions could develop.

1. *Delimitation of the subject*

The topic of the Symposium has been defined by UNESCO as "Patterns of cellular and sub-cellular organisation". The participants have been selected on the basis that we shall discuss matters relating to tissues, cells and sub-cellular components, but would enter very little into the chemical field; the aspect of biochemistry which would be most closely connected with our topic, namely, the replication of macro-molecules, will be the subject of a Symposium of the Society of Experimental Biology which will take place just after our meeting. Within the range of subject matter which extends from the EM-visible to the tissue, we shall be concerned with "patterns of organisation". The word "organisation" is, in ordinary usage, a somewhat vague one. It should be used to refer to phenomena in which, as it is commonly expressed, "the whole is more than the sum of its parts", or "the function of the part depends on its relation to the whole". We shall probably not wish to spend much time discussing the rather philosophical questions which can be raised concerning the interpretation of such phrases; but one may note that the "parts" need not be defined purely geographically, as spatially isolated entities (particles or the like), but must also include sub-systems defined by their function rather than by their localisation. Thus, another way of expressing our topic is by asking the question: "How far are the functional sub-systems of cells and tissues mutually inter-dependent in their operation?"

The general plan of the Symposium will be to start with the smallest functional units of cells and to work up towards the larger units, finishing with the consideration of tissue-interactions.

2. *Organisation within the chromosome*

Since we are intending to intrude as little as possible into the chemical field, we can take the gene as the "lowest" unit to be considered in detail. We shall need to consider questions such as the following: To what extent, and in what contexts, can we still consider the gene as a unit? In regard to its epigenetic function, how can the gene-unit be defined? Is the "*cis-trans*" criterion* the best we have available? What is the relation between the functional gene-unit defined in this or any other way and the possible sites of mutational or recombinational events? (And, overlapping into biochemistry, what is the relation between these and nucleotide or amino-acid chains?) Do cistrons overlap, i.e. may one mutational site belong to two of them? In a compound locus in a higher organism, such as *white* or *lozenge* in *Drosophila*, are we dealing with a few discrete cistrons, or with a stretch of chromosome with a greater degree of internal coherence than that would imply? How far do the facts suggest that genes which act sequentially on a metabolic reaction-chain are in bacteria arranged in sequence in immediate contact, while in organisms of moderate grade (e.g. moulds), they sometimes are and sometimes are not, while in higher organisms such an arrangement is rare? In so far as this is true, what is its significance—is it simply a consequence of the bacterial cell possessing only a very small number of each type of molecule, so that it is advantageous for them to be near the next member of sequence; or, perhaps, are bacterial genes less differentiated out of some primordial unspecific nucleoprotein?

In a larger size-range, we ought to consider some of the problems of "position-effect" in what may now be thought of as the old-fashioned sense. To what extent can we account for phenomena such as *Bar* or the *cubitus interruptus* position effects by ideas similar to those developed in connection with pseudo-alleles? What is the evidence, from light-microscope work, on patterns of metabolic activity spreading along chromosomes? We have the old data about heterochromatin and variegation; is there anything in the newer observations on *Chironomids, Rhynchosciara*, and newts which bears on the influence of one part of a chromosome on its neighbourhood?

3. *Visible evidences of gene action*

We shall want to hear the most recent data from the investigations of giant chromosomes of the salivary and lampbrush types. What is known about differing activities of alleles of the same locus? How is the cytological expression of a given region of chromosome related to different tissues and to different stages of development? Is the general pattern of banding constant from tissue to tissue, and stage to stage, or are there changes of pattern which might perhaps indicate that the boundaries between the active units are not always the same? Presumably the pattern exhibited by the chromosomes in a particular type of cell is an expression

---

* Two contiguous and similarly acting genes are said to belong to the same "cistron" if their effect in the "*cis*-configuration" (AB/+ +) is different (usually or always ? stronger) from that in the "*trans*-configuration" (A+/+B).

of the manner in which the genes operate in that variety of cytoplasm; is there any experimental evidence that the pattern can be altered by treatments which change the cytoplasm? What is known, for instance from histochemical or tracer studies, of the nature of the metabolic activities which are connected with the general banded or lampbrush patterns, or with such special appearances as puffing or nucleolus-formation? Is there any cytological evidence suggesting that some genes may be totally inactivated in some tissues? How far does the evidence from nuclear transplantation, and from studies of metaplasia, warrant the conclusion that some genes may during development become irreversibly inactivated or mutated or otherwise altered?

4. *Activities of the nucleus and traffic from it to the cytoplasm*

Passing from the scale of the gene-locus to that of the whole chromosome or the entire nucleus, one might begin by considering the recent tracer investigations on the mechanism of chromosome reduplication—does the chromosome split to form sister chromatids or does it lay down a new replica to give a mother-and-daughter pair? How far is the answer to this likely to be relevant to the problem of how genes form physiologically active products? Recent studies with the electron microscope have produced some very suggestive pictures of chromosomes apparently passing materials through the nuclear membrane into the cytoplasm. What can be said about the relations of these materials to the chromosome, to the formed structures of the cytoplasm, and to the nuclear membrane? In other types of cells, the nucleolus seems to be the site of the most intense protein metabolism or turnover. There is considerable recent auto-radiographic evidence bearing on older theories of the functions of nuclear constituents in protein synthesis, and on the passage of synthesised substances from the nucleus into the cytoplasm. The evidence needs considering in connection with DNA and protein as well as RNA. How can the evidence about the great activity of the nucleolus—which would appear to be merely connected to, rather than an actual part of, the chromosomes—be brought into line with the genetic evidence that many individual specific genes are operative during the development of a cell? Is the nucleolus merely an assemblage point, where the products of many separate genes are collected before being released into the cytoplasm (in which case it ought not to be fully developed in isolated part-nuclei)? In this connection we need to consider the evidence concerning the synthetic activities which continue in cells whose nucleus has been removed, or which have been provided with a nucleus of different genetic constitution. In some cases, e.g. *Mytilus* polar lobes, amino-acid incorporation falls off very soon after separation from the nucleus; in others, particularly *Acetabularia*, protein synthesis continues at a rapid rate for a considerable time. In the latter situation, is there any evidence about the specificity of the proteins formed? When, instead of the nucleus being simply removed, there is a substitution of a new one (as in *Paramecium* or by transduction in *Salmonella*) the specificity of the proteins produced is altered extremely rapidly.

5. *Cytoplasmic structures and activities, and their influence on the nucleus*

The electron microscope has shown that there is often an elaborate structural organisation even in parts of the cell which previously appeared to be more or less homogeneous cytoplasm, in which it seemed plausible to envisage the reactions in purely biochemical, molecular terms. We shall need to survey the direct evidence on this point, and it may be worthwhile considering shortly the structures of some of the more obviously formed elements which are produced by certain cells (e.g. flagellae, muscle fibres, spermatozoa, etc.) as examples of the degree of complexity which cytoplasmic structure may attain. However, more generality attaches to elements such as mitochondria, microsomes, endoplasmic reticula, etc. which are of nearly universal occurrence. How far do these organelles show common features of organisation, for instance in being built up of double membranes? Is there any evidence relating their origin to either the nuclear membrane or the cell membrane? What EM-visible evidence is there bearing on their genetic continuity?

Turning from the EM mode of investigation, there is of course a great deal of information about the activities of particles isolated by differential centrifugation or rendered visible by *intra vitam* staining. We shall probably not wish to discuss in any detail the intra-particle organisation of biochemical activities, but we must be deeply concerned with the inter-particle and particle–nucleus interactions, which seem to play an important part in the unfolding of the specific developmental performance stemming from the genes. One may enquire, in the first place, how far different types of cytoplasm (in different cells, or in various parts of the egg) differ in their particle populations and cytoplasmic structures? How do these populations and structures change as differentiation proceeds? Can these changes be related to definite developmental events? If so, have these events any special characteristics; for instance, do changes in cytoplasmic organisation tend to coincide with times when we think that new protein syntheses are beginning? Is there any direct evidence of the influence of the nucleus on changes in cytoplasmic organisation, for instance, in enucleation experiments, in genetically controlled organisation of the ovum, etc.? There is plenty of evidence that influences impinging on the cell from outside may cause profound changes in cytoplasmic organisation; fertilisation or artificial parthenogenesis provide striking examples. How far, and in what way, are such alterations transmitted back to the nucleus? Some of the strongest evidence we have of the influence of the cytoplasm on the activities of the nucleus comes from the study of the differential effects of the various ooplasms of ova, for instance in controlling chromosome diminution is *Ascaria*, the formation of the Bildungscentrum in *Platycnemis* or the grey crescent in amphibia. The operative substances are known, in many cases, to be centrifugable. Is there any recent evidence which allows us to envisage in modern terms the type of cytoplasmic element which is effective in influencing the nucleus in this way?

Genetical methods of analysis yield evidence of a different type concerning the interactions of nucleus and cytoplasm, and demonstrate the existence of cytoplasmic particles or elements which have a considerable degree of autonomy in duplication. We shall have the opportunity to hear of the most recent results in yeast and *Paramecium*. In the latter organism, in particular, there seems to be a complex but closely integrated system of organisation by which the cytoplasmic state determines which gene shall be active in controlling the specificity of partially autonomous cytoplasmic elements, while the same genes also are involved in determining the stability of the cytoplasmic situation.

6. *The organisation of cell division*

There is one particular performance which cells carry out, namely, division, which provides a very favourable opportunity for studying the inter-relations between the various cell components. We shall presumably not have time to review the whole extent of our knowledge about cell division, but there have been particularly important advances recently in connection with the nature of the mitotic apparatus, of the energy sources utilised, of the extent and directions of the cortical movements and of some of the chemical events in the cortex. Over and above these new factual data, our particular interest should be in the interactions between nucleus, spindle and cortex, and also those between the physiological processes of growth, energy storing and liberation, and division.

7. *The cell as an organised chemical kinetic system*

We should now turn to consider other lines of investigation which, while in no way denying the existence of particulate and other structures, are mainly concerned with the ways in which the chemical processes of the cell are integrated into systems, and with the degree of stability which such systems may exhibit. One of the phenomena which has been most thoroughly studied from this point of view is that of adaptation by bacteria and similar organisms to the presence of particular potential substrates in the medium. Here we have data both on the mode of transition from one type of activity to another (i.e. on the mechanisms by which

adaptation is brought about), and on the nature of the interlocking reactions which allow the chemical processes of the cell to be organised into
two or more alternative systems. In differentiation, again, we have to deal
with a situation in which early cells of one single type later develop into
two or more distinct alternative types. There is recent evidence that the
supply of particular amino-acids can switch the cell from one type into
another of the possible modes. We shall need to consider some of the
recent evidence on these points, and also to discuss such questions as the
following: How far are the alternative modes of organisation sharply distinct from one another, either in physiological functioning (enzymatic
adaptation) or in development? Does the existence of a sharp distinction
between alternatives necessarily imply some degree of "feed-back" in the
system? If so, what forms may this feed-back take? Suggestions have been
made about competition for substrates needed in synthesis; about specific
induction of particular enzymes; about specific inhibition, by the products
of one reaction, of the alternative reactions. Are we always dealing with
very complex systems containing many reactants, or are the systems sometimes fairly simple? We need to consider the evidence that the sharpness
of the alternatives and their degree of stability (the "canalisation" of a
developing system) are under genetic control, and often respond to selection as though very many genes are involved; indeed in well-analysed
cases, as in *Drosophila*, we know that many genes affect any one developmental pathway.

8. *Tissue interactions: embryonic induction*

Embryonic induction is, on the one hand, perhaps the most thoroughly
analysed case, in multi-cellular organisms, of a choice between alternative
modes of organisation of intra-cellular processes, and on the other a
striking example of the type of interaction which provides the mechanisms
for organisation at the supra-cellular or tissue level. There have been
important advances in recent years in our knowledge about the classical
primary induction process in vertebrate embryos. These have come partly
from a close attention to the time relations of the process, in relation to
the character of the tissues induced, and from chemical study of inducers
derived from adult tissues; new techniques such as the use of radioactive
tracers have also yielded some information. Some of the questions that
seem to require discussion are: What is the chemical nature of the active
principles of the adult inducers, and how far are they similar to substances
active in the early embryo? Does the induction call forth definite regions
of the embryonic axis (archencephalon, posterior axis, etc.), or are we
dealing with inducers each of which evokes a particular tissue (neural
tube, mesoderm, etc.)? What is the site of the inductive process; cell
membrane, cytoplasmic particles, conceivably direct on to the nucleus?

Is the site of action related to the length of time the process takes? What is the status of the suggestion that all evocation processes involve some degree of damage (a "sub-lethal cytolysis") to the reacting cells? What are the similarities and differences as regards site of action, time required, etc. of different evocation processes (of neural tube, lens, etc.)?

It might be as well to devote a short time, if we have any to spare, to a discussion of the confused vocabulary of this topic. The conventional classical phraseology speaks of "organisers" which "induce"; but we well know that there may be inductions of things which are not organised in the usual sense (e.g. of structureless masses of tissue); and conversely organisation may appear in a tissue or group of tissues in whose origin induction has played no essential part. It has been suggested that, instead of using phrases which seem to imply an essential connection between organisation and induction, one might speak of "evocation" (= induction, whether or not the phenomena exhibit any organisation) and "individuation" (= organisation, whether or not induction enters into the picture). But these terms have been frequently misunderstood, and others may have some better suggestion for disentangling the different aspects of the whole complex "organiser reaction".

9. *The organisation of cells into tissues*

A collection of cells in contact with one another seems to be never, or very seldom, a mere assemblage of self-sufficient units. It seems to be the general rule that we find ourselves confronted with organisation in the classical sense that the functions of each cell depend on its relations to the whole. The situation may be expressed by speaking of the cell-group as a "blastema", or by saying that it is the site of a "field". Some recent important avenues of investigation of such problems have been, for example, the techniques of disaggregation and reaggregation of cell groups, or the differential killing of certain cells. How far do such studies throw light on the nature of the interactions between cells and of the field to which they give rise? What type of forces are involved in cell-adhesiveness, particularly when it is specific? Are we dealing with molecular interlocking, or with immunological phenomena (and how far are these really different)? What is the role of extra-cellular matrices, membranes, etc., and how do these acquire their sometimes elaborate structures? What suggestions can be made as to how morphological patterns arise within originally homogeneous masses, e.g. the appearance of a five-rayed group of pre-cartilaginous condensations within the mesenchyme of the limb-bud? What is the significance in this respect of initial slight inhomogeneities, or interactions with other tissues such as the ectodermal apical thickening of the limb-bud? Can any useful pointers be derived from the way in which genetical factors, e.g. for polydactyly, impinge on the situation? Can the unfolding of such a pattern be thought of in terms of self-inhibiting processes (each digit expands until it stops itself), or of self-reinforcing but competing processes (each digit expands until the others stop it)? How much individuality do we have to attribute to each element; at a very early age hind limbs cannot substitute for forelimbs, at a relatively early stage each digit acquires its own individuality—is this a chemical property, or is it demonstrable by immunological methods? To what extent is the co-ordination of different tissues in the normal body due to immunological processes? We need to consider also how tissue organisation breaks down in carcinogenesis. Firstly, is tumour induction a two-stage process; and, if so, is there any valid analogy with the two stages which have been postulated in embryonic induction? Is it conceivable that perhaps all induction processes are two-stage—firstly, a lessening of the existing organisation, and then a transformation into a new type of integration? Secondly, when a tumour arises, what kind of "social" behaviour do its cells exhibit, e.g. in adhesiveness, invasiveness, autonomy of growth, specificity in tissues attacked, etc.?

CHAPTER I

The Nature of Biological Organisation

WADDINGTON: I should like to open this meeting by saying a few words about the kind of symposium we are trying to run. To some people the word symposium calls up memories of Platonic dialogues, but I'm afraid I cannot lay on couches, hetairae and wine—at least, not at this hour of the morning. But still that is the kind of function we are aiming at, rather than the reading of formal papers. We want to discuss the bearing of the results which we have obtained, the nature of the problems we are trying to solve, and how they are related to one another. I'm hoping you will discuss very freely and possibly break in on one another, at any rate when you can do so without interrupting the other man too much. This is all being recorded on tape, and to help with the recording, I should like to ask everyone to speak fairly slowly; as Dr. Weiss points out, that might also have the advantage that if one speaks slowly one may have time to think before one says something. I do not imagine that we are going to reach any firm conclusions. In fact I do not think we are aiming at any sort of complete and conclusive summary of the questions we shall be discussing. We shall probably spend most of our time in a state of mind which is very graphically described by the philosopher Whitehead—the state of imaginative muddled suspense that precedes a great inductive generalisation.

We are going to start the session with some discussion with the general concept of organisation. The official title of the symposium is "Patterns of Cellular and Sub-cellular Organisation", and we should begin by considering what we mean by organisation in the most general sense. One of the main reasons for doing this is to see what kind of a focus we can make for a discussion on this general problem. There are two things we shall have to try to do. On the one hand, of course, we shall want to bring in all the most immediately interesting points, but, on the other, we want to try to prevent the discussion becoming completely chaotic and going off in all possible directions simultaneously. I think it is possible that the idea of organisation, if we keep that in mind as the problem we are aiming at, may provide some sort of a focus.

1

Organisation, to my mind, implies some sort of relation between the parts into which a complex entity can be analysed. You have a complex entity and you can break this down into parts somehow or other; and if these parts are related to one another in an orderly manner you can say that the complex entity is organised. That very general concept of organisation covers many varieties of it. For instance, the parts may be derived in a large number of different ways. They may be spatial parts; then spatial organisation will arise if these parts are related in some orderly way, in some sort of pattern or something of that kind. But, of course, the concept of organisation also applies when it is not into spatial parts that we have analysed the complex entity, but, for instance, into physiological functions. One can perfectly well have a kinetic organisation, in which the elements are not in any way spatially organised, but in which the processes themselves are interrelated in an orderly manner.

One of the major problems about organisation is how it comes into being. I suppose the standard idea is that it arises from the fact that the parts have certain characteristics which, as it were, only fit together in a particular way. Then the organisation arises when the parts have joined up with one another and have come into their appropriate relationships. That produces a rather paradoxical situation about organisation. In a way it is a limitation on the potentialities of the system. You have a lot of units or elementary parts, and if they fit in a certain defined pattern that eliminates the possibility of them being joined up in other ways. On the other hand, it is only by this fitting together, even though it is in a limited way, that the full range of properties of the elements ever emerges and becomes manifest. In fact, organisation, although a limitation in one way, often means that the units are exhibiting properties which they cannot show in isolation.

There is another very general point I should like to make about organisation and its origin. I should like to raise the question whether organisation always arises from some pre-existing organisation. Do we in biology only have to deal with situations in which originally very simple patterns gradually become more complicated as the interactions between their elements work out? If we only have to deal with such a complication of organisation, and perhaps with the transmission of organisation from one tissue to another previously unorganised one, then we can really avoid the question of how organisation originates in the first place. On the other hand, we may have to try to deal with the problem of how a pattern can arise in an initially completely homogeneous material in which no pattern was present to begin with. Some mathematicians, such as Turing [1], have worked on systems of that kind. He considers a uniform expanse of tissue, and certain processes going on in this which are subject to stochastic variability, so that there may arise certain centres in which by chance one of the processes is going particularly fast. Then he imagined that the fast-going process leads to the production of a substance which diffuses out from the centre, and also tends to inhibit the others, and he was able to show that a system of this kind would result in a periodic pattern of alternative waves and troughs of the rates of the key reactions, or of the concentrations of particular substances. You could in this way get a patterned system arising from a material which was completely homogeneous at the beginning.

That is an attempt to tackle what is perhaps the most fundamental problem about organisation, namely, how it could arise from a completely unorganised beginning. Personally, I rather doubt whether it has much application to, at any rate, the more important patterns in biology. Most of these patterns are surprisingly insensitive to variations in quantity; that is to say, the same animal shape can occur in a big one or in a little one. Turing suggested that his system might give rise to a periodic pattern which might explain, for example, the number of tentacles on a hydroid. But you tend to get the same number of tentacles on the hydroid whether it is large or small, and this is exactly what would *not* happen on Turing's system, where the periodicity would have a wave length of fixed size dependent on the chemical nature of the reacting substance. However, Turing's work is one of the few attempts to tackle organisation from this most fundamental point of view.

Those few remarks perhaps suggest the kind of concept of organisation which we should keep in our minds. I am now going to ask Paul Weiss to tell us some of the ideas arising from his experimental work on the appearance of organisation in tissues. I am afraid he cannot be here on the last day when we shall come back to tissue organisation, so I shall ask him to give us as much as he can now.

WEISS: I should like to start, in the spirit of this conference, with trying to come to grips with this word "organisation"—this stop-gap of ignorance —in a rather more operational manner than has been customary. I should like to present some facts for your consideration, and see whether we cannot extract from them an objective description of it, just like a physicist would of a new concept. What is it really that we are dealing with in biological systems that we call organised?

This is a box representing system S_1 (Fig. 1.1a). We have in this box a number of randomly-dispersed components of different kinds—acknowledging the principle of heterogeneous composition. Let us assume three kinds, symbolised by crosses, dots and circles. It does not make any difference whether the boxes and components are organs and tissues; tissues and cells; cells and cellular components; or nuclei and nuclear constituents, and so on, so long as you realise that we have here a system consisting of units with distinctly different properties. I shall now try to define organisations operationally in terms of the properties of the system, not in terms of the properties of the observer. Then we can make an objective test:

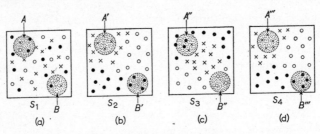

FIG. 1.1

If we take a micro-sample from the box, large enough to preserve the heterogeneity, say from the position A; then another sample of equal size from position B; then we can write that for such a random dispersed system the probability that the content of A will equal that of B is very high ($P_A = P_B$). Now, let us take another system S_2 (Fig. 1.1b), having the same content but which, for some reason, has a different, non-uniform, non-random distribution of components. The number of units of each kind is the same in S_1 and S_2, hence both would appear identical after homogenisation. We can describe the undisturbed system S_2 by saying that the probability that a sample taken at random from any one location, for instance, site A' will equal a sample from another location, for instance, site B' is very low ($P_{A'} \neq P_{B'}$). This sub-sorting is usually considered organisation. Now, I want to make the point that this is not a sufficient definition of organisation, because you can have systems of the same composition with many different types of distribution, for instance system S_3 (Fig. 1.1c), and for all of them the same formulation would be valid, that sample A and sample B are unlikely to be identical in composition, but the probability that sample A" of S_3 would turn out to equal sample A' of S_2, or sample B" of S_3, would equal B' of S_2 would also be extremely small ($P_{A'} \neq P_A''$).

WADDINGTON: I feel that you ought to add some remarks about the size of your samples A and B.

WEISS: They are identical in size.

WADDINGTON: But they've got to be big enough.

WEISS: They are identical in size with the sample of the original system, and that was large enough to include representatives of all the types of components—at least one of each.

If we can accept that, then we find this definition sufficient, as far as it goes, but it defines what we usually mean by *complexity*, and complexity is not enough to describe *organisation*. We have got to add the following to it—that we consider a system organised if this system follows the same rule as the other one ($P_A \neq P_B$), but furthermore that the probability of all samples from locations A of all such systems being alike, and all B samples being reasonably alike, is very high. That is, to rate not only as complex, but as organised, system S_2 would have to be so that when compared to another system of like composition, S_4 (Fig. 1.1d), the following formulae would apply: $P_{A'} \neq P_{B'}$; $P_{A'''} \neq P_{B'''}$; but $P_{A'} = P_{A'''}$, and $P_{B'''} = P_{B'}$. That is, samples taken from corresponding sites will be essentially alike. By "corresponding", I don't mean only geometrical correspondences but topological ones—the point is that there must be relations of some kind between the sites such that one can draw a network of relations through the system such that this network has a greater degree of invariance from one system to another than exists between different samples taken from one and the same system. For space that means there is a basic pattern. Such relational invariance means a certain constancy of over-all pattern beyond the flux of components at the next lower order of magnitude, and a certain degree of latitude, or freedom of detail. It bears a formal resemblance to the "uncertainty" principle, or "indeterminancy" principle—or, as it should be called, the "indeterminability" principle—of Heisenberg on the atomic level, repeating itself on the level of the organism. Whether there is anything in this comparison that is more than a formal analogy is something of a problem.

WADDINGTON: May I interrupt you there a minute. There is something I didn't quite get in this. Did you imply that there is only one network of relations along which you have to take your samples in order to get your basic relations of the probabilities being the same? Do you always have to follow the same path to get from A_1 to B_1, or can you do it in any order you like?

WEISS: For this model here, for the most general model, you can go through in any way you like. There must be isomorphism of relations, so to speak.

Now if it weren't for such systems, which repeat themselves despite their complexity, the problem of organisation would never have arisen. We would not have identical or similar entities of sufficiently frequent occurrence in our experience to give them a name, like "cell". The mere fact that we have a name for them already signifies underlying resemblance. There must be something at the back of this, therefore, separating mere heterogeneity from *ordered* heterogeneity. The element of order is more invariant, in mathematical terminology, than are the events in the constituent units.

Now, the same thing can be immediately transposed into temporal or chronological systems, where instead of location in space you have position in a time sequence (Fig. 1.2). You can have a chain of events consisting of the three components of this type (Fig. 1.2a). If the same links appear in another sequence (Fig. 1.2b), you would have sequential operations,

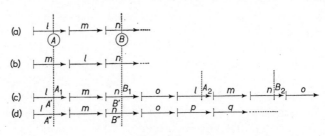

FIG. 1.2

but not yet organisation. Organisation would be present only if the following holds in addition. Instead of sampling space as before, we now sample time course. This is the time line (Fig. 1.2), and you take cross-sections, let us say at A and B. The probability of a given event at A being the same as at B—the probability then of any time sample being like any other time sample on the line—is low. In comparing the two differently arranged chains (Fig. 1.2a with Fig. 1.2b), we also note that the probability of events sampled at any identical intervals A,B being the same in both, is very low. Organisation would arise when the latter probability becomes very high. This occurs in periodic repeat systems, such as metabolic cycles (Fig. 1.2c, $P_{A_1} = P_{A_2} = \ldots$; $P_{B_1} = P_{B_2} = \ldots$), as well in aperiodic development (Fig. 1.2d) where the comparison is made not between successive phases of the same system, but between separate systems (Fig. 1.2d; $P_{A'} = P_{A''}$; $P_{B'} = P_{B''}$; etc.). This inner relation in the time pattern then raises a merely heterogeneous sequence to an orderly, or organised sequence.

Now, since most morphological products are not established by spontaneous generation all at once, but evolve along a time line, that means that it is going to be possible, and increasingly so, to reduce or resolve space patterns to orderly sequences of processes. Just where this breaks down is an empirical question of the future. Just as the orderliness of an assembly can often be referred to the orderly aggregation of the units, so order of form can arise from the order of the formative processes. Thus, the final shape of the organism can be resolved into the rules according to which the processes, the technology by which the egg evolves, are linked and timed. I believe that unless we keep this in mind, and come to grips with this time pattern, which we deliberately destroy when we go about determining the sheer inventory of a living system, of a cell or a living tissue, or a part of a cell, unless we study that which distinguishes the randomised or merely complex system from the organised system in which the order follows the outlined rule, we will not really face our problems and get on.

Now, the problem which Professor Waddington has raised is to what extent an over-all order in time or space resides in the elements; to what extent is a higher degree of organisation merely an expression of properties of the elements putting themselves into an expression or manifestation of a higher degree of order? Is the order inherent in the parts, or has something to be added from the collective of the parts, something present in the block of the parts all the time and handed down, passed down as a continuum of organisation. I think this is the problem that's been raised; and without entering into any further theoretical considerations I should like to expose you to three examples; one on a molecular or almost molecular level, one on the supracellular level, and another from a slightly different organism again on a supracellular level, where we find in one case molecular groupings according to a space pattern which does not reside, at least not specifically, within the properties of the individual molecules. I will strip them of all details and expose them very briefly.

This first slide is an electron micrograph of the basement lamella under the epidermis of larval frog skin (for illustration, see [2]). You will see it shows a remarkably regular structure. The black dots are cross-sections through cylinders of collagen fibres of the diameter 500–600 Å, embedded in a ground substance which we know now consists of a muco-polysaccharide. Then you see another layer and another one, all sandwiched and containing these tracts of true collagen fibres running parallel to the plane of the skin, but alternating in direction from layer to layer by right angles, In short, the membrane is built like plywood of a pile of about 20 layers of fibres, each a cylinder about 600 Å wide, that is, containing about 1000 molecular chains. But, when they have reached this size, they stop—why do they stop? Why don't we find them all giant or all small? So you see, here we have the problem of collective entities appearing. Then, at every 200 millimicra of height, their orientation changes sharply at right angles. Why? And the structure which has this degree of regularity grows with the body, and these fibres run, so far as we know, essentially continuously round the body.

We started to work on the origin of this thing, and the best way to study it is after it has formed and to study its restoration or regeneration after wounding. So we make a wound and open a hole through the skin and the following things appear.

Two slides will pinpoint this matter of emerging organisation which Professor Waddington has mentioned. We have here a scrambled collection

of two types of molecules (Fig. 1.3a) indicated by two types of symbols
—pins for dipoles and this type here indicating a molecule with a few side
chains—and this is a randomly orientated system. As soon as you have an
interface between two media of different properties you introduce an external factor which will take these systems in hand and force them to assume
some degree of structural order (Fig. 1.3b). You get the same thing in a
Langmuir monofilm or in the double membranes of various cell particles.

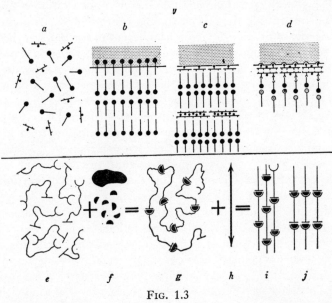

FIG. 1.3

You get some degree of self-ordering. Now you can see that this degree
of order was predicted on the properties of the constituent elements. It
arises as soon as there is a chance for the expression of those properties;
in this case due to an interface, which is a very simple thing. But I think
it is a model of what happens constantly in the arising of organisation.
It is something that I should like to come back to at a later occasion. It is
something we should keep in mind when we talk about induction; whether
we are merely introducing permissive conditions which make it possible
for the system to show what it can do; or whether we impart something
to the system which the system hadn't known in advance, so to speak.

If we add another molecular layer here now (Fig. 1.3c), as soon as we
have this other species, it can act as a go-between, an intermediary, and
we can have a new higher type of organisation (Fig. 1.3d). This is a model
then, let's say, of a myelin sheath with alternating layers of lipid and
protein molecules; so we can produce a three-dimensional space order of molecules emerging from the original two-dimensional order of the interface.

Now, this illustrates the basic principle of organisation emerging by virtue of the properties which reside in the basic elements of the system.

Here is another example: we take two chain molecules differing in end groups (Fig. 1.3e) and those can easily be polymerised by adding these little molecules (Fig. 1.3f) to the end, something like collagen fibre formation. They are cemented together by these fitting end-groups, and as a result we obtain long chains (Fig. 1.3g). Now, a chain is not a straight line. To get this we need an additional factor; for instance, stress to align the links in parallel order (Fig. 1.3h, i). This is a higher degree of orderliness now, but they are still randomly arranged laterally. It is necessary to have attractive forces between homologous elements to pull them into register (Fig. 1.3j), as we see in the muscle fibre, or a collagen fibre, giving us an over-all cross-striation. I put this slide on to show you that while some of the properties, like polymerisation, reside in the properties of the constituent elements of the substance, additional factors—physical factors—an interface in this case—stress in that—or again chemical forces like the lateral attractions—may have to be invoked in order to produce the eventual organisation.

Now, let me show you one more thing with reference to the Turing rings which Professor Waddington mentioned. We are now going to deal with the changes in a collective assemblage of cells, a further complication of the system. Here is an example (Fig. 1.4a); this is to represent a blood

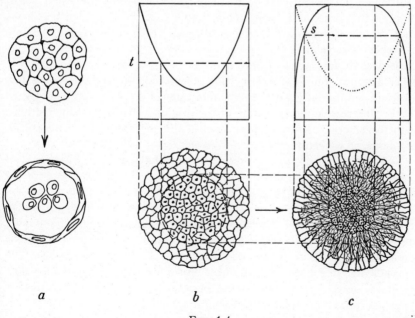

a b c

Fig. 1.4

island of an embryonic chick. In a blood island the cells are demonstrably alike; if they are isolated they are all the same cells. But they don't remain that way long. The outer cells soon form an endothelium, the blood vessel. The inner cells become stem cells and eventually give the haemopoetic system. From that time on there are two species of cells, which have emerged from one species; and who determines, or what determines, what is to become an endothelial cell or a stem cell? Their position in the system —their geometric position. The inner ones become blood, the outer ones become endothelium. Of course, if you cut the island in two, then a cell which used to be an inner one in the centre all of a sudden becomes an outer one, and that changes its future fate. And what really determines, then, the dichotomy between these cells is not really geometry but difference in physico-chemical exposure to the environment, or to their own collective activity, which is signified by their geometric position, "inner" or "outer". We have many such cases in biology or embryology; that is, of self-organisation of the system according to the differential conditions prevailing in different regions of the system.

The essential thing is not really the differential condition but the differential response of the parts, in this case, of the cells, to the particular local parameter. This differential response is again built into the individual units. They respond with a limited type of response; each cell seems to be able to do only one of two things at any one time, but out of these the position in the system chooses by favouring one against the other. Now, this can be worked out further (Fig. 1.4b, c). If these cells on the inside start actions of their own, then a third type of cells in between comes into existence as a result of the interaction of the first two. Before the newly created conditions we had only two, and now we have a third group of cells. I'm not going to elaborate this scheme; all I'm going to say is that a certain number of greatly diverse morphological results can be obtained by the progressive manifestation of the original cells in their interactions, with the emergence of new properties at the zones of the intersection of the fields, as we call them.

Now, let's go back to the basement membrane and see what some of these things mean. For illustrations, see [2]. Here is a diagram of a wound that is several days old (Fig. 1.5a). You can see the basement membrane (1) with its various layers at the left, with the epidermis cell (e) above. The wound edge is very sharply defined. This is the wound exudate here, and we are now considering what is happening inside it. This organised membrane will be fully restored later on. This cell underneath, the mesenchyme fibroblast (f), produces fibres into the ground substance which are needles with a 600 Å axial periodicity, and 200–250 Å diameter. They are quite random at first. Random material is the stuff out of which the later fabric will be formed. Then, after the material has been shed, an ordering process sets in, which I am showing here on the right-hand side (Fig. 1.5b). In the vicinity of the epidermal cell (e) you will see that these same fibres now begin to be orientated essentially in two orthogonal systems at right angles; the laminar arrangement of the fibres proceeds gradually from the epidermis downward. It is not a process of order arising out of molecular solution, but is order imposed upon a network of sub-microscopic or supramolecular units. How, we do not yet understand. The distance between the ordered fibres is about 600 Å, anticipating the later diameter of those fibres, and incidentally corresponding also to their axial period. It seems to occur like this. First, one layer is ordered. Its fibres are drawn parallel with their homologous segments, lined up laterally in register. Then a second layer is built on top of the first, then a third one on top of this one, and so on.

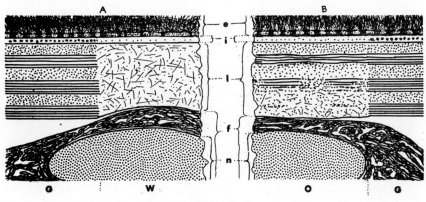

FIG. 1.5

Now, there seems to be a certain exclusion principle here which prevents any two neighbouring layers from assuming parallel orientation—which is too difficult to go into. But the upshot of it is, that the first lattice framework is an invisible one, establishing certain equilibrium points at the corners of a cubic space of something like 600 Å side length, which is rather beyond the molecular interactions which we know about, particularly in view of the fact that there must be lots of other things going on in the ground substance in between. Then later the space is filled. The organisation into layers proceeds distinctly from the epidermis down, by an influence from the inner surface.

That leaves one factor still unknown—the orientation of these fibres relative to the body. We have made some experiments on this recently, rotating an area of the membrane first and then poking a hole in it. We could thus determine quite crucially whether the orientation of the new fibres would conform to the body axes or something else. We found that

the actual orientation of the fibres was determined neither by the mesoderm nor by the epidermis, but by the polarity of the old fibres around
the wound edge. The new fibres are woven on to the old ones in whatever
direction that may place them relative to the rest of the body. The point is
that here, on the supra-molecular, sub-cellular level, we find patterns or
organisation determined, one might say, not by any one factor but by the
co-operation of three systems, ending up in this type of regularity. Now,
you see, there are lots of problems still contained here, which we can study
empirically; that is the whole point of going into this further.

I would like to go on right from here to expose you to a similar problem
on the supracellular level explored with the assistance of Dr. Virginia
McMurray. To save time I'll put a diagram on here. It concerns the
formation of fish scales in rows. The scales of fish, the hairs of mammals,
the feathers of birds, and so on arise in definite space patterns or grids.
And each feather, each hair, each scale, is a multicellular unit. Now,
development seems to be like this (Fig. 1.6). This is the lateral line

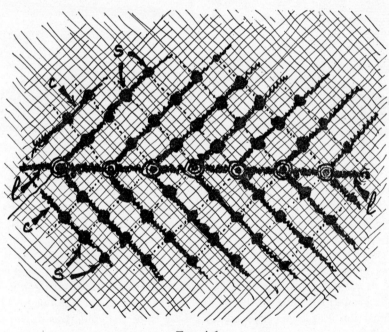

Fig. 1.6

system of the fish (1) and the scales develop from a germinal proliferative
cord along that line, sending out dorsal and ventral sprouts. When you
study the dermis of a fish—that's where the scales form—you find there
are two intersecting systems of fibres, very much like those in the basement

membrane we have just studied, except that there are only two layers. Now, a very interesting thing seems to happen when the scales form. Two sets of streams of cells (c) run off the lateral line, drawn out along the dermal fibre tracks by contact guidance, and following one of the two systems on the dorsal side, and the other on the ventral side. In addition to this contact orientation of cell cord growth, there must be a polarising antero-posterior factor that blows them backwards, so to speak, for between the two alternative directions, they choose the one that is bent backwards.

These are then the main cords of primordial scale cells, and now these cords break up into clusters of cells for the formation of scale(s). These clusters lie in exact extension of the second system of connective tissue fibres that's underlying them (dotted lines). So they are aligned by a different kind of influence, which is not growth; on the lower side here the same thing happens, only it is the other line system which takes the lead. In other words, the cells for scale formation are concentrating round the intersection point between the two line systems, one of which has furnished the material, while the other has furnished an influence which proceeds along a geometric line and determines again equilibrium positions which now mark the actual points of scale formation. Now you notice why I am bringing in this example. It links up with what we have just shown in the basement membrane—the appearance of equilibrium points at certain distances from each other which arrange themselves finally morphologically into a grid.

Let's turn now to the next example. The point of it is that whereas before we saw the intersects between two line systems in a lattice directly embodied in the deposit of the dark centres of collagen fibres, in this next case we do not see a direct morphological result, but the intersects merely become the foci for the occurrence of a secondary process of organisation; and you see how that links up with the emergent progressive complication of organisation by secondary interaction processes, which go back to relatively simple constellations of forces. This has considerable and rather amazing implications in the studies which are going on with dispersed randomised cultures of cells in the building up of larger complexes. I started work on the morphogenetic properties of dispersed cells back in '49 with Andres, who has done a superb job with it. There was no trypsin routine in those days, and we scrambled the embryonic cells mechanically, which incidentally can be done much more delicately than the chemical treatment. Then we injected these scrambled cells of the one or two day old chick embryo into the vein of an older embryo. They became either settled in the embryo—but I am not talking about that part—or some of them went into the yolk sac [3]. The yolk sac is very much like a tissue culture, lying beyond the organising influences of the embryo proper.

On the yolk sac, these scrambled cells built up organised embryonic complexes containing cartilage, joints, bone (the bone marrow induced in there comes presumably from the blood of the host), a spinal ganglia, brain, musculature, and so on. In some cases where we had skin cells, we found that the scrambled skin cells on the yolk sac could form, after reaggregation, perfectly good feathers in rather regular fields.

It was only one further step then to carry this into tissue culture, and Moscona, as you know, has carried this out on a large scale. However, contrary to Moscona's primary focus of interest on the aggregation of identical cells—problems in which I have been quite interested too—we shall concentrate more now on the self-organisation properties of the individual complexes. How do they do it? There is something said about their doing it according to their characteristics. But how do they do it then? When a suspension of 7 day skin, which had been fully dispersed, then centrifuged and reaggregated, was raised on a plasma clot it gave rise not only to a perfectly good keratinised skin, but to feathers as well.[4] That is, cells which didn't know their place in the whole before—except that they were skin cells—after forming a collective in a different environment knew how to put themselves together in such order as to give rise to the complicated manoeuvres that underly the morphogenesis of a feather.

Recently we have carried this thing with Moscona even further, determining the architectural self-ordering of dissociated pre-cartilage cells from locations with different morphological destinies. Limb cartilage, for instance, shows whorl-like cell arrangements, whereas the scleral cartilage around the eye grows as a plate, in the body as well as after explanation in tissue culture. We therefore went on to scramble pre-cartilaginous mesenchyme from the two types of sources; $3\frac{1}{2}$ day limb bud and 7 day sclera, because the sclera lags behind the limb. No histologist or histochemist could tell these two suspensions apart. Then we took the scrambled cells, aggregated them, and put them in tissue culture; the limb cells, forming a new collective, now build a well-shaped cartilage characteristic of the site of origin: The cells from the limb bud formed massive limb skeleton, while those that had come from the pre-cartilaginous mesenchyme of the sclera arranged themselves in a plate about three or four cells thick. On grounds of this kind, we feel we are not prepared at present to make any predictions as to how much in the way of supra-cellular organisation comes about by the harmonious interactive properties of the individual constituents, by grouping themselves according to their own rule of behaviour, with the differential response being, of course, innate in them; as against the properties that have to be derived *en bloc* as organisation from elsewhere.

Now, let me come on to the last word which I should like to throw out, in relation to the discussion of induction properties. This is one of

Moscona's pictures in which kidney tubules *in vitro* have formed in an aggregation of dissociated kidney cells. In the next, I show an old picture of ours from a normal kidney tissue culture, where you see free kidney tubules appearing in islands in the new outgrown zone. You see how very neatly these tubules are formed. Now, you remember the work of Grobstein; he shows the "induction" of kidney tubules by some action of the matching mesoderm, an operative action which can be transmitted across filters with certain degrees of porosity. Now, what does that mean—"induction" of kidneys? Does it mean that the cells you take out of a blastema do not know how to co-operate to form the kidney tubule by which we rate them later? Or, is it merely that in those cases where we don't see them form kidney tubules they haven't been given a chance to manifest or to express their capacity? You can't build a house out of one brick—it takes many bricks to build a house. And a single kidney cell, if it's not in the proper position, cannot form a kidney tubule.

We have now studied further this technology of kidney tubule formation. We are just at the beginning, but I will show you approximately what the results promise to be. Kidney cells cultured *in vitro* on a glass surface flatten out, and secrete something, and that's all they can do in that condition. But if you allow a group of those cells to come together in a bunch, then that secretion, instead of being given out at random, is given out in a polarised direction towards the interior of the cluster. It's like the example I showed you with the blood islands (Fig. 1.4)—it's the position, then, which begins to count when you have more than one cell. You've got to have three or four cells—you've got to have groups. When looking at Grobstein's picture—he pointed out, virtually, that in the area where the induction took place the cells were bunched and there were large groups, while outside that area of action they were spread out. Now, we found that spread-out kidney epithelia can form no tubules; they cannot at the same time spread out and contract, they've got to do either one or the other. You've got to give them a chance to bunch up.

We found now that if you take a slide and mark it with non-adhesive parts, for instance with cholesterol or other fat, and study how a culture of kidney cells behaves on that mosaic substratum, then on the unmarked part they will form a sheet which will never reveal to a morphologist that they are kidney cells, unless, of course, he could test their secretion and find successfully what was in it. But, over non-adhesive parts, over the islands of cholesterol, the same sheet of cells cannot adhere and does not spread out; instead it bunches up, and there you get incipient formation of kidney tubules. Did we induce kidney tubules by cholesterol? It is rather that the non-coated portions of the substratum prevented the manifestation of the kidney-formation abilities which we use as a signal of the morphological capacity of the cells. We prevented the signal from being

3

unfurled, by making them actively spread out. So the question is, in all of these cases—I don't know whether this really is the answer to Grobstein's case, but it looks like it—whether the "induction" is not simply the removal of a condition that actively prevents the mechanical arrangement necessary for tubule formation. In our case, the factor that prevents tubulation by promoting adhesion seems to be in the horse serum. If mesoderm contained something that counteracted or cancelled out this factor, one could understand why mesodermal effects would be vital for the actual appearance of kidney tubules in nephrogenous blastemas.

Well, I think I've taken as much time as I want to, to emphasise that there is appearing over the horizon at least an opportunity to study the appearance of higher organisation by the co-operative collective action of constituent elements; and this can be studied at all levels, from the supra-molecular to the supra-cellular level.

WADDINGTON: Thank you very much, Paul, for giving us these examples. As I understand it you contemplate organisation arising on the basis of three main principles. Firstly, interactions between the elements according to their own individual properties; then questions of spontaneously arising new conditions: once you've got a mass of elements—cells or particles—processes go on within them, and build up conditions which may distinguish the outside from the inside, and things of that kind. And thirdly, you must sometimes take account of general external conditions, which may be a gradient in the surroundings, or a polarity, or something of that sort. But I should like to hear something from Lehmann, whether there isn't a fourth factor in some of these cases. Organisation has been, rather unfortunately in some ways, mixed up with this question of the so-called organiser. The justification for this mix-up is, I think, that sometimes the organiser does seem to impose an organisation on what it induces. In many cases this may not be so, and the so-called induction merely creates conditions under which the induced material can express its own characteristics. It is then purely permissive as you, I think, sugggested. But in some cases there is at least a suspicion that it does more. For instance, in the amphibian organiser the induced material, the neural system, fits exactly with the mesoderm which induces it. That led to the suspicion that the mesoderm has not merely a releasing capacity, but is actually imposing the detailed spatial configuration. Now, I know Lehmann, and Toivonen, and the people working with organisers, have ideas about this. How far do you think you can reduce the organisation in an embryonic induction purely to the release of inherent capacities of the reacting system? Or, does it involve some imposing of order from outside?

LEHMANN: There are several points about the organiser and I would like to come back to that one later. I want to remember first that animal organisation is produced by a long course of evolution. The organisation now present is passed on from one generation to another. At the same time we ought to be aware of the fact that the organism lives in a particular environment which exerts a high selective pressure on it. The organisms nowadays have been highly selected. This important point has to be kept in mind in a discussion about fitness of organisation.

What we can do now is simply to investigate organisation as an existing phenomenon. In the living systems there are obviously very close relations between structural and biochemical events which are difficult to analyse. A further point I want to make in these general considerations is to indicate that organised biological systems are stable in one and very flexible in another respect. And the next point is, if we consider a metazoan organism as a living system, we have to think of its subunits, the organs, and the thousands of elementary units, the cells which form the organs. The delimitation of the cellular dimensions is given in some way by the order of magnitude of intracellular organelles (mitochondria, nucleus etc.) and the kind of biochemical function carried by these organelles. It is already clear that there are always several types of organelles necessary to constitute a cell. These different types are, as we see from submicroscopic morphology, localised in a characteristic, intracellular pattern which represents the structural aspect of intracellular organisation [5]. All these particulates seem to be biochemically active and functionally correlated. So you get already at the intracellular level a very close interrelation of these different cellular constituents.

Then, we have also to consider the two antagonising groups of factors which are in all structural levels (inside the cells, in cell populations, in different organs) always interlinked, on the one side the inhibiting, on the other side the activating, factors. We recall here the regulation of enzyme activities by metabolite controlled feed-back mechanisms, and the induction of enzyme activity by some substrates. Then, on different levels and in many cases there are very interesting threshold effects, where with a given intensity of action the processes are guided in one way and with another intensity they will take a qualitatively different direction. Concerning such special biological events, we are usually ignorant, so to speak, what such or such a process means in the life history of an organism. Whether these processes run in this way or in the other way, in both cases it is sufficiently justified to assume that the processes have a definite meaning for the selective value of the organism. The arguments for evolution are now well founded and we are entitled always in experimental considerations to take into account the functional meaning of a process for the organism in relation to its fitness in selection. Of course, we are not here discussing evolution, but it seemed necessary to mention these points in connection with the general problem of organisation.

Now, about the question of the organiser. Professor Waddington, may I ask you again for your questions so that I may exactly answer what you have in mind?

WADDINGTON: I was saying that the organiser was named as such because it appeared, at least to superficial examination, that the mesoderm imposed on the reacting ectoderm a certain pattern. The mesoderm appears to determine that the fore-brain appears here, the hind-brain there, and the neural tube in a certain position. Then the neural system fits in perfectly with the somites and you get a complete orderliness in the body, which appears to be imposed on the extoderm by the mesoderm. Here you have got the conceptions of induction and organisation completely mixed up. I personally have always tried to separate them by my words "evocation" and "individuation". These were intended to separate the two concepts of induction and organisation.

The question I was asking really is this—we have a lot of information now about chemically pure, or reasonably refined, extracts which specifically induce either fore-brain or more posterior parts of the nervous system, and in these experiments the pattern of the fore-brain—which may be perfectly well shaped and have its eyes in the right place and so on—has certainly not been imposed by the mouse kidney or whatever it might be that has induced it. It must have been produced by the self-organisation, or self-individuation as I call it, of the reacting tissue. But can we now say that this self-individuation is the whole story, or must we still suppose that the mesoderm *sometimes* transmits a pattern? If we have organisation transmitted from one tissue on to another, that is a good place to try to catch it on the way, and analyse how it works. If it is not transmitted, and you merely liberate capacities of the reacting material, then you have no chance to catch it in transit.

LEHMANN: Yes, I see your point. Concerning the different regional properties of the induced neural plate, there is not much difference between the living roof of archenteron and a dead neural inductor for the traditional opinion. In both cases the ectoderm is activated by a stimulus of regional character. Subsequent to the kind of stimulus archencephalic, deuterencephalic or spinocaudal self-organisation takes place [6, 7, 8]. A transmission of a pattern from the inducer to the induced neural plate is not suggested by any known experiment. Only a transformation of the original tendencies present in a neural field might be secondarily brought about by posterior parts of the roof of the archenteron (Nieuwkoop [9]). So we have to assume that the characteristic pattern of brain or spinal cord arises autonomously within the neural plate as a process of self-organisation or "self-patterning". The peculiarity of the "organiser" of the dorsal lip of the blastopore is illustrated best by the fact that this blastema is inducing neural plate *and* organising itself into a proportional pattern of notochord, somites and lateral mesoderm. This was also Spemann's idea, proposed in his latest publications [10].

WADDINGTON: I am quite ready to admit that a great deal of the organisation in the archenteron roof and in the ectoderm is self-organisation. The question I was asking is if we can rely completely on self-organisation. I can't agree with your statement that "a transmission of pattern from the inducer to the induced neural plate is not suggested by any known experiment". Surely the classical organiser experiment demonstrates clearly that the inducing archenteron roof determines the position of the mid-dorsal axis of the induced plate. Again, reduction of the size of the archenteron roof, for instance in halved gastrulae, shows that it is the inducer which normally determines not only the anterior-posterior sequence but also the length of the various organs of the neural system, and finally also their width. I should have thought that it was impossible to maintain that in normal development the archenteron roof is organising itself, and the neural plate was also "self-organising", and that these two processes are quite independent and proceed without any information passing between them. The only question to my mind is just how detailed is this information. Does the inducing system merely determine that here there shall be an archencephalon and specify its overall size and leave it at that, for the rest to be done by the reacting ectoderm? Such phenomena as the occurrence of cyclopia following reduction of the archenteron roof, and the very precise fitting-together of inducer and induced, which is so commonly seen, suggests to me that rather detailed information about the organised structure may, sometimes, be transmitted; although, as I have said before, it is clear that the ectoderm can do quite well even when it is not receiving such detailed instructions.

There is something else which comes into this question, I think. In nearly all the cases of self-organisation which Weiss has been able to analyse the pattern of organisation is relatively symmetrical—either it is regularly symmetrical, or something imposes a polarity on it, but even that is relatively symmetrical. Now in the nervous system of an amphibian you have a highly complicated *linear sequence* of different parts. Or take another example which we are going to discuss later, Zwilling's story on the formation of a pentadactyl limb. You have a lump of mesoderm, and you have an ectoderm which has a more or less linear ridge—the apical ridge which is very important for the process—and somehow in that system just *five*—well, I've forgotten exactly how many toes a chicken has, but whatever the number is—condensations are produced; and where exactly do you get that number from? If one is going to rely on self-organisation as an explanation of all these organs, one's got to go a step further than we've heard yet, and produce an explanation for orderly but non-symmetrical organisation, and that seems much more difficult.

WEISS: In the first place, the feather is not one of your symmetrical systems, it's not very symmetrical, it's a complicated process. And secondly, if the factor in these cases was not working on a homogeneous population but, as in the body, on a population of different ages and different histories, then the result of that symmetrical action would be asymmetrical; and the time sequence might make for instance another sixth finger, or seventh finger—some sort of hyperdactylism—come out. So it is partly the historical complication which will develop the simpler system. And along that line I must contradict in a way—well, not contradict, but I would like to raise one point where I have not been understood. Lehmann emphasised biochemical processes. Now I've been talking about chemical processes all the time, but chemical processes going on in a test-tube are not the same as processes going on in a living body. We, as biochemists, could provide the biochemical reactions with the optimum conditions of pH, ingredients, and everything that is necessary, and we can keep the conditions constant; the body does not. It produces those conditions in a unique place; there is a matching between the biochemical background and the reaction. All I am trying to do here is to define how and where such unique places can arise. For instance, in the case of collagen we see a direct product of the reaction, which is precipitated as collagen right there. All I'm doing is calling for evocation, so to speak, in this place, where the medium provides a setting for the efflorescence of biochemical reactions leading to a scale. For that reason I do not think you can ask the question in the way you did—in the induction of the neural plate is there anything imparted by the mesoderm, or is it merely evoked?— because one has to break down what is a neural plate, what is a nervous system; it's a hodge-podge of all kinds of processes ending up in what we call a nervous system. Something like polarity certainly can't impose all of them.

WADDINGTON: I think Nieuwkoop has something to contribute to this problem, namely, bringing in what you just mentioned—the temporal sequence. Changing the time relations may give you another way of getting away from a regularly symmetrical system. Would Nieuwkoop like to expand on that?

NIEUWKOOP: It seems difficult to make any very clear-cut comments on such a problem. In the induction process we have strong indications for self-organisation, which Professor Lehmann already mentioned, and which have been clearly demonstrated in Professor Waddington's Institute. The mesoderm can organise itself according to its own capacity, but the organisation capacities of the ectodermal system are also extremely high; I am hoping to show this before the end of this conference. The whole problem is however much more complicated; it is not only that there are two systems organising themselves, but they are also interacting. It looks as though the first phase of interaction is rather simple; it has more or less the character of liberating processes in one or both systems. Then starts the process of self-organsation, but as soon as a certain level is reached in one of the systems or in both, there comes into play a series of secondary interactions. In that phase, I think your question can be answered in a positive sense. There is a transmission after a certain pattern has been established in both systems, but it may not actually be a pattern which is transmitted, but may have more the character of gradients which are rather simple.

WADDINGTON: I think now in this first session we've succeeded in bringing the problem of organisation to our minds. We are coming back to the particular points about organisation in relation to induction and tissue interaction at a later stage. We will now break off and have coffee, and we will start again afterwards with a quite different point of attack.

REFERENCES

1. TURING, A. M. (1952) *Phil. Trans.* B **237**, 37.
2. WEISS, P. (1956) *Proc. Natl. Acad. Sci., U.S.* **42**, 819.
3. ANDRES, J. (1953) *J. Exp. Zool.* **122**, 507.
4. WEISS, P. and R. JAMES (1955) *Exp. Cell Res. Suppl.*, p. 381.
5. LEHMANN, F. E. (1956) *Ergeb. med. Grundlagenforsch.* **1**, 109.
6. LEHMANN, F. E. (1942) *Naturwissenschaften* **30**, 518.
7. TOIVONEN, S. (1940) *Ann. Acad. Sci. Fenn.* **55**, 7.
8. YAMADA, T. and K. TAKATA (1956) *Embryologia* **3**, 69.
9. NIEUWKOOP, P. (1955) *Exp. Cell Res. Suppl.* **3**, 262.
10. SPEMANN, H. (1936) *Experimentelle Beiträge zu einer Theorie der Entwicklung*, Berlin.

CHAPTER II

Organisation at the Gene Level

WADDINGTON: We will now start again at the bottom, as it were, by considering organisation at the gene level. Although the phenomena we shall be dealing with are very unlike those we considered this morning, we shall probably find that they exemplify rather similar principles. I shall ask Pontecorvo to introduce this session.

PONTECORVO: I will say only one thing, and that won't take long. The picture—I won't put it stronger than that—of the organisation at the chromosomal level has changed in the last ten years from that of a linear series of beads on a string—genes A B C D — to that of a linear series of building blocks — a b a c d e a b d e f a b a c d e f e — with the A gene corresponding to a b a c d e a; the B gene corresponding to b d e f a b a c, and perhaps C, in some cases at least, to b a c d e f e, i.e. partially overlapping with B. We now realise—I think everybody would agree with that—that we don't need to assume discreteness in the structural organisation because we find discreteness of functions. In other words, the genes are units of function arising from an aperiodic sequence of structural elements, like words arising from particular groupings of letters. In genetic jargon this scheme says that we can get crossing-over between parts of genes as well as between genes. The old estimate of Muller for the structural basis of one gene has a maximum of something like 1000 Å; this included the possible non-genic linkages which were thought to exist at that time. The present estimate is of the same order. Is that enough to open the discussion?

WADDINGTON: I think there is really plenty to discuss in what you've said.

PONTECORVO: These are, of course, as you have seen, statements completely *ex cathedra*, just to open the discussion.

WADDINGTON: Well, does nobody feel like saying something about this?

WEISS: I should like to have some information. Is the regularity of that order based on structural stability, or merely on some rule of composition?

Is it based on the separate parts of the gene being separable and then getting together again in the same order?

PONTECORVO: There is very little doubt about the linear arrangement of the individual elements.

WEISS: That I understand; but is it due to the continuity of a string along which they are strung up, or is it due to the fact that each one can combine only in a particular way?

PONTECORVO: Do you mean each of the functional elements, A, B, C, or each of the structural elements a, b, c, d, e, f?

WEISS: A, B and C, let us say.

PONTECORVO: A, B and C can combine in practically any way in linear order. What is still doubtful is the partial over-lap of B and C. In other words, whether, of the elementary structural elements (a, b, c, etc.) which determine function B, some are also shared by function C. This is not likely to be the usual situation, but there is already evidence that it may happen.

WEISS: What I'm asking about is the structural stability of that arrangement in interphase. I know you can see re-arrangements in mitotic chromosomes, but is the persistence between the times when you can see them based on an underlying structural continuity, or is there something there which makes them join up again in a particular linear order?

PONTECORVO: Well, if there is something which makes them arrange themselves in a linear sequence in the same order, then that is what we call the gene arrangement. I mean we have to have the linear order somewhere.

WADDINGTON: I think the point that Weiss is making could be put in this way. When you have something like transduction, which involves a little bit of chromosome picked up from one cell and put into another, for instance by phage, the transduced piece sticks into place—or may stick into place—instead of the section of host chromosome that should have been there. One possible way of interpreting that is to suppose that the chromosomes break up at some stage in the life cycle and then re-form, and in these instances you get the wrong bit going in. What do the experts on this subject say about that possibility?

PLAUT: Shouldn't we ask here what you mean by a gene? How do you measure it? I gather it's mainly a functional definition.

PONTECORVO: Yes, function, that's the only definition we are left with.

PLAUT: One possible way to answer Dr. Weiss's question would be to ask a second question. Can you always measure this function? You, Weiss, were asking something about the *structural* stability, and Pontecorvo replied something about the *functional* stability.

WEISS: Perhaps that was so, but I'd like to see the two linked up somehow.

BEERMANN: Perhaps we can contribute something to this, from the giant chromosomes of Dipteran larvae—these are certainly interphase nuclei—they should be considered as such functionally, and why not structurally also . . .

PONTECORVO: They are non-mitotic chromosomes.

BEERMANN: Well, ones which are working.

BRENNER: I think that Dr. Pontecorvo has taken Professor Waddington's instructions too literally, and particularly his restriction about not going down to the molecular level. If I may be disobedient . . .

WADDINGTON: Yes.

BRENNER: Perhaps I can indulge in two sorts of statements; the first of which is theoretical, the second speculative.

I think that Professor Pontecorvo's work, and that of several other people, has shown adequately that the old idea of beads on a string is wrong, and that, in essence, the material between the genes is like the genes. Put in a simple form, the genetic structure consists of a single strand of some chemical material which carries information. Of course, as you all know, a hot favourite for this material is DNA. Now, you may ask for the evidence for DNA being the genetic carrier, and most of the evidence is based on microbiological studies; and you may ask whether experiments with micro-organisms have any bearing on experiments with higher animals. What I'd like to show, in a quite speculative way, is how they have a bearing on organisms which have a higher degree of organisation.

I shall not go into the evidence—I take it that we all know the evidence —on which we base the idea that DNA carries what we like to call genetic information. What we should like to understand is exactly how genetic information gets transferred to the rest of the cell. Now, in this sort of story we really needn't be concerned with the detailed biochemical processes. We can formulate it in an abstract sense and deal with it in that way. Then we can also look for a physical counterpart of any theory we may have.

The simplest picture, and the one that appeals most to the imagination, is that the DNA composing a functional unit—which I shall leave undefined for a moment—carries information which is coded into a sequence of the purine and pyrimidine bases. As you know, DNA has a duplex structure consisting of two chains wound helically around each other and held together by hydrogen bonds between complementary pairs of bases. Thus adenine pairs with thymine, and guanine with cytosine. It is important to realise that the doubleness of the structure does not in any way increase the informational content, since a given sequence of bases on one chain automatically determines the complementary sequence on the other chain.

Now, we may put forward a rather radical idea straightaway, which I am prepared to defend, and that is that DNA has no other function at all except to transfer information to protein, and specifically to transfer information to enzymes.

WADDINGTON: But surely the genes have to re-duplicate themselves?

BRENNER: Yes, including re-duplicating themselves. But I want to emphasise the functional aspect of the genes, and that, in their expression, genes do not make small molecules. The genes do not make substrates for reactions; and genes do not affect other genes directly in the same genome; they carry out all their effects by the agency of protein.

WADDINGTON: You restrict them to specifying proteins, and not RNA?

BRENNER: I don't want to be concerned with any intermediate now. I do believe that DNA makes RNA, and that the RNA specifies the protein, but the theory would work equally well if there were 300 informational intermediates, or if there were none.

WADDINGTON: Could you put it in the form of saying that you believe that between the gene and anything smaller than a protein there always comes a protein?

BRENNER: No. Some polysaccharides may be larger than protein molecules and they are made by protein enzymes. I just mean that the DNA specifies enzymes, and that the enzymes produce other things; they may make small molecules or they may make large molecules.

Our picture, then, of the DNA is that it is a long strand with the information carried in a code composed of four digits, that is, the four nucleotide bases. A language which we could symbolise like this ... A B D C C D B A ... I've just made it regular in this case. Now we may ask ourselves whether the protein looks anything like this? Has it any topological resemblance? Here are simplified diagrams of some proteins about which we know a little. I'll put three of them up on the board. (Fig. 2.1) Ribonuclease consists of a single polypeptide chain which is cross-linked in four places, so that it would be constrained to fold in a very odd manner.

Insulin has two polypeptide chains held together by two disulphide bridges. Haemoglobin is a di–mer, consisting of two identical subunits each of which in turn contains two non-identical chains which are, however, not joined together by covalent disulphide bridges. Since both ribonuclease and haemoglobin have spherical or nearly spherical molecular shapes the polypeptide chains must be folded in a number of places. Recent work by Kendrew [1] on myoglobin has shown that this folding can be very complex.

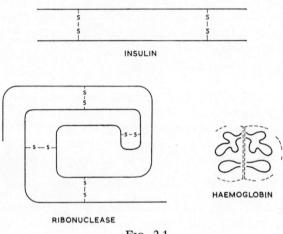

FIG. 2.1

Here, then, we have very crude models of three proteins which have physiological actions and what we want to ask ourselves now is how can something as simple as the linear code — A B D C C D B A — specify structures of this range of complexity?

We can begin by destroying the secondary and tertiary structure, and look at the primary structure. If you could take a protein molecule by its two ends and extend it breaking all cross-links, what you would find is that it can be pulled out into a long polypeptide chain. There is no evidence for any branching in protein molecules, and the only known cross-links are disulphide bridges. It seems that all protein molecules which have been well studied possess this primary structure of a single chain. This chain can now be represented as a unidimensional array of symbols, . . . aklghbbe . . . , each symbol standing for an amino acid residue. Since twenty different amino acids are found in proteins, the polypeptide language has twenty different digits. Thus the polypeptide chain is topologically similar to the DNA chain but whereas the former has twenty different units, the latter has only four.

The hypothesis that we can now propose is that the functional genetic unit—a length of DNA in the genome—determines the details of a length of protein in the cytoplasm. Immediately we are confronted by a new problem. What determines the folding of the polypeptide chain? The simplest view of this is that the folding is, so to speak, self-organising, that is, it is given by the sequence of amino acids in the chain. This theory is called the Sequence Hypothesis by my colleague, Francis Crick, and good arguments can be made to accept it as a working model. We may leave this aside for the moment and proceed to ask what happens when a gene makes a mistake during replication. Suppose that instead of inserting an adenine in a daughter chain a guanine is inserted instead. This means that the new chain will have a different sequence of bases, and if the instructions are wrong the product is going to be wrong. In other words, a mutation which changes the base sequence of DNA will change the amino acid sequence of the protein which is being specified. Instead of one particular amino acid in a given position in the chain, another one will be found.

WADDINGTON: You've got a four digit language in your DNA, but a twenty digit language in your protein. How can this mean that when you make *one* mistake in your DNA, you make *one* alteration in the protein?

BRENNER: Let me first give the experimental evidence. Ingram in the M.R.C. Unit in Cambridge has recently shown that the difference between normal and sickle cell haemoglobin resides in a change in a single amino acid [2]. That is, the two haemoglobins are nearly identical, and in the subunit which contains about 300 amino acids, only one is changed. The change is now known to be a change from a glutamic acid to valine. In addition, he has recently been able to show [3] that in haemoglobin C there is another change in the same place (Fig. 2.2).

Haemoglobin A (normal) . . . his.val.leu.leu.thr.pro.glu.glu.lys . . .

Haemoglobin S   . . . his.val.leu.leu.thr.pro.val.glu.lys . . .

Haemoglobin C   . . . his.val.leu.leu.thr.pro.lys.glu.lys . . .

FIG. 2.2.   Sequence changes in haemoglobin mutants.

WADDINGTON: That's very nice, but isn't it a contradiction to the idea that the change is determined by a single base in nucleic acid, because each base in the DNA must determine several words in the aminoacid language?

BRENNER: No. That depends on the coding. This raises a question of cosmology, if I may put it that way, which I'll come to at the end, as it is more speculative.

We can now classify the consequences of changing an amino acid in a protein. Firstly, the change might be phenotypically unrecognisable; for example, the species differences in insulin cannot be recognised as they all have the same insulin activity physiologically but they do differ in a few aminoacids. This could still be called a mutational change but we shouldn't know it unless we got hold of the different proteins and analysed the aminoacid sequences.

The second possibility is that we may get a partially inactivated protein, that is, a protein which may perform its function but perhaps under different conditions of pH, or temperature. The third consequence is that you may get a totally inactive protein.

We can now predict that if a lot of mutants of a single protein were collected it would be found that the mutant proteins need not be necessarily altered in exactly the same position. You could change the physiological function of the protein by mutations in different parts of the gene. The reason for this is as follows. Suppose we consider an enzyme with a highly folded polypeptide chain. Somewhere on or in this spherical molecule there will be an active centre which catalyses the reaction of substrate molecules. The specific configuration of this active site is most likely to be determined by the relations between a number of polypeptide chains. If the molecule were deformed into its single polypeptide chain, the regions which determine the active site would be found at different places along this chain. Hence, when the phenotype is recognised by a modification of the activity of an enzyme, we do not expect to find an isomorphous relation in the DNA, since it is topologically related only to the extended chain. It is therefore not surprising that there are no gradients along the gene for certain physiological effects, and Demerec's finding that mutations which produce similar defects are found distributed in all parts of a gene is also not surprising but exactly what we would expect.

So far we have discussed the functional genetic unit in terms of its control of a single enzyme. In some cases it is not possible to show biochemically that a single enzyme is involved, since the actual biochemical step involved is not characterised. This applies particularly to mutants in bacteriophages. The use of the so-called *cis-trans* test makes it possible to define functional units more exactly. In this test, two different mutant genomes are inserted into the same cytoplasm by making heterozygotes, heterokaryons or, in the case of phages, by infecting the same cell with two different phages. The phenotype of the complex, with the mutants in the *trans* configuration, is then observed. If the phenotype is mutant, then each mutation affects a unit which cannot complement the other's function. On the other hand, if the phenotype is wild type, then the mutations affect different functional units. Functional units defined by this test have been called cistrons by Benzer [4]. Very frequently, cistrons affecting what appears to be a single phenotype are very closely linked. For example, the two r_{II} cistrons in bacteriophage T4 appear to be contiguous, and the fine mapping studies of Benzer [5] on this system does not reveal a gap between them of any considerable length. Professor Pontecorvo [6] has also described cases of contiguous cistrons affecting what appears to be a unitary function. On the other hand, Demerec and his co-workers [7] have shown that the genes which determine the enzymes synthesising tryptophan and histidine are also closely linked and in the same order as the biosynthetic sequence. In this case it is certain that each of the genetic units controls a different enzyme with a different unitary function. There are many explanations for this correlation which I can't discuss now; what I would like to discuss is why there is close linkage between the two r_{II} cistrons in Benzer's case. Since the two cistrons can perform their functions adequately when they are in different genomes, their contiguity is clearly not essential for their expression. One immediately asks how this close linkage could have arisen.

WEISS: Could I ask a question? In the beginning you said you were going to leave out any spatial or other realistic interpretation of this seriation, and now you bring in proximity.

BRENNER: There is no way of studying the sequence except by genetic methods. There is no way of chemically defining it. No one can do sequence studies on DNA yet.

WEISS: So you infer that this genetic linkage means proximity in the chain?

BRENNER: Yes. The important point is that when a large number of mutants are mapped by genetic means they always give a uni-dimensional linear sequence in the cistron.

WEISS: You are coming back to the spatial description through a genetic means.

BRENNER: Yes. There is no way of determining directly the detailed spatial organisation of DNA, except the genetic.

WEISS: Well, that's what I meant. You're back in the groove.

BRENNER: We're not back in the groove. Or at least if we are, it's a jolly good groove to be in.

PONTECORVO: If you can suggest any other system which will give a uni-dimensional arrangement, except a linear structure . . .

WEISS: Oh, no.

PLAUT: Now the reason you do not postulate the impossibility of a member of another cistron in this place is simply that it has not been found yet.

BRENNER: No, that is . . .

PONTECORVO: Yes.

BRENNER: No.

PONTECORVO: What is the evidence?

BRENNER: In this case here?

PONTECORVO: Yes.

BRENNER: The reason is that if there is another cistron it would be exceedingly small.

PONTECORVO: The fact is that we know already of cases of overlapping cistrons.

BRENNER: Is this the Lederbergs' case [8]?

PONTECORVO: No. This is our own [9].

BRENNER: Well, I think I can give an explanation of yours. To return to the question of two contiguous cistrons. The simple hypothesis is that originally there was one cistron which specified the structure of an enzyme with a single polypeptide chain. Later a mutation occurred in this cistron which had the effect of destroying the information for a single amino acid, so that a gap appeared in the middle of the chain. I will discuss later how such gaps could be produced. The two pieces of polypeptide chain could still come together and fold correctly to produce an enzyme with intact physiological activity but which would now be made of two different chains. The effect of this would be to split the single cistron into two cistrons. These would remain closely linked since the space between them need only be one nucleotide pair in the DNA and the chances of a translocation cutting exactly at this point would be extremely small. The prediction is that insulin and haemoglobin, for example, are each controlled by two cistrons. [Since the Conference, Richards [10] has described an interesting model system with ribonuclease which illustrates the points made above. He has been able to split ribonuclease into two pieces with the enzyme subtilisin. Each fraction can be purified and neither has any enzymatic activity when tested alone. However, when mixed together, the resulting complex has enzymatic activity. The single polypeptide chain is not reformed but the two pieces can still fit together and produce the correct configuration. If this were mimicked by a mutation, then this would result in the appearance of two different cistrons each responsible for the synthesis of a piece of the protein.] The significant feature of this hypothesis is that a single enzyme which acts unitarily physiologically may nevertheless be controlled by more than one cistron.

The last point that I want to make is general and speculative and concerns the coding problem. Exactly how does a DNA sequence transfer information to a polypeptide sequence? Now, it is quite clear that if there is a four digit language to code a twenty digit language, one digit of the first code cannot correspond to one of the second since there would be insufficient information. At least three elements of the DNA code must be used to determine one element of the polypeptide code.

PLAUT: Your are assuming a single chain here. What is the possibility of a regular double helix, as an unsplit entity, forming your protein molecules?

BRENNER: The doubleness of the helix doesn't really matter, because by having two chains you don't get more information.

PLAUT: One determines the other?

BRENNER: Yes. From the information point of view, they amount to a single sequence, although from the stereo-chemical point of view there are problems, which I am going to raise. But first I shall deal with the abstract problem. What I shall discuss is not a perfect theory; in fact, I am going to show what holes there are in it, and how we can try to fill them.

Gamow [11] was the first to suggest a definite solution of the coding problem, but it is known to be incorrect. His ideas were based on false assumptions, but it is useful to discuss them. He began by assuming Astbury's numerological identity; that is, the vertical distance between the bases in DNA, which is 3·3 Å, is almost the same as the chemical repeat between amino acids on a polypeptide chain, which is 3·5 Å. The true crystallographic repeat of a polypeptide chain is 7·0 Å, because the amino acid residues lie on alternate sides of the backbone.

Gamow proposed that three bases are used to code for each amino acid. There are, therefore, $4^3 = 64$ coding triplets but only twenty amino acids. This meant that the code was degenerate, that is, more than one triplet coded for each amino acid. The demand that one base was stereochemically related to one amino acid made the coding overlapping as follows:—

DNA: ... A B B D C D A ...

polypeptide ... a k g e ...

4

Such overlapping triplet codes are, in general, restrictive on amino and sequences although the feature of degeneracy loosens the restrictions considerably. Gamow proposed one way of degenerating the 64 triplets into twenty but it was quickly shown that his code could not code the sequence of insulin. However, if one is prepared to allow free choice in degenerating the 64 triplets the number of possible overlapping triplet codes is immense and it would be impossible to enumerate each one and test it with the existing data. Fortunately, it is possible to show by a simple proof that *all* codes of this type are impossible and the paper dealing with this has just appeared in the Proceedings of the National Academy of Sciences.

This has led to the study of codes which are non-overlapping. Let us consider a non-overlapping triplet code of the type

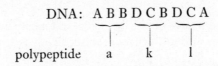

DNA: A B B D C B D C A

polypeptide   a   k   l

This class of codes immediately raises two new problems. The first is how the amino acid finds the triplet that codes for it and does not jam up the template by sitting on overlapping regions. In other words the code must have a comma in the information, which breaks up the string of digits into groups of three. This problem has been ingeniously solved in the commaless code proposed by Crick, Griffiths and Orgel [12]. They divided triplets into two classes: sense triplets which coded for an amino acid and nonsense triplets which did not code for any amino acid. The condition was that whenever two sense triplets were juxtaposed all possible overlaps should be nonsense. That is if ABB and CDA are sense triplets in the sequence ABBCDA then both BBC and BCD should be nonsense. They showed by a simple elegant proof that it was impossible to code for *more* than twenty amino acids, but, what is more, they were able to write down a code—in fact 192 codes—for twenty. These codes place no restriction at all on sequences of amino acids, and they possess a further interesting feature. In the Gamow type of code, all mutations, and certainly those involving substitution of bases, must replace one amino acid by another. In the commaless codes, however, it is possible to go from a sense triplet to a nonsense triplet by mutation and thus interrupt the polypeptide chain. Thus, they provide a mechanism whereby a localised mutation can not only produce a defective protein but also result in the complete absence of a specific protein.

WADDINGTON: Well, there are some points you've left out. You've dealt with the point I was raising earlier as to why a change in one of the bases should affect only one amino acid, by your idea of this non-overlapping code, but you did not say how you again get the amino acids close enough to one another.

BRENNER: This, of course, is a problem. We have several ideas which I could briefly enumerate.

WADDINGTON: Well, let's have at least one.

BRENNER: One idea is very simple. In the cytoplasm there is a linear template of RNA, say, which carries information transmitted to it by DNA. Each amino acid, by the agency of an enzyme, is attached to a trinucleotide which carries the coding triplet for this amino acid. These pair up on the coding template, in the correct order and the trinucleotides are then joined to form a new RNA chain which has an amino acid attached to every third nucleotide. This chain is then coiled up, essentially with a threefold screw, so that the aminoacids lie above each other, and can join up to form a polypeptide chain. This, of course, is speculation.

There is another point I should like to discuss, which concerns the question of why there are chromosomes? I think that this is an important problem, but it doesn't seem to have been talked about much. I should like to begin by trying to define under what conditions we find chromosomes, and under what conditions we find pure DNA.

Let me say at the outset that this will be speculative. In electron micrographs of sectional bacteria, no nuclear structures can be seen. There is no nuclear membrane and the cytoplasm contains lumps or strands in a vacuole which are probably DNA. But, in sections of a yeast cell, or *Chlamydamonas*, a definite nuclear membrane can be seen and the nucleus is very similar to any nucleus in a metazoan cell. Now, the remarkable thing is that the only organisms which do not have typical nuclei are bacteria and blue-green algae which are closely related. Genetic evidence also suggests that in bacteria the genes form one linkage group, and operate through DNA, and not through exchange of chromosomes as in the higher organisms. Bacterial transformation can be accomplished by pure DNA and in transduction it is almost certainly DNA which is transported by phage, and the recent work of Jacob and Wollman [13] at the Pasteur Institute suggests that during conjugation, a DNA strand is injected by the donor into the recipient. The strongest evidence that the genetic system of a bacterium is not a morphological chromosome, but is a long strand of DNA, is the fact that phages are genetically homologous with bacteria.

Well now, let us ask why, or how, this transition occurs from a pure DNA nucleus to the normal type with chromosomes. It seems to me that the most reasonable assumption is that this is correlated with the association of the DNA with a certain class of proteins. I can find no evidence at all that when you extract bacteria for DNA you also extract something like a histone: whereas when you extract an animal cell the DNA comes out with a histone attached.

We cannot define at the moment how this came about, but we may look at the advantages of having a chromosome as a way of organising DNA. Well, the first advantages are, of course, that it gives you the possibility of much more genetic variability. In the bacterial genetic structure there is no obvious way of integrating pieces that fall off. In other words, if a piece is lost there is no way of transposing it to another place. This could explain, for example, why deletions are very common in certain bacterial material, but no one has ever found anything which looks like a translocation. Thus, in pure DNA genetic structure it is not easily possible to shift the genes around the genome. Hence, the linkages, like those described by Demerec, may survive because there is no ready mechanism for redistributing the genes. It is only when you get a chromosomal mechanism that you can shift genes around from place to place. The last idea I would like to throw out is that the chromosome contains some mechanism which allows genes to be switched off; in another words, it is possible that differentiation cannot be accomplished with a pure DNA structure. All the genes have to go on working. Perhaps I'll return to this later in the Symposium. I am sorry to have taken so much time.

PLAUT: I gather that your mechanism of information-transfer from gene to protein does not preclude the possibility that this initial transfer also involves the replication of the initial chain of DNA?

BRENNER: There's nothing to exclude it; in other words, DNA makes RNA and RNA makes DNA, although I doubt it.

PLAUT: Not protein?

BRENNER: No. Here we may state what Crick calls the Central Dogma. That is, that once information gets into protein it can't get out; in other words, protein can't code back. It can't make specific RNA. But let me just make one clear distinction. When I say protein can't make RNA, I do not mean there are not protein enzymes involved in making the nucleotides and putting the pieces together. What I mean is that information in an aminoacid sequence can't be transferred to a nucleic acid. There are two grounds for saying this, which I think are too technical to go into.

PLAUT: If one sticks to this dogma then, and seeks an indirect mechanism for DNA replication, then one might suggest that RNA is involved first.

BRENNER: There is, of course, a good case for DNA making DNA. It would be very interesting to know from the people who work on autoradiographs whether, when DNA is making DNA, it makes RNA at the same time. That's a very important question.

WADDINGTON: I haven't got quite where the RNA comes in. You've got transfer of information between DNA and protein, provided the RNA . . .

BRENNER: The RNA is a messenger. What we postulate is that the DNA specifies the RNA, and the RNA does the work of specifying the polypeptide chain.

WADDINGTON: You're assuming, then, that the RNA has a sequence of bases like the DNA?

BRENNER: I won't say similar, I'll say it has a sequence of bases. It may be quite completely dissimilar, but it carries the information.

WADDINGTON: But what about your arguments about the translation from a four digit to a twenty digit language—the four digits of DNA to the twenty digits of protein—unless RNA has the same sort of four digit system the argument does not apply.

BRENNER: No. But the point that I was making was this, that if the DNA has a sequence adenine, thymine, guanine, adenine, it does not mean that the homologous RNA contains the same sequence.

WADDINGTON: No. But it must have four bases of some kind.

BRENNER: Four bases certainly, which suffice to carry the information. RNA, of course, does not contain thymine, but uracil.

BRACHET: But we do not really know the structure of RNA. You are basing your idea of this on what we know about the structure of DNA; but if we have to think of RNA as an intermediary, you have to imagine it has a rather similar structure. But is RNA linear?

BRENNER: I think that all the chemical evidence shows that RNA is linear, but there is no X-ray evidence.

BRACHET: One of the troubles with the problem of protein synthesis is where do you get the activation energy.

BRENNER: Well, there I can give you a scheme, and this is only a scheme, I underline, where we have few experimental facts. We'll start in the nucleus with a piece of DNA, which is a duplex. One chain runs in one direction; the other chain runs in the opposite direction. This is obvious because you must be able to flip over the base to accomplish the base pairing. We then assume that in some way this makes an RNA chain which is nuclear RNA, template RNA, and which carries the information. Now somewhere, either in the nucleus or in the cytoplasm, this RNA is packed into a microsomal particle. We know very little about the structure of these particles but we can assume that the RNA is inside a protein shell which is purely structural, that is, has no information and is composed of sub-units which repeat. The simplest form of this theory is that every microsomal particle, irrespective of what product it makes, has the same structural protein. These particles could be made in the nucleus and extruded as formed structures, or the RNA could leak out and be wrapped up in the cytoplasm. Next, we know that in the cytoplasm there are enzymes called activating enzymes. These activating enzymes catalyse the formation of an amino acyl AHP compound from ATP and an amino acid. There is good evidence that there is one activating enzyme for each amino acid. The tryptophan-activating enzyme has been crystallised by Lipmann [14].

Now it is known from experiments on homogenates and isolated fractions that amino acids can be incorporated into these particles. The assumption is that what we call incorporation is the same as synthesis. There is, however, evidence for this. It has since been shown by pulse experiments that in whole cells amino acids flow through the microsomal particles on the way to protein. For example, if reticulocytes are exposed to ^{14}C-leucine, then killed at different times after that, the isotope enters the microsomal fraction rapidly and then the activity declines in three minutes. Thereafter, the radioactivity of haemoglobin increases [15]. In other words this is good evidence that most of the protein in the particle is inert, and that the protein synthesised in the microsomal particles is subsequently leaving it. Each amino acid has the same AMP when activated so that this nucleotide cannot function in the coding. There must be some way of transferring this to a coding system, and Hoagland [16] has recently found that these amino acids are transferred to cytoplasmic RNA. Now, somehow the amino acids go from the cytoplasmic RNA into the particle and there are three theories. One is that this whole piece of RNA goes in and is lined up by the template RNA. This seems to be nonsense because the amino acids presumably have the correct order and you wouldn't need the particles. The second is that this RNA is chopped into small pieces, each attached to an amino acid, and that these find their way into the particles where they are lined up. Three, that the compound which actually goes into the particles is an activating enzyme with, attached to it, a small piece of RNA and the amino acid. One prediction of this theory is that the template RNA will be metabolically relatively inert. It also predicts that there is an independent cytoplasmic RNA, which can be made in the absence of the nucleus, and which turns over rapidly.

BRACHET: My question is whether this AMP part should not have DNA.

BRENNER: No.

BRACHET: What is the relation between the architecture of the template mechanism and the architecture of the protein molecule?

BRENNER: Consider the old idea of a template which was current in thinking about this problem some years ago. The template presented a surface with a lot of specific holes into which the different amino acids fit. Let us ask this question: how do we make a template which can distinguish between valine and *iso*leucine which differ only by single methyl group? We may assume that the error rate of protein synthesis is not more than 1% and very probably lower than this. A template would therefore have to distinguish between valine and *iso*leucine with an accuracy of greater than 99%. This cannot be accomplished by van der Waal's forces though there are ways of doing it that are too technical to discuss now. But the significant point is that no structure of RNA or DNA can be conceived which can accomplish this distinction. These are polar structures and their surface forms a pattern of hydrogen bond acceptors and donors. They have no hydrophobic niches. Thus we must conclude that amino acids do not go on to nucleic acid templates as amino acids. We are driven to consider what may be called the Adaptor Hypothesis which was suggested by Crick in 1955 [17]. That is, the amino acid is first combined with some adaptor molecule for which the template is sensitive. Since this combination is specific, there must be twenty different enzymes for the twenty different amino acids. The activating enzymes are good candidates for this function.

PLAUT: I wonder if this would be a good time to present what little evidence there is suggesting that in the chromosome DNA does not make DNA directly.

WADDINGTON: Yes, I think you might as well do it now.

PLAUT: I'll try to do this rather briefly. The evidence comes from the *Crepis* experiment which Mazia and I did earlier [18], plus the work I've done since then. If one obtains an unsymmetrical distribution of newly synthesised DNA in mitotic division, then it becomes extremely difficult to think of DNA replication by the system of a splitting of the double helix and a re-synthesis of partners. If you look at the molecule after it has done this, then both of the double helices ought to be equally old and new; that is, equally labelled. If one obtains pools of such molecules the same will apply and they ought to be equally labelled. If they are not, then the average DNA molecule can't replicate by this system, it can't involve the permanent split of the double helices, unless one makes the rather difficult assumption that only a few of the chromosomal DNA molecules replicate, the rest do not, and these few replicate by the Watson–Crick system.

PONTECORVO: What about Taylor?

PLAUT: Well, I've tried to qualify it. This is from the *Crepis* work and if that turns out to be wrong I should be very much surprised, but I am assuming now that it is not, but that it is correct. Taylor's work [19] as far as I can see supports neither one nor the other. I don't think it can be used to give critical support for the replication scheme.

BRENNER: There is a possible way of investigating this problem in bacteriophage. We ask what happens when a mistake is made during the replication of DNA. We assume the Watson–Crick mechanism of replication, namely, that the parental duplex separates and each chain guides the synthesis of a complementary partner. Since the parental chains are inviolate, the mutation occurs in the newly synthesised complement so that the product expected is a molecular heterozygote, containing one wild type chain and one mutant chain. When these structures replicate again they should produce one wild type and one mutant duplex. These molecular heterozygotes should be matured like any other DNA, so that one could expect to find infective phage particles which give a mixture of wild type and mutant progeny. We have not done any serious work on this, but plan to, using mutagens which increase mutation rate a hundred fold. This makes the problem technically feasible.

WADDINGTON: Of course, the same difficulty really arises in much greater form in higher organisms, when you are dealing with chromosomes which are certainly composed of a large number of double helices running in parallel. In forms where you have a DNA genetic system, you have only one continuous chain, but in higher organism chromosomes, at any time you can see them, the chromosomes are certainly much thicker and have many parallel chains.

WILDE: I would like to ask a question for information. Where does the recent report that many of us heard at St. Andrews, by Allfrey and Mirsky [20], fit—that the incorporation of amino acids in thymus nuclei could be mediated equally well by DNA, RNA, the hydrolysis and dialysis products of DNA, and polyadenylic acid? According to this paper all of these were essentially equally efficient in favouring the uptake of aminoacids. It was an isolated system, of course, and I'm just asking from ignorance.

BRENNER: Well, I think if I can make a comment on that; if you study the sequence of some of the papers of Mirsky, there has been a progressive dilution in the interpretation. The first paper said that you had to have DNA, the second paper postulated that you had to make an RNA, and the third paper showed that even small polynucleotides were efficient. I should recommend that one should wait a while before giving a firm interpretation of this. They suggest that the polynucleotides are functional in making ATP.

WADDINGTON: It is not clear, is it, that those amino acids have been taken up into chromosomal protein?

BRACHET: No, a protein associated with DNA showed very high incorporation, but it was not a histone.

PONTECORVO: If it is in order to go back to the idea of the cistron, I would like to raise a question. I didn't quite catch Brenner's point of a protein that has evolved by duplication. How can you explain a thing like the results in *Aspergillus* published by Calef [21] and expanded recently by Martin–Smith [22]? You have this sort of arrangement. There are a number of mutants which are phenotypically identical; they determine a requirement for adenine and are arranged in the following order: 33, 13, 9, 17, 15, 32, within less than one unit. 17 and 15 belong to different cistrons by the test of complementarity. 17 and 32 belong again to different cistrons for the same reason. All the other relations of all of these six two by two indicate that they belong to the same cistron, and that is their order.

BRENNER: Well, we can find a good explanation of this, I think. Let us ask ourselves what happens when you do the heterokaryon test.

PONTECORVO: It's really the heterozygote test.

BRENNER: Would you accept it would work in a heterokaryon?

PONTECORVO: Yes, I know it.

BRENNER: Good.

PONTECORVO: It's the same, at least qualitatively the same.

BRENNER: Now let's ask ourselves exactly what must occur to reconstitute the wild type. Let us assume that here we have the case of a protein constructed of two polypeptide chains each determined by a different cistron. When two nuclei, damaged by mutation in different cistrons, are put into the same cell, the enzyme can be made, because the two polypeptide chains will still be produced, even if the information is present in different nuclei. This is reasonable, since if the information in each cistron is transferred to the cytoplasm, for example in an RNA template, these templates would have no way of knowing whether they came from the same or different nuclei. We now assume that this RNA template carries the information from *both* cistrons. Hence, each template makes two protein chains, which under normal conditions would fold up, and interlock to produce the functioning enzyme. Let us now consider the case of anomalous mutants. First, consider one of the templates. This makes one good polypeptide chain while the other has some mistake in it. If these combined with each other, a non-functioning enzyme would be produced, but, what is more, there would not be an excess of the good chain available for combination with the intact product of the other template. In other words, preferential combination in some mutants leads to breakdown of the *cis-trans* test. This is not purely theoretical since this anomaly is known to occur at a higher level of protein organisation. The haemoglobin molecule has a molecular weight of 68,000 and is built up of two identical halves, each of molecular weight of 34,000. Although each half-molecule contains two non-identical chains, this fact need not concern us here. In sickle cell anaemia, the individual is homozygous for the mutation and the haemoglobin molecules differ from normal ones, possessing two negative charges less per 68,000 unit. An individual with the sickle cell trait is heterozygous and has one normal gene and one sickle cell gene. What sort of haemoglobin molecules should be found? I would say that this individual should have three kinds of haemoglobin: one composed of two normal half molecules, i.e. normal haemoglobin; another composed of two sickle cell half molecules, i.e. sickle cell haemoglobin; and a third, new, type, composed of one normal half molecule and one sickle cell half molecule. These should be in the ratios 1 : 1 : 2. The remarkable fact is that this expectation is not realised and the "hybrid" molecules are *not* found. Instead, the heterozygous individual produces roughly equal quantities of normal and of sickle cell haemoglobin. In other words, here preferential combination occurs always between identical halves and although this is not a *cis-trans* test it is a model of what I have been discussing. Incidentally, this very feature of the haemoglobins would make *cis-trans* tests very difficult to interpret.

WADDINGTON: You mean that in the actual case the sickle cell heterozygote does not produce the three types?

BRENNER: The heterozygote does not produce the three types. In other words, it can't mix even at the level of the half molecule.

SOMEBODY: The heterozygotes are always the same, are they?

BRENNER: In the heterozygote you find the two haemoglobins. You find SS in about a half and AA in about a half. In other words, you find the sickle cell haemoglobin and normal haemoglobin but you do not find the haemoglobin which is intermediate. This applies to all of the traits that have been investigated. It applies to the CA trait, the CS trait and the ES trait. I think this is an illustration of how the *cis-trans* test could break down. I am emphasising the possibility that there may be conditions which result in the preferential association of products of the same nucleus.

I think this is quite an important point to bear in mind and you could expect to find anomalies of this sort appearing now.

WADDINGTON: Well, I think it's time now that we brought this morning session to a close. We have now had a good time on the DNA chain. This afternoon we'll deal with the chromosome on a more complex level, but with this material in the background we'll try to make some bridge between them.

REFERENCES

1. KENDREW, J. C., G. BODO, H. M. DINTZIS, R. G. PARRISH and H. WYCKOFF (1958) Nature, Lond. 181, 662.
2. INGRAM, V. M. (1957) Nature, Lond. 180, 326.
3. HUNT, J. A. and V. M. INGRAM (1958) Nature, Lond. 181, 1062.
4. BENZER, S. (1957) In The Chemical Basis of Heredity. Ed. McElroy, W. D. and B. Glass. Baltimore: Johns Hopkins Press.
5. BENZER, S. (as 4).
6. PONTECORVO, G. (1956) Cold Spring Harbor Symp. Quant. Biol. 21, 171.
7. DEMEREC, M. and Z. HARTMAN, also P. E. HARTMAN (1956) Genetic Studies with Bacteria, Carnegie Institution of Washington Publication 612, pp. 5 and 35.
8. LEDERBERG, J. (private communication).
9. PONTECORVO, G. (private communication).
10. RICHARDS, F. (1958) Proc. Nat. Acad. Sci., Wash. 44, 162.
11. GAMOW, G. (1954) Biol. Medd. Dan. Vld. Selsk. 22, No. 2.
12. CRICK, F. H. C., J. S. GRIFFITH and L. E. ORGEL (1957) Proc. Nat. Acad. Sci., Wash. 43, 416.
13. JACOB, F. and E. L. WOLLMAN (1958) Symposia Society Experimental Biology 12, 75.
14. DAVIE, E. W., V. V. KONINGSBERGER and F. LIPMANN (1956) Arch. Biochem. Biophys. 65, 21.
15. RABINOVITCH, M. and M. E. OLSON (1956) Exp. Cell Res. 10, 747.
16. HOAGLAND, M. B., P. C. ZAMECNIK and M. L. STEPHENSON (1957) Biochem. Biophys. Acta 24, 215.
17. See CRICK, F. H. C. (1958) Symposia Society Experimental Biology 12, 138.
18. PLAUT, W. and D. MAZIA (1956) J. Biophys. Biochem. Cytol. 2, 573.
19. TAYLOR, J. H., P. S. WOODS and W. L. HUGHES (1957) Proc. Natl. Acad. Sci. U.S. 43, 122, 1957.
20. ALLFREY, V. G., A. E. MIRSKY and S. OSAWA (1955) Nature, Lond. 176, 1042; (1957) J. Gen. Physiol. 40, 451.
21. CALEF, E. (1957) Heredity 11, 265.
22. MARTIN-SMITH, C. A. (1957) Microbiol. Gen. Bull. 15, 20.

CHAPTER III

Organisation of the Chromosome

WADDINGTON: Perhaps it's about time we reminded ourselves that biology is a material science. Let's go on this afternoon to the chromosome as a material structure. We've got quite a large array of talent on this subject here now. I believe that Mick Callan is willing to start things off by showing us some pictures of his beautiful chromosomes.

CALLAN: What I think I'd like to do is to run through the document I've circulated and point out a few things that are not mentioned in it. I should like first to give you some idea of what lampbrush chromosomes look like [1]. You can find lampbrush chromosomes in the oocytes of a wide variety of organisms. This slide shows the complete complement in a newt oocyte. There are twelve bivalent chromosomes and the longest of these chromosomes (I) is some 700 μ in total over-all length. The next slide shows simply one chromosome. As it happens it is the smallest chromosome (XII). Each chromosome has an axis, which I shall be talking about in a moment, and lateral loops which give it this characteristic appearance. It is possible when you've studied these things for some time to get to know your way about these preparations and to be able to return time after time to consider one and the same locus on a chromosome. It's not, of course, anything like such a straightforward affair as following one locus on a salivary gland chromosome, but in some respects it is perhaps more informative.

I would like to show you what a small part of one of these lampbrush chromosomes looks like (Fig. 3.1). There is first of all a chromosome axis, which may not be resolvable in the light microscope: there's no certainty about this, but it's quite clear that along this axis there are a series of things which can be resolved, and one calls them chromomeres. They have different shapes and sizes. The order of magnitude of these chromomeres when they're clearly visible is about 1 μ in diameter. Coming from these chromomeres on the axis there are pairs of large lateral projections. The axes in these lateral projections can occasionally be seen in some loops in the phase contrast microscope. They're almost certainly really submicroscopic but Dr. Gall has clearly shown that they exist, by means of electron microscope work and pepsin digestion. Some at any rate of these chromomeres have an axis in the loop and some very fuzzy material which is scattered around the axis. One can't help having the impression, from the majority of such loops, that this material which is sticking out from the axis consists of a series of little fibres, but whether that's really

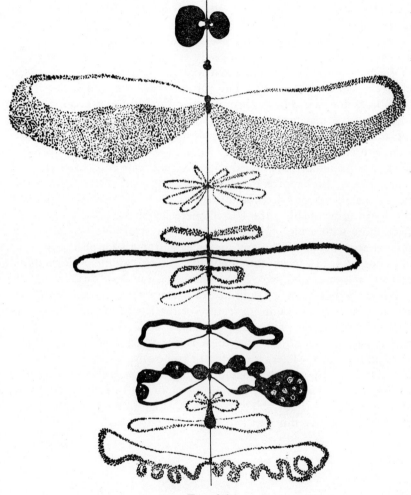

Fig. 3.1

so or not I wouldn't like to swear. Embedded in this material are very often, in some loops at any rate, granules which are highly refractile, and others have been clearly shown to contain RNA. They may have a particular orderly distribution along the loop and there are quite frequently signs of a spiral organisation in the whole affair. Well, that's merely what one particular type of lampbrush looks like; there is in fact an enormous range in the morphological picture. If you go from one end of a chromosome to another, and look at different chromosomes, the morphology of these loops is tremendously varied. It is not even constant at any one locus, because if you compare for any particular locus the appearance in young and old oocytes there are considerable differences.

Some of the points I would like to make are these. If you follow an individual locus which you can easily recognise, and study the situation in early oocytes, in medium sized and in older oocytes, there is quite clearly a sequence of events. The chromosomes start out with very small lampbrush loops and large chromomeres, then in the process of development the loops may get bigger and bigger and if you happen to have chosen a giant pair of loops they may stretch out to a quite remarkable distance from the chromosome axis, 2 or 300 μ in some cases. By the time the loops are maximally developed there is practically no chromomere left. This process also happens in reverse. We start with a structure which has large loops and a small chromomere: as the oocyte continues to mature the loops grow smaller, the chromomere larger, and finally you end up once more with a big chromomere and very small loops. This developmental sequence is not by any means synchronous for all the loci on the chromosomes. It looks extremely likely that chromomeric material is actually spun out into these loops and makes up their axes.

Now, another point I would like to make is this. If you look carefully at lampbrush chromosomes a feature of the lateral loops is that they are all asymmetric. Each has a thin end and a thick end, and of the material that is massed around the axis, there is very much more of it on one side than on the other. There are at least two possible explanations as to why this should be the case, but one possibility at least is this. In the process of loop axis extrusion from the chromomere the extrusion starts, say, at this region which I am going to mark X (Fig. 3.2) and always continues from there; that is, this part here (Y) is the part which has been extruded

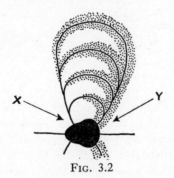

FIG. 3.2

from the chromomere for the longest time. As the loop extrusion proceeds more and more gets piled on to the Y side so that while the recently extruded stuff is still by the point X the most antique loop axis, the part that's been extruded longest of all, is on side Y. There's a great deal of evidence, coming from a number of sources that I'll not go into, that what are produced on these loops are primary gene products which periodically slough off or disperse in some fashion into the nuclear sap. From then on I don't know much about what happens to them. Well now, this interpretation of loop asymmetry I have given depends on the assumption that synthetic processes have been occurring longer at point Y than at point X.

There is an alternative interpretation. The axis of each loop may be some sort of assembly-belt system where material is drawn in at one region, passes along the loop and when it has passed through a sufficient number of transformations it is pushed off as the finished product. I personally favour the first explanation because stuff which sloughs off from these loops does not slough off only at the "finished" end; it can also slough off at intermediate places.

Let's just consider orders of magnitude for a moment. You may assume each loop to be about 20 μ in length. If anything this is an under estimate. You may consider that there are of the order between 6 and 10,000 chromomeres in the entire chromosome complement. Neglecting the fact that from many of the chromomeres multiple loops project, you will have a total length of loop axis which you can work out for yourselves. Yes, if you consider 6000 chromomeres to be the number and 20 μ the average loop length, then the genetic material of these *Triturus Cristatus Carnifex* nuclei is in fact of the order of length of 25 cm. Now, I think Dr. Gall might very well have something to say in a few moments as to how many strands of DNA may possibly be involved in a formation of this kind. There can't be very many. No one in fact to my knowledge has estimated the amount of DNA in a newt oocyte nucleus but it would be my guess that it is in fact only four times the sperm amount.

BRENNER: How much is the haploid amount of DNA?

CALLAN: You can answer that, Joe, I think.

GALL: I was just going to make one comment first. Alfert and Swift [2 have measured respectively the oocytes in the mouse and the grasshopper and in those two cases there is the 4C amount of DNA, at least during the early stages when the oocyte is sufficiently condensed for photometric methods. In regard to the total amount of DNA, the C amount for the frog, or at least for *Rana pipiens*, is 7.5×10^{-12} which works out to around 15 cm of DNA per chromosome.

WADDINGTON: Per chromosome, or per nucleus?

GALL: Per chromosome, yes. Now, in the newt there is probably something like five times that much.

CALLAN: One further point I would make is this. There is pretty good evidence in this material that one can directly see allelic differences at specific genetic loci and I think that's really a rather spectacular sight. I would like to show you just one slide.

PONTECORVO: Now, these are paired chromosomes in diplotene?

CALLAN: Well that is rather a moot point. My interpretation of the situation is this. At the chromomeres carrying twin loops they are in diplotene, but between the chromomeres, well anyone's guess is as good as another's; I personally see only one strand. The chromosome is in effect a series of single-double single-double structures. It is certainly diplotene in the sense that the chromosomes are held together, homologue to homologue, at places which are almost certainly chiasmata.

WADDINGTON: At the chromomeres there are always at least one pair of loops?

CALLAN: Yes, excepting—I will mention an exception which in effect proves the rule—excepting in the parts of the chromosomes where the axis is quite definitely double, as at the ends of chromosome XII and in the middle of chromosome XII, where the axes are split: the chromomeres there, or at least some of the chromomeres there, carry single loops.

Figure 3.3 shows chromosome XII and one particular locus which I've

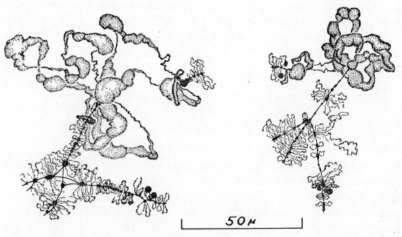

50μ

FIG. 3.3

studied very carefully is the great multiple looped thing in it. Let me tell you straightaway that it can be absent on both the homologues of chromosome XII or present on one chromosome XII and absent on the partner. The other thing in this picture, by the way, is chromosome XI which has a giant loop at this locus and in this particular instance it's a homozygote. The next slide shows another example of chromosome XII where again this loop is present on one homologue but absent on the partner. Perhaps you'd better also see it drawn. This is an accurate drawing of that particular loop. The multiple loop locus happens in this case to have broken in a very characteristic way within the chromomere, so that part of the loop is pulled out in this fashion and the homologous region down here is something like that, and the corresponding loop in another cell like that. Now when you find the situation in a given individual, it happens in every oocyte at the stage when the particular loop locus is sufficiently large to be seen, and if you go back to the same newt several months later you find precisely the same picture as you were finding several months before.

One other reason, incidentally, for supposing that these loop axes are part of the fundamental permanent genetic axis of the chromosome is that when you stretch a lampbrush chromosome, as very often happens by accident in preparation, and break it, the breakage occurs so that two lampbrush loops span a break (Fig. 3.4). The asymmetry of lampbrush loops is seen clearly in the broken region. That is, the break has occurred through the chromomere, and that is an absolutely regular feature. In other words, if you pulled out the chromosome you would have a long chain structure, single-double, single-double, single-double.

WADDINGTON: I don't quite understand how you reconcile this with the heterozygous effects, in which one of the giant loops is absent in one of the arms. If it is part of the genetic material, this would be more like a deficiency than a failure of expression in the heterozygote.

CALLAN: It's certainly not a deficiency, because you can in fact find at precisely the same locus either a small loop whose morphology looks very similar to the developed big one—I've got a drawing of this somewhere—or one which looks like the generality of the loops in the sense that it's a pretty ordinary one.

WADDINGTON: But when you've got a large loop developed on one chromosome you have got there a long length of genetic material, whereas on the homologous chromosome you've only got a short length.

CALLAN: Ah, but a much larger chromomere.

WADDINGTON: Oh, you've a larger chromomere? So you think the length of the genetic material may be similar in both arms?

5

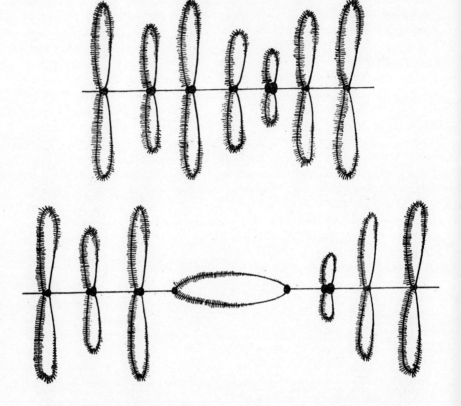

FIG. 3.4. Diagram showing how an axial break in a lampbrush chromosome comes to be spanned by two lampbrush strands. Above, unbroken; below, broken.

CALLAN: Yes, and it's merely by extension that the locus comes into synthetic activity.

WILDE: Homozygosity and heterozygosity are genetic terms which are concerned with the transmission of genes. Your evidence for using these terms is that you find similarity from oocyte to oocyte, not only contemporaneously but also through extended time; it is not from crossing experiments? Is that right?

CALLAN: No, the crossing experiments are underway at the moment, but I should like to say a little bit more on this point. Calling these things, for the time, plus or minus, I have worked the situation out for 13 individuals for two loci. The evidence is that they run in a genetic way.

These are simply counts of the numbers of individuals with the various constitutions (Table 3.1). And these numbers fit beautifully with the

TABLE 3.1

TRITURUS CRISTATUS CARNIFEX

Individual	Chromosome X			Chromosome XII		
C	$-/-$			$-/-$		
D	$-/-$			$-/-$		
E	$+/-$			$-/-$		
F	$+/-$			$-/-$		
G	$+/+$			$-/-$		
J	$-/-$			$+/-$		
L	$+/-$			$-/-$		
M	$-/-$			$+/-$		
N	$+/-$			$-/-$		
O	$-/-$			$-/-$		
P	$-/-$			$-/-$		
Q	$+/-$			$+/-$		
R	$+/+$			$+/-$		
	$-/-$	$+/-$	$+/+$	$-/-$	$+/-$	$+/+$
Observed	6	5	2	9	4	0
Expected	5·6	5·9	1·6	9·3	3·4	0·3

standard $P^2 + 2PQ + Q^2$ formula. That is, assuming they're genes. Several appropriate crosses are underway at the moment and I shall study them and then be able to say definitely.

BRENNER: What is this spot between the chromomeres?

CALLAN: The loop axis is resistant to pepsin digestion as Gall has shown, and the interchromomeric material is also resistant to pepsin digestion. I have shown in the EM that the dried and somewhat stretched inter-chromomeric axis is about 200 Å wide. But, before you start thinking of lots of strands I would like you to remember just how extensible this stuff is. You can pull on these chromosomes in natural conditions, and stretch them $2\frac{1}{2}$ times in length before they reach an elastic limit. Now, if the material is not pulled out from the chromomeres, but if in fact all the stretching is taking place in these regions between chromomeres, as simple observation tends to suggest, then the actual chromonema between chro-momeres is being stretched just about ten times.

WADDINGTON: Aren't these newts giving a somewhat old-fashioned look at the way we expounded the structure of the chromosome this morning?

Here we are getting what appears to be a distinction between the beads on the string and the string itself, possibly between genes and connecting-genes. Is there any sort of basis for supposing that the genetic behaviour of the material that is in the part of the string that comes out in loops might be different from the part which is in the connections?

CALLAN: No.

WADDINGTON: Couldn't they conceivably differ in their recombination frequencies, or something of that sort? Certainly the appearances suggest a distinction between two kinds of genetic material, if both the axis and the loops form part of the genetic string.

CALLAN: Yes, that's frankly my opinion, although I haven't any very strong evidence about it.

RIS: May I add something here. From my own experience with lamp-brush chromosomes [3] I have arrived at a picture that differs in many ways from Dr. Callan's. This concerns especially the structure of the "loops". The electron microscope shows that these "loops" look just like a chromonema in other chromosomes, for instance, in leptotene of insects or of lilies or *Tradescantia*. It is a bundle of coiled fibrils and definitely not a single thin strand with granules attached to it. The "chromomeres" or, as I prefer to call them, "heterochromatic segments", consist of the same sort of fibrils but they are here more densely packed together. The "loops" are Feulgen negative, but give a reaction for protein and RNA. The heterochromatic segments are Feulgen positive. During the development of the "loops" the chromosome increases many hundred fold in mass and volume, yet even at its maximum size it consists throughout of typical microfibrils. New material must have been added in the form of such microfibrils. Since it is pretty certain that neither DNA or histone have increased, this material must be mainly non-histone protein and RNA. From chemical studies of chromosomes of various cell types we know that such an increase in non-histone protein and RNA always occurs in chromosomes of actively synthesising cells. As a working hypothesis I have suggested that the formation of "loops" is the visible expression of this chemical change. Now it appears that "loops" are part of the continuous chromonemata which are coiled up tightly in the heterochromatic sections and less so in the "loops". If this is so then the loop material must have been added to the chromonema internally between DNA containing sections. Thus the chromonema increases in length as the non-histone protein increases and this expresses itself in the formation of loops. According to this view, the chromonema consists of segments that contain mainly DNA-histone and are more or less constant and in between these other regions containing the non-histone protein which increases or decreases in length depending on the physiological state of the cell. How this is brought about is difficult to understand at present, but I think this tentative picture fits best with the cytochemical and electron microscopic observations.

BRENNER: I am not sure of the orientation of the loops in relation to the main strand.

RIS: The "main strand" is not in reality continuous because the chromonema goes out into the "loops". I think some of the apparent continuity of the chromosome "axis" is due to the stickiness of the heterochromatic segments and these sticky connections break if the chromosome is stretched. We see then two heterochromatic segments connected by stretched "loops" as Dr. Callan has described.

CALLAN: Can I ask just one question? How do you reconcile that, Ris, with the statement I've made, and that I'm sure is right, that if you follow one specific locus, the loops, when they're very small, are attached to resolvable chromomeres, and when the loops have maximally developed there are virtually no chromomeres at all at this point of origin?

RIS: I have not made any measurements on "chromomere volume" during loop formation, but it is not my impression that the total mass of all "chromomeres" or heterochromatic segments decreases in any way. "Chromomeres" may be smaller in fully developed lampbrush chromosomes but this may be due to splitting up of large "chromomeres" into several smaller ones during chromosome growth.

CALLAN: Well, there is an extraordinarily precise inverse relationship between the loops size and the chromomeres size, that is all I'm trying to point out.

GALL: I don't want to emphasise the difference between Ris' view and mine and Callan's, since there is general agreement that the ribonucleoprotein material is part of the chromosome and that the loop forms a portion of the continuous stand. However, I would like to remind you of what happens when one puts the chromosome into dilute saline [4]. The loops, as far as one can see in the light microscope, just disappear and you are left with the chromomeres in their normal order and relationship. Often you don't even see the very fine connections between the chromomeres. This experiment led me, at first, to think that the loops are ancillary material and that structural continuity exists only along the chromosome axis. Later, Callan's evidence from stretching experiments indicated that the loops are part of a continuous strand, and I went back to examine dissolved chromosomes more thoroughly. For technical reasons I used chromosomes treated with pepsin rather than dilute saline, but these look very similar. Well, if you look at such digested chromosomes in the electron microscope, you will find a very fine undigested loop axis with dimensions about the same as the strand in between chromomeres. This means that the fundamental, or if you will, continuous strand is a sub-microscopic one and that the ribonucleoprotein material, at least from a structural point of view, can be removed completely from the chromosome without interfering with the integrity of the strand. For this reason I disagree with Dr. Ris in putting the ribonucleoprotein right into the structural axis of the chromosome.

It is important to give a dimensional analysis of what we have here, as Dr. Callan has mentioned. Now, if you simply multiply the number of loops by their average length you get a chromosome of the order of 5 cm. The total length of all the DNA molecules in such a chromosome is about 90 cm. Our estimate of chromosome length is made simply on the basis of the length of all the loops, ignoring any material which is wound up in the chromomeres and which would increase our estimate considerably. I think the important thing you can say from this is that the total length of the chromosome approaches the total length of all the DNA molecules of that chromosome.

Here I would like to put in the rather heretical viewpoint that perhaps the chromosomes of higher organisms may have the sort of simple DNA structure that everyone talks about for viruses and bacteria. Rather than assume that chromosomes of higher organisms are multiple stranded we might at least keep an open mind to the possibility that they are not highly multiple. Most of the evidence for multiple strandedness is based on cytological observations right at the limit of resolution of the light microscope. In other words, just for the non-cytologist, let's say that this doubleness, quadrupleness, etc., of the chromosome is not the sort of thing you can demonstrate easily to an unbiased observer. It seems to me that many lines of evidence are more easily interpreted in terms of a single stranded chromosome. Without going into the details of the Plaut–Taylor argument, Taylor's experiment is certainly interpretable—although he doesn't himself make exactly this interpretation—on a single DNA strand type of chromosome. We have the obvious evidence that crossing over occurs between chromatids and not between sub-units. The chromatid, which is the unit of crossing over, contains the unit amount of DNA for each organism, and this is the amount of duplication also. So following these lines of evidence it seems to me a very real possibility that the chromosome of higher organisms is in fact built along a single chain type of structure.

WEISS: Could I ask if the nuclear sap, so called, is solid in these nuclei?

GALL: I would say yes. It varies considerably in consistency in different organisms, but it's generally speaking a gel.

CALLAN: It varies quite a lot from stage to stage to within a single oocyte. The sap around the chromosomes in fact tends to disperse rather more easily in older oocytes than in very young ones.

WEISS: Why I asked the question is that it is very fundamental for organisation. If you are assuming here a single molecule of enormous length strung out, it must be somehow protected against disruption by the random movements of its surroundings.

CALLAN: It's very well protected.

WEISS: It is.

MITCHISON: Could you tell us about the action of DNAase.

GALL: Before that could I make just one comment? I did not mean to imply that the chromosome must be one single molecule. It could be a chain of DNA molecules with breaks along the chain, structural continuity being supplied by protein or anything else.

WEISS: I thought that was what you inferred by the comparison of the DNA values and the length and total volume in the calculations you have just given.

GALL: Whatever the form of the DNA, I only meant that it is laid out continuously rather than having a lateral redundancy.

WADDINGTON: How do you envisage the mechanics of recombination in this thing? You've got your chromosomes laid out pretty well unravelled and it's going to be rather complicated to cross over from one chromosome to another in this situation.

GALL: Well, that raises a serious problem, but it's really not more serious than with a multiple strand chromosome which has to cross over in many strands all at the same place.

PONTECORVO: Could we discuss this differentiation business now?

BEERMANN: I would just like to remind you here, that from radiation experiments, as far as I am informed, it is very well known that many chromosomes are multi-stranded. There are breaks, and recombinations between breaks, not only in chromatids and chromosomes but also in sub-chromatids—at least in half-chromatids, I do not know whether anything has been found where it is something still less which is broken in one chromosome.

GALL: I'd like to hear some of the radiation people discuss this because I only know two or three examples of this. A half-chromatid break could perhaps be a break in only one of the two stands in a DNA molecule.

WADDINGTON: What has Miss Auerbach to say?

AUERBACH: Well, I'm like you, I only know one or two examples. There is LaCour's story, then there is Marquardt, and I think there are one or two others [5], and as I am not a cytologist I really don't know how convincing they are. They show these pictures, and they say they are half chromatids . . . but then I think Ostergren explains LaCour's experiments as something else—I forget what it is. But, even those few are somewhat doubtful.

BEERMANN: But, it is very well known that you get these mosaics in *Drosophila*. You get these by irradiating sperm and this is supposed to be single-stranded at that time.

AUERBACH: No. I would say that the remarkable thing is that you get so few of these mosaics and this has always been taken by Muller to show that it is not yet double-stranded.

RIS: But, we know that radiation on metaphase chromosomes can split them in place, and they are four-stranded. In coccids, for instance, they do not come apart, they have diffuse spindle attachments and you can easily see this, as Mrs. Schrader has shown [6].

AUERBACH: Yes, yes, I saw that.

PLAUT: Well, I think we can safely say, from the light microscope observation of the telophase chromosome, that it is at least double. Beyond that it is difficult to go, but the duality is, I think, well within the limits of resolution and is quite clear, particularly at the chromosome ends.

CALLAN: You have evidence?

PLAUT: I have photographic evidence, though not here. You can see ends which go out in two directions. You could of course argue that this is perhaps a mechanical splitting, but I think that would be rather far-fetched.

PONTECORVO: There is one very indirect argument which favours the multiplicity; although I may be wrong, I think we should keep it in mind. If we take the total genetic maps of various organisms from phage to mouse and divide that by the amount of DNA per nucleus then we find that between the phage and the mouse there is a factor of 10^4 in the amount of DNA per unit of genetic map. It may not be . . .

GALL: I defy you to get 10^4 strands into 500 Å.

BRENNER: I think there's another interpretation there.

PONTECORVO: Yes.

BRENNER: And that is, what sort of magnification, if I can put it this way, the recombination unit has? Bacteriophage T2 has a very high recombination rate. The closest markers are at 0·01% recombination—I mean of that order. Whereas in *Aspergillus*, if I remember, the order of magnitude of recombination frequency is about 100 times less.

PONTECORVO: Well, it's more, but still . . .

MITCHISON: Could I ask again the effect of DNAase on it. Does it break it at the chromomeres or what? Or does it digest away the whole lampbrush?

GALL: If I use DNAase alone it does not disrupt the chromosome, and I have some evidence, although this needs rechecking, that if you use DNAase and follow by proteinase the chromosome falls apart even between the chromomeres, but not without the preceding DNAase; but that certainly needs reconfirming.

WEISS: May I ask, please, for information: How thick are the microscopic strands connecting chromomeres?

CALLAN: My evidence, for what it's worth, is simply this. They are 200 Å wide in chromosomes which were prepared quite a long time ago when I wasn't quite sure how much I'd stretched them. They may have been stretched by a factor of 2, I should say, at the outside, and they're really very uniform at that width in between several chromomeres. That's of course dry, naturally enough.

GALL: In the light microscope the connection between chromomeres is invisible although you can tell the chromosome is continuous because it is waving around with Brownian movement and doesn't fall apart, although in some cases you can see just the slightest indication of a strand.

WADDINGTON: Would somebody remind us what is the thickness of the DNA chain.

GALL: 20 Å.

WADDINGTON: So, if the chromosome was stretched out into a single DNA chain it would be totally invisible light microscopically and . . .

BRENNER: You'd have to be a Robley Williams to see it in the electron microscope.

WADDINGTON: I mean we got the idea of the single strand from consideration of length, but considerations of width also come into it.

BRENNER: There is one experiment in the literature which has been interpreted as showing a multiple structure of the chromosome. I refer to the paper of Friedrick Freska and Kaudewizc [7] on P32 incorporation. They fed *Amoebae* on P32 and then they watched what they called lethal mutations, and the generation when these lethal mutations occurred was consonant with about 16 units. Now, what I should like to know from people who work with *Amoebae* is this. The result is also consistent, of course, with the genetic material being 16-ploid; is there any evidence for this?

PLAUT: Well, *Amoeba proteus* has—I don't think they've been counted exactly—but at least 700 chromosomes. There is only one nucleus and you can neither claim that it is polyploid or diploid or haploid, it is non-sexual. The question is wide open.

BEERMANN: There are some relevant observations just to this point. I have found that there are strains apparently of *Amoeba proteus* which do not have one single big nucleus but many, many small nuclei. So it might very well be that it is polyploid in the normal strain.

BRENNER: I should like to make one additional comment if I may. That is, that the molecular weight of DNA that has been prepared from cells is going up. Early preparations contained DNA with a molecular weight of 1 million or 1·5 million. Today it is customary for molecular weights to be running into 10 or 12 million. So that it is possible that there could be a single strand, though the molecular weight would be immense, but that it has fragmented during the preparation. As the technique of preparation improves one may be able to find very large pieces.

PONTECORVO: But what does molecular weight mean in a periodic system of that kind? I can't understand. Does it have any significant meaning?

BRENNER: Yes. In DNA it means that unit which has a continuity of covalent bonds. I mean the molecule starts at one end and you can follow the covalent bonds right to the other end.

PONTECORVO: But is it perfectly decent, in physical chemistry, to think of the whole chromosome as a single molecule?

BRENNER: It could be thought of in that way. In fact, recent work suggests that you could isolate all the DNA of a bacterium as one piece, and that you can't separate the genetic markers by ion-exchange chromatography unless the DNA has been fragmented by the preparation.

WEISS: But that's not quite correct. It's not the whole chromosome, it's only the DNA in the chromosome, that corresponds to a molecule.

BRENNER: Yes.

MITCHISON: Could you tell us how long a molecule of a molecular weight 12 million would be?

BRENNER: Well, 6 million would be 10^4 nucleotide pairs, which would be 30,000 Å, which would be 3μ.

SOMEBODY: It's getting on for the length of a short chromosome.

BRENNER: In phage T2 there is evidence for one big piece of a molecular weight of 40 million, which behaves genetically and isotopically as one unit.

MITCHISON: But that would have to be wound up like a ball of wool.

BRENNER: Yes, actually in a phage head all the DNA has to be packed very tightly to get it all in.

RIS: There are at least two experiments which indicate that, even if the chromosome strands are continuous they can fall apart into regular pieces: Mazia's and Bernstein's [8] and even better Doty's [9] work. Doty used versene also, isolating nucleo-protein from calf thymus. He finds pieces which light scattering indicates are about 4000 Å long, which is about what Mazia found, and about 40 Å thick; and it's chemically a nucleo-histone. When the histone is removed the DNA is about 7000 Å long and 20 Å thick, indicating that it has been wound up as the nucleo-histone.

PONTECORVO: Are they of uniform size or is the 4000 an average and they vary from 1000 to 10,000.

RIS: It can vary a little bit around 4000.

BRENNER: It varies considerably. In DNA, isolated from thymus nuclei, the molecular weights have a very wide distribution. This has been shown recently by a new method of sedimentation in a density gradient.

WADDINGTON: Plaut, would you like to say anything more about the multiplicity of strands?

PLAUT: The autoradiographic studies of chromosome duplication may have some bearing on this question. Perhaps a brief summary of the agreements and disagreements is in place here. Unfortunately we can only speak of the DNA component of the chromosome at the present time.

Two experiments have been carried out in which the newly synthesised chromosomal DNA was followed through division. One of these experiments was done by Mazia and myself [10]; we examined the distribution of newly-synthesised DNA in mitotic division in root tips of *Crepis capillaris* by measuring the amount of ^{14}C-labelled thymidine in the two post-metaphase chromosome sets and concluded that a significant number of such sets showed an unequal distribution. We suggested, rather speculatively, that the data could be explained by assuming that each anaphase chromosome consists of three units of DNA synthesis. These units could be called strands if one keeps in mind that they are not defined in this case on a morphological basis. If we assume three such units per anaphase chromosome we would have six units in the metaphase complex. The random segregation of these into two anaphase chromosomes would lead to a distribution pattern of new and old DNA consistent with our data. However, the possibility of two rather than three units per anaphase chromosome should by no means be considered excluded. The main points which emerged from this study are that the products of chromosomal replication are not necessarily equal in their content of new and old DNA and that the number of independently behaving DNA-containing units is small.

The second experiment of this type was carried out by Taylor and his co-workers [11]. Using the mitotic cells of *Vicia faba* and tritium-labelled thymidine they were able to make the individual chromosome the unit of analysis and thus overcome the statistical complexities inherent in the analysis of whole sets of six chromosomes in *Crepis*. They found that the distribution of newly synthesised (labelled) DNA in the first division following synthesis was equal but that at the following division, preceded by synthesis in the absence of labelled thymidine, a clear segregation of the labelled DNA occurred between the two daughter chromosomes.

Both of these studies lead to similar conclusions as far as the number of independent DNA-containing sub-units of the chromosome are concerned: this number is small. Both studies point to the fact that chromosomal DNA is conserved: the old is not degraded. The disagreement between the conclusions drawn by us and those of Taylor lies in the postulated mechanics of chromosome replication and segregation; while the *Crepis* study suggests that the DNA-containing independent sub-units assort randomly into two anaphase chromosomes, the *Vicia* data seem to indicate a non-random assortment. The possibility of a significant assymetrical distribution of newly synthesised DNA in the division following the marking synthesis is excluded by the *Vicia* data as interpreted by Taylor and his colleagues.

Quite aside from the fact that the occurrence of significantly unequal distributions of newly synthesised DNA would have a direct bearing on our visualisation of the mechanics of chromosomal DNA replication at the molecular level, while equal distribution would not, the question of random versus non-random assortment of chromosomal DNA sub-units is of considerable importance in our understanding of the fine structure and mechanism of replication of the chromosome as a whole. Consequently an attempt must be made to explain the apparent discrepancy between the two experiments. Since it appears unlikely that mitotic chromosomes of one species behave differently during replication from chromosomes in another, we must look for errors in interpretation in one or the other or, for that matter, both experiments.

The *Vicia* study was the more direct one, and is therefore more reliable on general principles. I have, for that reason, spent a good bit of time in trying to find some flaw in the *Crepis* experiment or its interpretation. The labelling asymmetry we found, when subjected to statistical evaluation, turned out to be significant beyond the 99% level of probability. The possibility that the unequally labelled post-metaphase cells were not first but second divisions has been ruled out: essentially the same results were obtained when incubation time was cut to a period well below any conceivable mitotic cycle time in this organism. Some of the original preparations were re-autoradiographed and the same distributions of auto-radiographic grains were obtained. In short, the inequality of labelled DNA distribution in *Crepis* is not readily explained away, the initial conclusion still stands. One must now ask whether the design and inter-pretation of the *Vicia* experiment are subject to re-evaluation, whether the apparent directness of the experiment made the conclusions indeed safer. Recent repetitions of the *Vicia* experiment suggest that it is not as direct as had been thought initially: the use of colchicine and high levels of tritium beta particle irradiation introduce problems which must be investigated in detail before the conclusions drawn are fully acceptable.

What, then, do these experiments tell us about the fine structure of the chromosome? Most importantly, whatever the structural arrangement of the DNA molecules within the chromosome, these molecules behave as though they were packed into a small number of independent units: two per anaphase chromosome according to Taylor, more than one and less than four according to the *Crepis* study. If the microfibrils seen by the electron microscopists are indeed in whole or in part DNA structures and if these microfibrils are arranged with their long axis parallel to the long axis of the chromosome, we are faced with the exceedingly difficult problem of explaining how these fibrils duplicate as units but still behave as though they were part of a much larger unit of synthesis and segregation. One can set up a series of *ad hoc* hypotheses of chromosomal structure which might deal with this complexity more or less satisfactorily. Until we know more about the rest of the chromosome's structural components and have a clearer understanding of the nature and place of the micro-fibrils such structural models are, in my opinion, premature and not likely to lead very far.

WEISS: Could I complicate the question by asking, if there are multiple units, what holds these units tied together laterally at corresponding places, so that they are in register? Without that the whole thing wouldn't work.

PLAUT: Well, one can invoke a protein.

WEISS: You have the same phenomenon in myosin, collagen, and all the way through. I think it's about time that we tackle now, not only the linear regularity but also the question of the forces of lateral association and register. What puts strands together and lines them up over long distances in close packing and in register?

PLAUT: Well, in the polytene chromosome the fairly large number of strands is presumably held together by their intertwining. How this coiling comes about is not known.

LEHMANN: Callan was saying something about the question of the position of these filaments. Could you return to that topic; it seems to come in here.

CALLAN: Well, first I was going to say something in answer to you, Professor Weiss. Simply that if you look at these chromosomes within isolated nuclei in media in which a minimal amount of the dispersion of the nucleus sap has taken place there is more or less no Brownian movement taking place at all. There is a very stiff jelly in which these things are embedded. For purposes of observation you have to disperse that sap because first of all you want to get the chromosomes reasonably straight so that you can look at them in one field of focus. And, secondly, you want to get as large a difference in refractive index between the medium and what you are looking at, and that's why one disperses this sap. But, in life I have no doubt at all that these things are pretty rigidly embedded.

WADDINGTON: Is it time that some of the people on salivary chromosomes stepped in? There we are undoubtedly dealing with chromosomes which are multiple stranded. I don't know if Beermann or Pavan would like to say something?

BEERMANN: I may also have something to say about the questions that have just been discussed, such as multiple strandedness of the chromosomes, and local extension of the chromosomal fibrils in relation to gene function. However, I think it best to introduce you first to the general characteristics of the phenomena which form the basis of my contribution. These phenomena involve local structural changes in giant polytene chromosomes, in close correlation to cellular function, and have been described in detail in several publications [12, 13, 14, 15]. As contrasted to Dr. Callan's material we have here chromosomes that belong to pretty differentiated somatic cells.

WILDE: Could we make the note here that an oocyte is a reasonably differentiated cell.

BEERMANN: I should have said the cells of differentiated organs such as the salivary glands are certainly limited in their functional capacities as compared to the growing oocyte. This brings me to the first point. There is no doubt at all that Dipteran giant chromosomes are just a special type of interphasic chromosome, in terms of the mitotic cycle. They belong to "resting", i.e. really functional nuclei, and it should be stated right at the start that changes in the structure of resting nuclei, in relation to cellular differentiation, are by no means a peculiarity of Dipteran giant cells. They may be observed, though on a much cruder scale, in mammals, for instance, as reported by histologists in the 1880s already [16]. One of the most striking examples is the formation of large heteropyknotic blocks, or chromocentres, within the nucleus of the retinal rod cell (cf. Fig. 2 in [17]). It is tempting to speculate on the nature of this phenomenon, in terms of differential heteropyknosis, perhaps in relation to gene inactivation. Experiments relating to this point have not yet been devised. The great advantage in working with giant polytene chromosomes, as contrasted with normal interphasic chromosomes, is, of course, that you have a reliable system of reference in defining the structural changes occurring, and that this system, the so-called banding pattern, shows an enormous wealth of definable detail. In other words, in addition to seeing just that something has happened you can tell where it happened, down to the single gene locus. In order to do so, naturally, you need to be certain about the reliability, i.e. constancy, of your reference system itself. One might, for instance, argue with Kosswig and Sengün [20] that cytogeneticists, for more than 20 years, used to confine themselves to the study of one and the same type and functional state of cells, in studying the banding pattern of giant chromosomes, namely, those of the salivary glands of prepupae of *Drosophila*, and that the constancy found here might not be genetical after all. My work, therefore, had to start with comparing the banding pattern of homologous giant chromosomes from as many different types and stages of cells as I could get in one and the same individual, or in different individuals of the same genetic strain.

In *Chironomus*, such an analysis is feasible with the Malpighian tubules, the midgut, and the rectum, apart from the salivary glands of the larva. It was evident from the beginning that all the major bands of the chromosomes are in corresponding positions, just as a preliminary study in Sciara had shown long ago [21]. As one proceeds to the finer bands, however, the analysis meets with two difficulties. One of these is a matter of technique: the finer a band, the easier will it be overlooked, depending on the quality of the preparation. Obviously, therefore, you cannot expect to count exactly the same number of bands in any two different specimens of the same chromosome, especially if the two stem from different organs. The proportions of the chromosomes, their coiling, and their state of extension all come in here. In laying the emphasis on this type of difficulty, you may if you wish even go so far as completely to deny the genetical constancy of the banding pattern [20]. I think the main value of such sweeping negations lies in the stimulus they create for a critical re-investigation of the problem. Slizynski, [22] Breuer and Pavan, [23] and I myself [24, 12] could not confirm Kosswig's and Sengün's claims. On the contrary, with at least 95 per cent of all resolvable bands being in cor-responding positions, it became a problem to make sure that there are any clear differences at all, beyond those that might simply be due to the variations inherent in the quality of the preparations. And this leads to the second type of difficulty mentioned above.

It was found, both in *Chironomus* [12] and in *Rhynchosciara* [14] that real differences exist, differences which may even sometimes conceal the under-lying homology of the banding pattern. If you compare a small chromo-some section, say one comprising 20 bands, taken from the salivary glands, from the Malpighian tubules, from the rectum, and from the midgut of a full grown larva of *Chironomus*, you may find that there are two or three bands which look different in different tissues. That it is really the same bands you compare follows, of course, from their position in relation to their unchanged neighbours. Morphologically, the differences in the appearances of homologous loci may be described as being due to different degrees of swelling, accompanied by a proportional loss in density which expresses itself in a loss of the staining intensity. I shall come back to the question of staining later. Now, this swelling may sometimes result in the formation of a large "puff" which will necessarily obscure the position of adjacent bands, thus providing another pitfall for the naïve observer. So much for the technical difficulties of the analysis itself.

Let me now turn to the question of the biological significance of the variation just mentioned. Throughout the following discussion, I shall use the terms "puff" and "puffing" in talking of the structural modification of the bands, with the exception of Balbiani's rings to which I shall return presently. There are several questions that one may ask in considering the different aspects of one and the same band in different cells. Is there any regularity in the phenomenon, and if so, how much? Can we correlate the changes to something in the character or state of the cell? As to the first of these questions it suffices to point out that every one of the pictures that I am going to present here (cf. [12, 13]) is representative of the situation as found throughout the tissue or organ of the particular indivi-dual studied, at least qualitatively so. If you find a band puffed in one salivary gland cell you will find it puffed in all, except for those which, in some cases, can be demonstrated to produce a different kind of secretion. I shall return to this type of intra-organ differentiation later on. As regards the precise degree of puffing I am at present unable to give you reliable information. It may very well be that there is a slight amount of quantitative variation which might have to do with short term functional cycles, e.g. secretion cycles in salivary gland cells. I should save this functional viewpoint for the later discussion.

Right now, we may conclude, in a preliminary way, that the puffing of certain bands is closely correlated to the character of the cell. Puffing is tissue-specific, which, however, does not imply tissue specificity in the behaviour of the single band as such, in the sense of tissue-specific genes. Specificity, as observed in *Chironomus* giant chromosomes, rests in the specific spectrum of bands that become puffed in one tissue as contrasted with the puffing spectrum in others. Thus, a single band may, and often will, become puffed in more than one type of cell, as you may have noticed from looking at the slides.

Having established this state of affairs we are led to ask another question: Just when and how did the selective puffing of certain bands come about, and does the puffing ever change again? With regard to the first half of this question, we are certainly at a loss at present, and this is the more to be deplored since the general problem involved is of so much importance to embryology. We are touching the problem of the interaction of chromosomes and cytoplasm in the process of embryonic determination. Unfortunately, however, we have no giant chromosomes in embryos since, evidently, all of the larval organs become determined long before their cells begin to grow and form giant polytene chromosomes. So, as regards chromosome morphology, we are left to extrapolation and, perhaps, to electron microscopy. As regards the latter I shall not go into details here —the work is just beginning. As regards extrapolation, I am referring to the fact that as far back as the first larval stage one is able to recognise one of the largest puffs in salivary gland nuclei, the so-called ring of Balbiani. I am coming to this type of structural modification presently.

Much more information, of course, is available with regard to changes in the state of puffing going on during the last period of larval life. I found that when the imaginal disks and the gonads begin to grow under the stimulus of the pupation hormones there occur striking changes in the chromosomes of the salivary glands and of other organs of *Chironomus* [12]. On a much larger scale such changes become apparent in *Rhynchosciara*, and Dr. Pavan will certainly tell you more of his analysis of the phenomenon. What happens in *Chironomus* is that a series of new puffs appear while others that had been present during larval life disappear. Interestingly enough it seems that the newly developed puffs form at homologous loci in organs that differ as much as the salivary glands, the Malpighian

6

tubules, and the rectum. One can hardly escape the conclusion that changes in the composition of the larval haemolymph must be responsible for the simultaneous puffing of homologous loci in different parts of the body. It is evident that the situation calls for much more careful analysis before one can decide whether a direct action of hormones is involved or whether secondary factors such as the appearance of histolytic enzymes, changes in the ion concentration, etc., intervene. At any rate the situation provides a model for what might happen during embryonic determination when changes in internal and external conditions induce changes in the functional state of the chromosomal loci, thus switching on a new type of metabolic steady state, or nucleo-cytoplasmic feed back cycle, within the cell.

I should like to illustrate what has been said here just by presenting an especially striking example. As early as 1881 Balbiani [25] described a peculiar ring-like structure in the nucleus of *Chironomus* salivary glands. This structure is not a nucleolus though it has often been called one. Balbiani's ring really represents a particular type of puff of, in most cases, considerable dimensions [12]. As yet no *Chironomus* or other Chironomid species has been found which did not show at least one such giant puff in its salivary gland nuclei. Balbiani rings, as contrasted with nucleoli, have a diffuse outline just as normal puffs have, but the puffed material appears to be pushed out of and arranged around the chromosome in a ring-like fashion. Such an arrangement, and the rotational symmetry it shows, are a necessary consequence of the cable-like structure of the polytene chromosome if you make one additional assumption: the constituent elementary fibrils of the chromosome must, in this instance of puffing, have remained unpaired from the very beginning of polytenisation [12, 17]. The argument runs as follows: if one tries to imitate Balbiani's ring formation on some sort of wire cable or rope, one has only to pull out all of the single elements radially at one place. Now, whatever forces are involved in the act of pulling out of the loops in the natural chromosome, the process obviously meets with difficulties if there are several thousand intimately united strands present; at least it has never been observed that a Balbiani ring developed when the chromosome already had a high degree of polyteny. So I assume that the ring develops step by step as the strands of the chromosome reduplicate, an assumption which implies presence of the puffed state from the beginning of cellular growth in late embryogenesis and which it is not necessary to make in interpreting normal puffing, even if the puffs as such reach dimensions larger than those of Balbiani's rings. Thus, it seems to me that the rings are not just manifestations of transitory changes in gene function, as normal puffs might often be (if you come to think of functional cycles, variations in nutrition, temperature, etc.). On the contrary, the distribution of Balbiani's rings ought to provide information about long-term nuclear differentiation as established during embryonic determination itself. There are some observations which support this conclusion.

In view of what happens in the case of normal puffs and diffuse bands it does not surprise one to find that there are differences as regards the occurrence and distribution of Balbiani's rings in different organs and tissues. In *Chironomus tentans*, for instance, one has three such rings in the fourth chromosome of the salivary glands. None of these is present in the fourth chromosome of any of the other investigated tissues. Conversely, you may find Balbiani rings in the Malpighian tubule chromosomes which have no counterpart in the salivary glands, and so on. All this, even if it is very spectacular, does not come unexpected and is only mentioned in passing, so to speak. But there is one type of observation which, apart from being illustrative, permits further conclusions to be drawn on the nature and significance of Balbiani ring formation. I am talking about specific differences in the distribution of Balbiani rings between cells which, functionally, must be so closely related as to differ only in one special aspect of their physiology, cells which belong to one and the same organ and which fulfil the same general type of function.

Such a situation has been found to be the rule in the salivary glands of practically every Chironomid species studied. These glands usually consist of some 20 to 50 cells, the number not being fixed precisely. Now, a small group of these, not more than 10 in most cases, can always be demonstrated to be different from the rest as regards cytoplasmic morphology, or fine structure, or stainability, and also as regards the kind of secretion produced. These cells are located near the duct of the gland as if they were to add some special component to the bulk of the secretion. No profound differences exist between these cells and the rest of the gland as regards dimensions and shape of their polytene chromosomes. The chromosomal situation has been worked out in detail in *Trichocladius* [13] and in *Acricotopus* [15]. Bauer [26] and I myself have found similar conditions in *Cryptochironomus* and a great number of other Chironomids, including *Chironomus tentans*.

Consider, for instance, the conditions in *Acricotopus*, as studied by Mechelke [15]: Both dimensions and shape of the chromosomes are similar in the two types of cells and, at first sight, since the two show, within their nuclei, two Balbiani rings each on the same two chromosomes, one really does not suspect that anything is wrong at all. However, much to our satisfaction, the rings are not in corresponding positions on the chromosomes, i.e. if you follow the banding pattern of the chromosomes involved you find that the rings are in different arms. The distinction is as clear cut as possible: there are no transitions so that for the single Balbiani-locus one registers either presence or absence of a ring. It is interesting to see that such a differentiation exists, in the case of *Acricotopus*, long before the functional difference between the two types of cells becomes visibly manifest, for it is only at the onset of metamorphosis that the special cells begin to produce a secretion which, in contrast to that produced by the rest of the gland, has a dark brown colour. Moreover, Mechelke could demonstrate that, as soon as this type of secretion begins to appear in a cell, the Balbiani rings of this cell begin to regress and shortly thereafter will completely disappear, leaving only a slight disturbance of the banding behind. Incidentally, this correlation does not hold for other types of puffed bands and not for the normal cells of the gland.

Such observations would hardly lend support to any hypothesis which assumes that the engagement in the production of secretion is a direct one in Balbiani's rings. It seems to me, rather, that the Balbiani loci are part of a nucleo-cytoplasmic feed-back mechanism that establishes and controls the character of the cell, particularly of its cytoplasm, so that it is competent to react in a specific way to a specific stimulus. This is, of course, in line with current ideas on nucleo-cytoplasmic relationships in general. To illustrate the point a little further, I should mention that, in the salivary glands of the related species *Trichocladius*, the cytoplasm of the "special" cells, throughout larval life, is characterised by the presence of numerous granules which all other cells lack. Here, as contrasted with mere products of secretions, we may actually have it to do with entities whose existence is directly linked to the presence of Balbiani rings in the nucleus.

Before I change to another aspect of the matter, I should just add two more points here. From what has been found in *Acricotopus* and *Trichocladius* you may have got the impression that the differences between normal and special cells in the salivary glands, as regards Balbiani's rings, always are of the mutually exclusive type, each type of cell having its own specific set of Balbiani rings. This is not so in members of the genus *Chironomus*. In *C. tentans*, for instance, you have two Balbiani rings in common in both types of cells, in addition to two "differential" ones. The second point is that conditions like those just described are by no means confined to the salivary glands. Only recently I found beautiful Balbiani rings in the Malpighian tubule nuclei of *C. tentans* [27], and at first, it was a little unexpected to see that one of these regularly failed to develop in the distal two-thirds of the tubules, for I did not know of any functional differentiation within the Malpighian tubules of *Chironomus*. However, on consulting the text books of insect physiology, such a functional differentiation turned out to be not so improbable, and, on closer inspection, the cytoplasm of one of the two cell types was at times found to be packed with small crystalline particles.

How can we integrate all the morphological and developmental data on Balbiani's rings? I think that the answer to this question has been implicit in the presentation of the data, especially since I have not made serious attempts to keep it clear of the functional viewpoint. Balbiani's rings in Chironomid nuclei seem to be those genetic loci which in each type of cell establish and dominate the specific type of nucleo-cytoplasmic inter-action. We may now turn to a short account of the genetic behaviour of the loci involved in puff and Balbiani ring formation in one or the other type of cell. In other words, we may ask, is there a genetic component which contributes to the variation in puffing, in addition to obvious developmental and environmental factors? Is it possible that a chromosomal locus changes its puffing behaviour by way of mutation? Obviously, what one has to do first, in being confronted with this sort of question, is to look for heterozygotes, i.e. cases of heterozygous puffing. From the slides that I have presented here, as well as from the many illustrations that have been published [12, 15], you may yourselves have drawn the conclusions that heterozygosity must be extremely rare in puffs. This conclusion is the more justified since most of the animals used in our studies stem from natural populations which, on general grounds and on account of the abundance of chromosomal polymorphism, ought to contain a great store of genetic variability. Not even crosses of animals from as far apart as Sweden, Germany and England [28] will result in an appreciable increase in puff heterozygotes. The same holds true for the hybrids of *C. tentans* and *C. pallidivittatus* [28], two sibling species which must have had ample time to evolve in different directions. If you take the fourth chromosome pair of such an F1 hybrid, for instance, you will see, in spite of the peculiar manner in which the two partners are paired ("end to end"), that all three of the Balbiani rings are in corresponding positions in both partners.

WADDINGTON: How are these chromosomes paired end to end?

BEERMANN: The fourth chromosome is telocentric, i.e. probably has an invisibly small second arm which is heteropyknotic and which causes the two partners to stick to each other, end to end, at the centromere.

WADDINGTON: Do the long arms ever pair side by side?

BEERMANN: They do, but in consequence of inversions which differentiate the two species the pairing is irregular and often absent. The homology can nevertheless be established.

Now, as regards the low frequency of heterozygosity in puffs, one might of course simply consider this as an indication of the rarity with which genetic heterozygosity occurs at the loci in question. Simple as it may be, this is certainly not the correct interpretation of the facts. It is by no means proven, nor is it a probable assumption, that mutation of the gene necessarily changes its puffing behaviour. This is sometimes forgotten in discussing lines of experimental genetic work on the puffing phenomenon where you might hear suggestions like 'the following: Just try and find mutations of, say, salivary gland function, look for heterozygosity in one of the puffs of the salivary by conventional cytogenetic methods. It is evidently much more promising to proceed from established cases of puff heterozygosity first, and then try to find out biochemical differences between the two types of homozygotes.

A few cases of puff heterozygosity have actually been detected in *Chironomus* (see [12]). I shall take as an example a further case which has been established only recently [29, 27]. The puff in question, a Balbiani ring, develops, if present, at a locus of the third chromosome, both in *C. tentans* and in *C. pallidivittatus*, either heterozygous or homozygous. What type of genetic mutation is involved? Nothing like a deficiency or duplication can be detected in heterozygotes if one inspects the banding pattern of the critical section in the Malpighian tubules where, of course, the puff itself is never manifested. By definition, then, this is a case of true unilocal "gene" mutation. Its phenotypic effect on the whole individual is unknown, but it would be hard to believe that it had no effect on nuclear and cellular metabolism in the salivary glands. In order to explain its occurrence in both species one could speculate on two different lines, heterosis and exceptional mutability. I cannot go into details here, but, at any rate, both types of explanations lead to the same conclusion, namely that the puffing behaviour of the genes normally seems to have an extraordinary genetic stability. Such a situation fits in well with the basic assumption of my work in general. I have stated repeatedly that, in my opinion, puffing is an expression of gene activation, in a quantitative sense. Activation is defined as an increase in the rate of turnover brought about by an increase in the supply or availability of the specific substrates of the gene [27]. Hence, mutations which change nothing but the type of reaction catalysed by the gene, without changing its substrate specificity, cannot be expected to change the microscopical appearance of the corresponding locus. On the other hand, those mutations leading to changes in substrate specificity would be expected to do so. Now, it seems plausible to me that mutations of just this second type will rarely be found, even if they occurred with normal frequency, for any change in substrate specificity would most probably lead to the complete loss of the activity in some, and a sudden appearance of activity in other types of cells or situations, a condition which ought to be lethal in most cases.

Now, in concluding this contribution to the discussions of today I should like to raise one last question: What evidence do we have that the changes in local chromosome structure actually indicate changes in gene activity? I must confess that all the evidence I am able to put forward here, in addition to the arguments derived from the description of the phenomenon as such, will be of a circumstantial nature. I am not yet in the lucky position of Professor Waddington and of Professor Brachet to tell you about incorporation of labelled metabolites in puffs. Briefly, my observations are as follows. In *Chironomus* a very simple experiment can be done, just putting the larvae into a cold room and heating them up again. When you do this, after a certain amount of time, two hours more or less, droplets begin to accumulate in certain parts of the salivary gland chromosomes. They contain RNA and protein. Later, after about 8 hr, all these droplets will have disappeared. Now, it is fairly clear from my observations that these droplets always appear in places which have the diffuse or puffed modification of normal structure, as shown for the Balbiani rings and also for one of the puffs of *Chironomus* salivaries (cf. [18] and [27]). It can also be seen that the reaction is different in different puffs and Balbiani rings. Droplet formation may be taken as an indication of a relatively high turnover rate at the loci involved.

A second type of information derives from cytochemical reactions. Caspersson and Bauer [30] had concluded from u.v. spectrography that Balbiani rings must contain high amounts of protein in addition to nucleic acids. Using enzymes and the familiar staining reactions it is possible to specify this a little further. For instance, if you stain giant chromosomes with a combination of orcein and light green you will find the Balbiani rings and many other puffed regions staining deep green, thus indicating high concentrations of (non-histone) protein. If, on the other hand, toluidin blue, a basic stain, is applied in the proper way, you will find most of the puffed regions stained a deep violet, as contrasted with the blue–green appearance of the normal bands, but in agreement with the staining of ergastoplasmic regions in the cytoplasm and with that of the nucleoli. Illustrations may be found in [27]. RNase treatment has shown that the toluidin blue staining of the puffs is due to RNA.

Of course, such observations are not entirely new. Similar results, by means of contrast staining, have been mentioned long ago by Professor Brachet and others. The point in returning to this type of study at all is that you have here a nice tool to locate all bands that are presumably active, even if their puffing is very slight, and that on the basis of such a study you can proceed to test the parallel between RNA and protein synthesis from locus to locus, using adequate additional techniques. At any rate it becomes quite clear from the staining reactions that puffed loci contain, or produce, something in addition to normal, non-puffed, ones. As regards chemical composition, therefore, the situation may be restated as follows: The interphasic chromosome shows a constant genetically fixed pattern of DNA (and, probably, histone) distribution. On this pattern is superimposed a sequence of points of ribonucleoprotein accumulation which changes in close correlation with the functional character of the cell. The points of RN-protein accumulation seem to be identical with those, which on purely morphological criteria, have been designed as puffs and Balbiani rings. The presence of ribonucleoprotein at these places is a further indication of increased synthetic activity, since RNA is always found at places of protein synthesis.

A further contribution from electron microscopy. In ultra-thin sections of one of the two large Balbiani rings of the fourth salivary gland chromosomes of C. *tentans* [31] one finds an enormous number of small, globular particles. Most of these appear attached to the thousands of loosened, spongy elementary fibrils of the puffed region (cf. Fig. 7 in [17]), but you find them distributed all over the nuclear sap.

WEISS: Could I ask if these little granules are of the order of magnitude of microsomal granules?

BEERMANN: They are definitely much larger, about 300 Å, i.e. more than twice the diameter of Palade's microsomal particles. This is just the point that makes them so fascinating to me, for it should be easy to demonstrate the presence of particles of this size outside of the nucleus; but this has never been found, showing that the particles, if they are carriers of information, evidently have to transfer this information to some other carrier, or have to undergo changes themselves, in order to bring the information into the cytoplasm. The place of transfer is the nuclear membrane. It would be very interesting, of course, to know something about the chemical nature of these particles: Are they a specific type of RN-protein macromolecules? Preliminary observations indicate that ribonuclease destroys the particles, whereas a lot of different fixatives does not impair their structure.

In talking about electron microscopy of Balbiani's rings I should like to add a final word here on chromosome stretching. This bears a direct relation to what Professor Callan has found in Amphibian oocyte lampbrush chromosomes. You will remember that a single not puffed band never exceeds 1 μ in thickness, i.e. length, in terms of the single strand. Now, as we have seen, puffs and Balbiani rings arise from single bands by a process of structural modification, involving the loosening and stretching or unfolding, of the constituent fibrillar sections. In the electron micrographs of the Balbiani ring these fibrillar sections, which in cell types other than the salivary glands remain compressed into a thin, compact band, show a length of at least 5 μ, i.e. they are stretched by a factor of from 5 to 10. Thus, unfolding of the gene seems to be a necessary condition or corollary of activation, both in polytene and in lampbrush chromosomes and, hence, probably in all chromosomes [27].

WADDINGTON: Would any of the other chromosome experts like to come in now?

CALLAN: I would like to make another point, because I didn't say much about it when I was talking about the lampbrush chromosomes. In the course of the development of the oocytes the appearance of a particular locus may vary enormously. This region (near centromere of chromosome II) has a particularly large chromomere at this late stage with quite a small loop, but in a very young oocyte the loop extends about 200 μ from the axis. These objects ("spheres"), which are very characteristic of the two chromosomes 5 and 8 of *Triturus cristatus carnifex*, are visible only in the old oocytes, and it is very hard even to find the loci in young oocytes. These two giant loops (chromosome XI) are big and very evident structures in older oocytes but hardly visible at all in young ones. One has a similarity in this respect with the things Dr. Beermann has been telling us. My interpretation of the situation is that at particular phases in oogenesis particular genetic loci come into particularly active synthetic activity whereas other loci don't. In fact, this is one of the great difficulties in studying lampbrush chromosomes, and makes it impossible to make a map of the whole chromosome set, because the map changes in the course of development. A map I have prepared is valid as an over-all picture for all the time of oocyte development but for specific loci you have to bear in mind the age of the oocyte which you are studying. The agreement with Dr. Beermann's observations is, I think, extraordinarily good.

WADDINGTON: One point that seems to the outsider rather a difference, in the two pictures that you people present, is that in a salivary chromosome there seems perhaps rather a definite distinction between a Balbiani ring and a normal band, whereas in the oocyte all the chromomeres seem to have considerable loops on them, although some are admittedly bigger than others. Possibly it is because Beermann studies highly differentiated tissues that there is more difference between the "puffs" or Balbiani rings and the normal loci. I suppose one might claim that in oogenesis the cell has to make practically every kind of protein the genes are capable of making, while in differentiated tissues the metabolic activities are much less widespread, or something of that kind.

CALLAN: I think that's the logical way of looking at it.

WILDE: To the person who examines different salivary gland chromosomes, the cytological or living picture of the "puffs" would seem to represent a condition more like that seen in life in vertebrate cells during interphase. I wonder if we couldn't turn this picture around and consider whether the "puff" state might not represent the state of the interphase nucleus, whereas condensation of the sort that results in the visible polytene chromosome might be indicative of the specific differentiated phases of the salivary gland cells, or of the variously different cells which contain polytene chromosomes, such as those in the alimentary tract.

WADDINGTON: Perhaps we should go on to the question or the reversibility of "puffing", which Dr. Pavan has got some evidence about. I think this question of reversibility has many implications, particularly in connection with the complete inactivation of genes as suggested, for instance, by the recent experiments of Briggs and King.

PAVAN: The work I want to tell you about [32], done in collaboration with my colleague M. E. Breuer and lately with Dr. Adrienne Ficq, of Brussels, is on *Rhynchosciara*, a Dipteran which we find in Brazil. We have about a dozen species, of which we have described two, *R. angelae* and *R. milleri*. I think it is important to spend a few minutes explaining the biology of this animal, to give a better idea of the methods used and of the results obtained. *R. angelae* is a large Dipteran, the adult being about 0·5–1 cm in length, and the larvae may reach 2 cm. The larvae have salivary glands which may be 2 cm long. It is, therefore, quite easy to work with this material. The animal has some characteristics which make it excellent for the type of work we are doing. A female will lay about 2000 eggs at one time, and these eggs develop into larvae which stay together in groups. In these groups every animal is doing exactly what the others are doing. When one of them is walking, they're all walking; and when one stops, they all stop. As they all develop together, and were all produced by eggs laid during a short period of about an hour, the whole of a group have the same age. If we sample the group, we find all the members of the sample at the same stage. When they get to be full grown larvae they cease eating, and start to look for a place to pupate. When they find it, they stop and secrete a material which makes a cocoon around themselves, with all the larvae inside. Normally, in nature, a group breaks up into two or three, and instead of having thousands in a group you will get 500 or 200 or even 100, but at any rate the members of each group pupate together in a group. If the group of larvae finds a convenient place it just stays there and pupates, but if they don't like it, they move to some other place, stop there and start pupation. When they settle down, we get a group of animals lying side by side like cells in a honeycomb. After about 60 days from the egg stage, you have the flies hatching, and about 200 or 300 flies may hatch in a few hours. We have observed that after 60 days of development there is not more than 12 hr difference between the first and last flies to hatch. So you can see we have a wonderful animal to analyse the development of the salivary and other chromosomes.

Another peculiarity of these animals is that they have really beautiful polytene chromosomes in the salivary glands, in the Malpighian tubules and in the intestine. These beautiful chromosomes are easily prepared in squashes. I may say that the chromosomes in the Malpighian tubules are as good as the best salivary chromosomes in *Drosophila*. So, just as

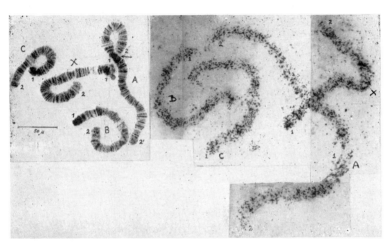

FIG. 3.5. Photomicrograph of a full set of salivary polytene chromosomes of a full grown larva of *R. angelae*. The letters indicate the chromosomes, the number 1 indicates the centromere region and the number 2 the distal end of the chromosomes. The scale represents 50 μ.

FIG. 3.6. Photomicrograph of an autoradiographed full set of salivary polytene chromosome of *R. angelae*. The indication of letters and numbers are the same shown in Fig. 3.5. The magnification of this photomicrograph is little greater than Fig. 3.5.

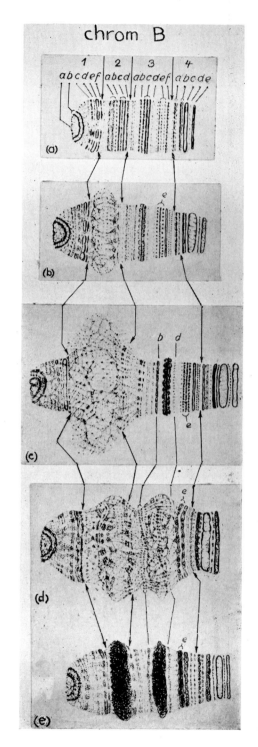

Fig. 3.7. Camera lucida drawings of the distal end of chromosome B at five different stages of larval development. Phase *a* is from a full grown larva, *e* from a larva beginning pupation about 6–8 days older than *a*; *b*, *c* and *d* are intermediate stages. The scale from Fig. 3.8 is valid here also.

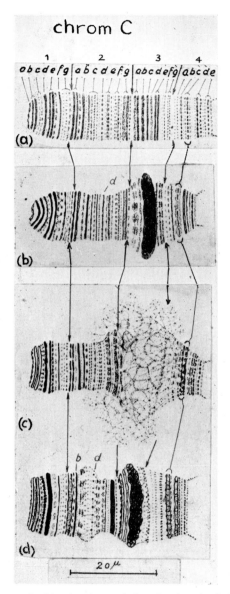

FIG. 3.8. Camera lucida drawings of the distal end of chromosome C at four different stages of larval development. Phase *a* is from a full grown larva and phase *d* from a larva at beginning of pupation. The scale represents 20 μ.

Beermann has done, we have studied the banding patterns in the salivary glands and Malpighians, and we have reached the same conclusion as Beermann and others, that the banding pattern in these organs is constant.

I would like at this point to show to you the chromosomes of *Rhynchosciara*. In the nucleus of an oocyte of *Rhynchosciara angelae* one can see ten elements. Eight of them are somatic. The other two are the "limited" chromosomes, only present in the germ line cells. Figure 3.5 will show you how good are the salivary chromosomes. There are four salivary gland chromosomes, A, B, C and X, easily distinguishable by the sizes and the banding pattern. The chromosomes from intestinal cells have been figured by Pavan and Breuer [33]. It is very easy to compare the banding pattern of them with that from the salivary gland chromosomes.

Now, *Rhynchosciara* shows still other peculiarities of development. You can have good salivary gland or Malpighian tubule or intestine chromosomes at any age, in old or in young larvae, or in larvae starting pupation. You will always get chromosomes which are wonderful to analyse. Here also we have been doing the same kind of work as Beermann has done in his animal. In general, we have reached much the same conclusions. In our case, we were able to follow in detail the development of the "puffs" in the chromosomes, sampling the group of larvae every day, or more frequently. *Rhynchosciara angelae* has, as we have said, four pairs of chromosomes in somatic cells. We selected certain bands in two of the polytene chromosomes, and followed the behaviour of them during development, to see whether they remained the same or whether they changed their shape. In Fig. 3.7 one can see what happens with the bands in the distal end of chromosome B in salivary gland cells during larval development. The figure shows camera lucida drawings of the same distal end of the chromosome at five different phases of larval development. The tip represented in *a* comes from a full grown larvae. The tip represented in *b* comes from a larva two days older than *a*. The chromosomes swell, and you get a big "puff" (*c* in Fig. 3.7). If you follow it you will see that this part regresses and the chromosome reassumes its original banding pattern, having, however, an increase of the Feulgen positive material on the particular loci where the puff was formed. We followed this process several times, and we always see that at this stage of development you have the chromosome with this "puff". In this puff of chromosome B, the accumulation of the extra DNA is shown after the puffing process, but if we follow the development of the bands of the distal end of chromosome C, in Fig. 3.8, we will see that this accumulation of DNA in a particular band (band *d* of section 2) precedes the formation of the puff. The block of DNA at the specific point is very condensed before the puff (*b* in Fig. 3.8), is vacuolised and dissociated in very small particles during the puff's formation (*c* in Fig. 3.8) and returns to the condensed stage again after the process (*d* in Fig. 3.8).

By sampling the group you can find the time when the structure of this chromosome goes through these changes, and here also the puff always occurs at the same stage of larval development. This accumulation of DNA in this region of the chromosome, as well as all the puffing formation is due to only one band of the chromosome; the other bands near by, are, as regards the puffing process, passive elements, and they may break up in small pieces because the formation of a Feulgen-negative substance inside the puff increases the diameter of the chromosome at the specific point, influencing in this way the integrity of the adjacent bands. If we compare the time when the change of tip of chromosome B occurs with that of the change in the tip of chromosome C, we will see that when the puff in chromosome B is in its full growth the one in C is still in phase *b* of Fig. 3.8. Figure 3.9 shows the relation in time between the puff's development of chromosomes B and C. (For more details see [32].)

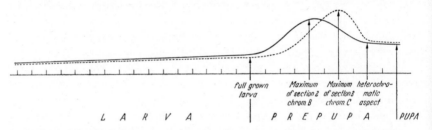

FIG. 3.9. A graphic representation in arbitrary units of the increase of the diameter of the puffs at distal end of chromosomes B and C. The plain line represents the chromosome B and the dotted, chromosome C. The divisions on the baseline represent approximately the time scale in days.

Together with these analyses, we studied the same bands of these two chromosomes (B and C) in cells from the Malpighian tubules and there we found there is no "puffing" formation on them. There is, however, some other "puffing" which you get in other parts of the chromosomes in the Malpighian tubules, and which you don't get in the salivary glands.

What we saw in the puffing of these two bands are very striking changes in chromosomal loci. You find that sort of thing in 20 or 30 different loci in the salivary chromosomes. Smaller changes are much more frequent. Both types are fairly general in these chromosomes.

The next thing we did was to stain these chromosomes at different stages of development. If you take the puff regions just mentioned, and try to stain them in different stages of development with Feulgen and methyl green-pyronin, you will see that before the puffing the region or the band responsible for the puff has only Feulgen-positive material.

During the puff you have a net formed by this Feulgen-positive material, and inside this is a pyronin-stained substance, newly produced. After the puff the pyronin-stained substance is released from this region of the chromosome, and only the Feulgen-positive material is retained as a compact block.

If you take regions of chromosomes without evident puffs you will see Feulgen-positive bands, and Feulgen-negative regions which stain with pyronin, like the nucleolus, showing that there is a distribution of something like RNA in these places also. If you use RNAse, the staining disappears. You have this substance spread through the whole length of the chromosomes, and its concentration is variable in time also; you can have an increase or a decrease at variable times through the larval stage (see [32]).

WADDINGTON: Is this a "puff" formation by the RNA, as well as from the DNA bands?

PAVAN: We think that sometimes in the interbands there is an increase of RNA, and we interpret it as a relation between two DNA bands which are near together, or due to a faint DNA band located at the specific point, but we still have not got evidence in these cases as we have for the puffs.

What we find in our observation is that you have some bands which have the same aspect in all stages of larval development, while others show varying aspects at different tissues. These last types of bands at some stage go through a "puffing" process so that they get swollen and then they go back again. That is a completely reversible system; but we have also something else, like what we have seen in the tip of chromosome B. In this case, the bands are at first like any other band, then they go through a "puffing", and when they go back to the banding stage they show an increase in Feulgen-positive substances at a specific point. This is also a reversible system but after the "puffing" you get this increase in Feulgen-positive substances, which is not found in the previous types.

Then you have still another type of band, like the one in the distal end of chromosome C, which gets an increase in the Feulgen-positive material before the "puffing", and then after the "puffing" returns to normal, with again an accumulation of Feuglen-positive material. This would also be another type of reversible system, as was the last described. These four types of bands are represented in Fig. 3.10. We have interpreted the result obtained in the last two types of bands as an increase in DNA material in the particular locus; or, putting it in another way, as an increase in numbers of the specific gene in this region of the chromosome, related to a specific activity of it at this stage of larval life.

At first, we did not have any proof of DNA increase by a quantitative method. We have sent some colonies of *Rhynchosciara* to Dr. Jack Schultz and to his assistants Drs. Rudkin and Corlette and they have now sent us positive results they got. They measured the quantity of nucleic acid in different parts of the chromosomes, by the method of u.v. absorption and enzyme digestion. They concluded that there is a differential increase in nucleic acid in this region of the chromosome after the puff has regressed. I still do not have the data on the measurements of the content

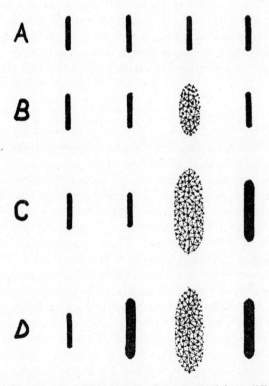

FIG. 3.10. Drawings representing the behaviour of four different types of bands found in polytene chromosomes of *R. angelae*. Type A would be a band which presents always the same aspect in all stages of larval life. Type B presents a puff at certain stage of larval life but returning to the original shape after the puffing process. Type C is like type B, but after the puffing process shows an increase in DNA higher than the one present in the neighbouring bands. In type D the increase of DNA is shown before as well as after the puff.

after treatment with RNAase and DNAase, but I am pretty sure that this shows an increase of DNA, because in the stage which they have measured you do not have any sign of pyronin-positive material there. (When I received the proof of this article to correct, I had the complete data from

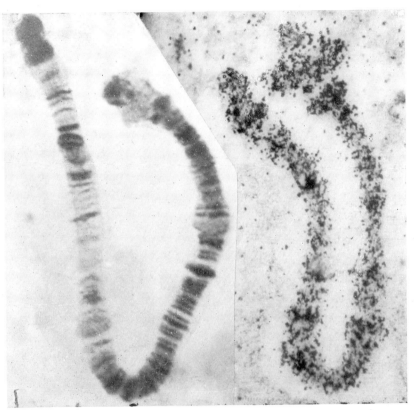

FIG. 3.11. Photomicrograph of an entire chromosome B by auto-radiography and stained by orcein. The stage of larval development corresponds to the full growth of the distal puff of this chromosome.

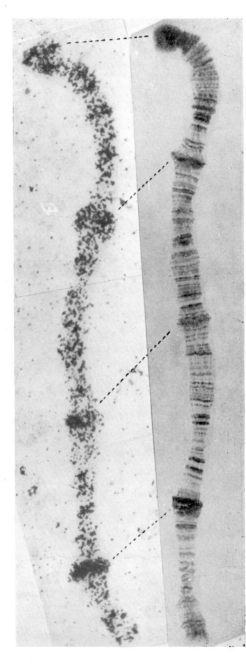

Fig. 3.12. Photomicrograph of an entire chromosome C by auto-radiography and stained by orcein. The stage of larval development corresponds to the one in phase *b* of Fig. 3.8. The distal puff is increasing.

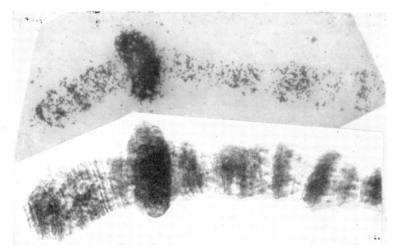

FIG. 3.13. Photomicrograph of the distal end of chromosome C by autoradiography and stained by orcein. The puff is in regression.

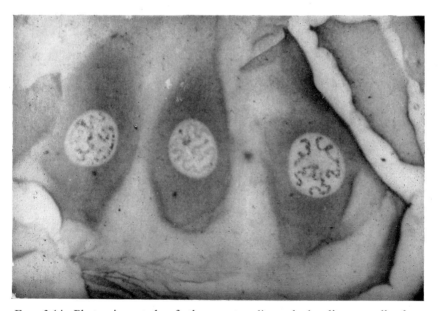

FIG. 3.14. Photomicrograph of three autoradiographed adjacent cells from the intestine wall. In the nucleus of the cell from the right one can see a high incorporation of tritiated thymidine, a much less incorporation in the nucleus from the left and no incorporation at all in the nucleus from the middle cell.

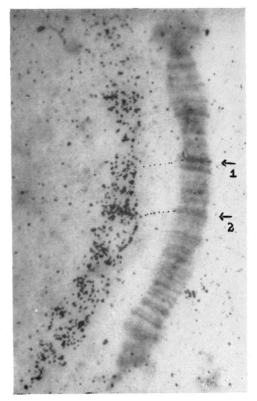

Fig. 3.15. Photomicrograph of the autoradiographed distal half of the long arm of chromosome A. During the staining process (Unna) there was a shift in the emulsion in such a way that the autoradiographic image is shown separately from the stained image of the chromosome.

The arrow 1 indicates a region with a high concentration in DNA but which shows a small incorporation of tritiated thymidine while arrow 2 indicates a region with less DNA but which shows a higher incorporation.

Rudkin and Corlette which confirm our data of the differential increase on DNA in different parts of the chromosome.)

Figure 4 from Pavan and Breuer [33] illustrates what I said about the distribution of the pyronin material along the chromosome. We can see bands stained with methyl green and bands stained with pyronin, and we could show that there are changes of this material along the chromosome during development. In these chromosomes you can see different regions where there are big puffs, and when a chromosome is starting to increase the puffing, you can see that there is pyronin-positive substance inside it. The pyronin-positive material inside the puff is the same as the droplets which you find throughout the nucleus. We could show that these droplets are inside the nucleus, not outside, and we could show also that they are made mainly of RNA. These micronucleoli are distributed all over the inside of the nucleus and often you can see many of them sticking on to the side of the chromosomes. Sometimes you have a nucleus without any visible micronucleoli, but with a background weakly stained red with pyronin. There seems to be a uniform distribution of this material inside of the nucleus in such cases.

The next thing we did, now in co-operation with Dr. Ficq, from Professor Brachet's laboratory, was the analysis of the behaviour of DNA in all these processes, using the autoradiographic method. We injected tritiated thymidine into this animal in the larval stage, and checked the incorporation of this thymidine, using a special photographic emulsion over prepared squashes of salivary gland and intestine walls. Figures 3.5 and 3.6 show a comparison between the entire set of salivary gland chromosomes as stained with orcein and as pictured by the autoradiographic method. At this stage of larval life there is no conspicuous puff, and the incorporation of tritiated thymidine is more or less uniform along the chromosomes. Now if we analyse the activity of DNA at a different stage of larval development we will see very different incorporation of thymidine at different points of the chromosomes. Figure 3.11 shows chromosome B at the stage where the puff of its distal end is in its full growth. In this stage the different activities of different regions of the chromosome are very obvious. Figure 3.12 shows chromosome C, and here one can see "puffs" being formed in at least three different parts of the chromosome which show high incorporation of thymidine. In Fig. 3.13 you can see a typical case where there is no doubt of the differences of incorporation. This is the puffed region in C when the puff is going back.

We have preparations and pictures of the chromosomes at all the different stages, and we can see that during development you have an increase in incorporation in the puffing regions at a certain moment of the larval life. When we inject the thymidine and wait for eight days and then make the preparations, the chromosomes have the same appearance, with a higher concentration in the regions where the puffing occurs, if the injection was made at a time when this process was going on. That means that you really have a synthesis of DNA there rather than a mere turnover.

Another point is, that beside what happens in the "puff" region, in any stage of larval development at which you make the injection, you have uniform incorporation of thymidine along the chromosome, giving a background of this sort (about the same which you see in Fig. 3.6). All the chromosomes are more or less uniform, in this incorporation, though there are of course some differences as we have seen in some points of the chromosomes. This background incorporation suggests that you have during development a duplication of the entire chromosomes and, beside this, you have also a different incorporation in the different parts.

Another important point in our work with Dr. Ficq is related to this picture (Fig. 3.14). We have here a case where three adjacent cells from the intestine wall were pictured after the injection of tritiated thymidine. We can see that these cells are in activity because of the puffing they show. One cell shows a very high incorporation, another a small incorporation and the middle cell does not show any incorporation at all, 24 hr after the injection. The middle cell must have been active in relation to the thymidine at some time, but, by that time, there was no more thymidine available [35].

In Fig. 3.15 the chromosome has shifted on the emulsion. In the region indicated by the arrow you have two bands very rich in Feulgen-positive material and almost no incorporation at the stage when the injection was made. These two bands are landmarks of chromosome A (arrow 1) and correspond to a region of the autoradiographic picture where you have only little incorporation, if you compare it with other regions of the chromosome with much less DNA. This shows that you can have bands with high amounts of DNA yet only little incorporation, so the quantity of DNA is not proportional to the incorporation of thymidine at all times [34].

WADDINGTON: How long was it after the injection that these autoradiographs were made?

PAVAN: Twenty-four hours.

WADDINGTON: I was wondering how far you could distinguish, as you were beginning to do in your last remarks, between an autoradiograph which indicates incorporation and one which shows purely the concentration of DNA, as it would do when the DNA is in equilibrium with the thymidine. You can get a higher number of grains in the autoradiograph either because the region has a high concentration of DNA, or because the DNA is metabolically very active. In some of your last slides you were beginning to distinguish these two; for instance, in that case where two bands had a high concentration of DNA but little incorporation. Presumably, in many of your "puffs" the high concentration of grains is produced by both factors; there is a large amount of DNA present and this DNA is very active at the time when the puffing is going on.

PAVAN: Yes. You can show for these two bands that there is a time in development when they incorporate a high amount of thymidine—they do just like a puff and at that time they are very active with radio-thymidine.

WADDINGTON: I suppose when you've got the full data on the absorption measurements from Schultz's group you will be able to get the rate of incorporation per unit of DNA. The autoradiographs, of course, just give you the amount of incorporation per area. One wants to be able to relate that to the amount of DNA present.

PAVAN: I do not know whether this can be done with the thymidine but it may be possible.

With the data we got from our work on *Rhynchosciara* we may conclude:

a. Although having the same banding pattern, chromosomes from different organs show different behaviour, the activity of each locus being different in different organs.

b. The activity of each locus is also variable when we consider the chromosomes of the same organ at different periods of larval development.

c. Although the more striking visible changes in the chromosomes during development are "puffs", which occur at certain loci at a specific time, less conspicuous changes in the bands are also very frequent.

d. In the puffing process, the DNA shows a very high activity proved by the incorporation of tritiated thymidine.

e. Our previous results, now confirmed by spectrographic method by Rudkin and Corlette, show that in many cases the puff processes are not entirely reversible. The post-puff chromosomes may show an increase in DNA in certain loci.

f. The activity of DNA may be higher in stages when its quantity is smaller, depending on the development period. By studying the incorporation of tritiated thymidine at different stages of larval life, Dr. Ficq and myself were able to show that bands very rich in DNA may be practically inactive at certain stages of larval life, although very active in other stages.

PLAUT: What you are getting here, especially over the puffs, is a measure of surface activity. You are not going to go down very far. You probably would not record a piece of DNA labelled 1 μ below the surface.

7

This means that when there is a difference, the true difference is probably greater than it appears.

GALL: Another interpretation, of course, of your unlabelled cells—what makes it so unpleasant—is that the production of DNA is discontinuous. You have one cycle of duplication followed by a period of no duplication, and the differences between the bands are dependent on times at which each band is duplicating within the total series of DNA duplications of the whole chromosome. This raises rather a difficulty for interpretation.

WADDINGTON: What are the implications of this increase in DNA following puffing?

BRENNER: I think that what Plaut and Gall have been saying is that there isn't really an increase in DNA in the bands, at any rate as judged by the thymidine incorporation. Is it possible to fit all these data into the theory that all DNA is synthesising the same amount irrespective of where it is found in the chromosome? If not, it means that some genes are replicating while others do not.

WADDINGTON: It sounds rather odd.

BRENNER: Well, I think what Plaut and Gall have been hinting is that this is not a necessary conclusion.

PLAUT: One possibility is that there are two kinds of asynchrony, one in time and one in space, but that essentially you are getting a polytenisation process.

BRENNER: In addition to the non-synchrony, there is the possibility that where the band is particularly condensed the beta particles would not be able to reach the emulsion, while where the chromosome was thinner you would get a better count.

WADDINGTON: But you don't get the same story with the Feulgen, without bringing in the thymidine? You get the same appearance of certain bands sometimes becoming more deeply staining.

BRENNER: That also wants adjustment for packing.

PLAUT: Do you mean packing without increase? It would, of course, come out with measurements whether that is really the case; for instance, the Jack Schultz measurements.

WADDINTON: I don't see why you reject the idea of the genes in these locations actually making more DNA. We know they can make DNA when they replicate themselves. They also make template RNA. Why shouldn't one gene at a certain stage in development start over-reduplicating itself and making extra DNA?

PLAUT: I don't think there's anything wrong with that idea, but it's too exciting to be accepted without eliminating every other possibility.

BEERMANN: There are very simple examples in higher organisms where you find production of DNA by chromosomes, not in the usual way of producing another chromosome, but producing a lump of material which looks like a nucleolus, but is definitely Feulgen-positive. This happens in the differentiation of the oocytes and nurse cells in some *Diptera*. Bayreuther (36) has shown this very clearly. You find that in prophase a thick lump of Feulgen-positive material develops in addition to the chromosome set and in contact with the heterochromatic sections of one chromosome pair. This lump is then included in only one of the daughter nuclei of the following division. While it is slowly dissolved, a new lump is formed in the same nucleus at the next division, and this cycle repeats three or four times. All the cells that get this lump are able to become oocytes and the others become nurse cells. So there is a case which, although it has not been measured, shows very clearly by pure morphological inspection that Feulgen-positive bodies can arise which are not chromosomes.

POLLOCK: In any case you're not showing net synthesis, are you, by this incorporation; it may be just increased turnover?

PLAUT: I believe that Pelc has evidence now which suggests that there is a low basal turnover in DNA.

POLLOCK: The localised turnover was a high basal turnover and the net turnover a low basal turnover. Isn't that right?

WADDINGTON: Again, if we take this back to the Feulgen evidence, the increase in Feulgen staining can't be due to turnover.

POLLOCK: Oh, quite.

PLAUT: Isn't it possible that the control of DNA synthesis is not the same in all parts of the chromosome? One might suggest that over most of the chromosome we have an exact duplication during synthesis at all times, but that in some parts, perhaps in the heterochromatic regions, the control is less tight, allowing for some deviation under some conditions. The apparent oversynthesis of DNA in specific regions of polytene chromosomes has been interpreted as evidence for metabolically active DNA. Could one distinguish between a locus at which the DNA is metabolically active and one where DNA synthesis is no longer controlled?

WADDINGTON: Isn't this a situation which seems to conflict with the dogma that the synthesis of DNA is absolutely controlled and that every gene just duplicates itself once in each mitotic cycle? Apparently these genes are not doing so but are producing considerable amounts of DNA. But, we haven't the slightest idea what this control is. It seems to me much less easy to understand why there should be such control than that there shouldn't.

MITCHISON: Isn't there also one point, that these cells are not going through a mitotic cycle? These are cells which are finished and will never divide again, and therefore you might expect their synthesis of DNA to be different from all the other cases of DNA synthesis which have been studied on growing tissue.

RIS: Furthermore, the cells are involved in endopolyploidy. We have this endopolyploidy in insects especially. It is usually found in gland cells, which are very active; and there is no reason why certain loci shouldn't be more active than others and make more strands.

WADDINGTON: Sirlin, who is studying the sulphur-containing proteins shown up by long continued labelling of salivary chromosomes, has got evidence that in certain cases whole chromosome arms have only about half the sulphur content that other comparable arms in other cells, or even other arms in the same cell, would have. Possibly they have a lower degree of polyteny than the other chromosome arms in the same cell. This suggests that the control of duplication in polyteny may not be so precise as the control for duplication in the mitotic cycle.

PLAUT: Pätau and Owczarzak at Wisconsin have measured the DNA levels in developing salivary gland nuclei and found that beyond a certain stage of polytenisation there is less than an exact doubling during synthesis. They suggest that the decrease in rate can be accounted for if one assumes that heterochromatic sections do not keep pace. This work has not yet been published.

WADDINGTON: Of course, there's a further point to put in here, that maybe these appearances, however we're going to explain them, could be related to gene functioning. It might be not merely a question of rate of polytenisation in general, but polytenisation in very close connection with gene functioning, which would make it very much more interesting.

PONTECORVO: But is it known whether the salivary gland chromosomes have any function, apart from producing saliva which is presumably the same from the earliest stages to the late ones?

PAVAN: I do not think they're the same.

BEERMANN: In *Chironomus* I have not observed the phenomena which have been seen by Dr. Pavan. During larval development everything seems to remain the same, which makes sense; but in other material it may be different.

PAVAN: But, I think in *Drosophila* there is some evidence.

BEERMANN: It is only on pupation that the function changes, which is the same as happens in *Chironomus*.

WADDINGTON: It seems to be about at pupation that you get most of these puffings. In the diagrams that Pavan drew—I don't know whether he meant this—the increase in a band seemed to come after the fully grown larval stage.

PAVAN: Yes, in these two puffs, yes.

BRENNER: There is a simple and attractive hypothesis which one can put forward and which really stems from Callan's observations. We think of the salivary gland chromosome as a kind of weaker lampbrush. That is, when a gene is switched off—talking in a very crude sense now—it is packed up tight. When it has to work and make RNA, then the chain has to be extended. We therefore have one piece of DNA extending from one end of the chromosome to the other, and in certain parts this is coiled up tight.

WADDINGTON: That is fine, until you come to this evidence of Pavan who seems to suggest that some DNA when it is extended makes, not RNA, but more DNA.

BRENNER: Well, we can always say that there you have local gene replication, so that you speed up the rate of RNA synthesis.

WADDINGTON: Yes, but in some of these things, for instance, in the last type of Pavan's bands, you get, in the first half phase of puffing, a lot of extra gene duplication with more RNA, more DNA, more Feulgen-positive material; then you unwind your gene, and presumably get its specific action; and finally, it shuts off, and packs up again, but the DNA sticks around it.

BRENNER: Or, alternatively, what you've done is that you have switched off in addition to that gene some adjoining genes in the interchromomeric stuff, which have become rolled up into the band as well. In other words, you have increased condensation.

PAVAN: You can show here very easily that you really have an increase in genic material in this region, with an increase in the chromosome nearby. If you measure the two bands here, instead of them coming nearer you have them going apart. You get a real increase of material here. They are very condensed also before the puffing. You have only Feulgen-positive material there. Here it's stained by the pyronin. You can't see anything here but the methyl green.

BRENNER: Well, that is a gene that must have really been switched off, but in addition it's got a lot of extra DNA which just remains there.

PAVAN: We tend to interpret this puffing rather as Beermann does. You have this DNA material here. It starts to form something inside by a kind of vacuolarisation, when you see stages a few hours different you can follow it very easily. You can see that something is forming inside and the chromosome strands nearby are being forced apart. You have the pyronin material forming here. This is a very active process which makes the chromosome increase in diameter. When you have a distinct band near the puff you can see that this increase in diameter causes it to break up like this.

BRENNER: Well, I'm saying exactly the same thing, except I'm pushing and you're pulling.

WADDINGTON: We shall have to stop fairly soon, but I think Weiss wants to ask some questions bringing us back to our general topic.

WEISS: Could I just return to differentiation. There is a fairly large body of evidence that shows that you can switch the cell alternatively— or make the metabolic energy of the cell available either for the manu-facture of specific products or for multiplication, and there is a certain alternativeness or mutual exclusion between the two processes. It must be rather unique if you can consider this process you've described here as something corresponding to polytenisation or in some way related to multiplication, because usually differentiation and multiplication are mutually exclusive. I've raised this because there's quite a lot of indirect evidence on that point, but if we note the significance of these beautifully analysed phenomena here for the process of differentiation, I hope at a later time we will come back to the question of whether they are really initiators of a differentiative change in the rest of the cell, or merely indicators of an already existing cytoplasmic differentiation.

Along that line I'd just like to ask Dr. Beermann a question from his own presentation. I was particularly struck by the heterozygous cell, in which one chromosome puffs but the other doesn't. Obviously both come from perfectly viable parents, each of which has obviously morpho-logically and physiologically hardly distinguishable features. I think this fact makes us think about the interpretation of this phenomenon, doesn't it? We have a few lucky cases, where a local reaction or response of a band or a gene system goes to the extreme of puffing up, but most of these active regions of chromosome do not have a similar morphologically distinguishable expression. Is that a fair statement of these heterozygous cases?

BEERMANN: Yes. I wanted to come back in any case to this question of whether bands which are not in the puffed state are really switched off completely. The experiment that has been done in some cases is to produce genetically mosaic individuals that lack these bands homozygously, and find out whether the cells still function in the normal way. There is one experiment reported by Demerec in 1933, I think, when he found that there are some deficiencies which are cell viable in the homozygous state in the integument of *Drosophila*.

WADDINGTON: But the remarkable thing about his results was how few they were. Much the greater number of deficiencies, although their genes were not known to operate in the integument, were actually cell lethals.

I suppose it's hardly fair to ask if you can see anything rather like heterokaryosis? In a heterozygote one might be able to see puffs on each chromosome, but of rather different kinds, and these two might be able to co-operate in some way.

CALLAN: In lampbrush chromosomes you can get in some loci a rather regular, but not invariable, situation in which a loop joins up with its partner loop to form a large mass from which two tails project back to the locus from which the loops come. This is really two sister strands producing something mutually. You can also get the situation, and very frequently at particular loci, where homologous lampbrush loops co-operate to produce a material.

PONTECORVO: That is four loops coming together?

CALLAN: Yes, or even more than that, if it happens to be a locus with more than two loops at the site. Aren't there two alternative propositions open here? Because we've not yet been able to pin down what the functional state of a gene in a cell is; is it covered up and loaded, or is it uncovered and unloaded? This, I think, is very important for those of us who are concerned with differentiation. It would be nice to be able to pick up an identifiable key in the nucleus that would indicate the active state of the genes. I think Dr. Beermann's proposal of the crossing experiment is absolutely essential before we can decide what is or what is not the functional state of the gene.

WADDINGTON: Isn't it true that these puffs are very active in incorporating the things concerned with protein metabolism as well as with

DNA? If so, that would indicate that in the puffed state that region of the chromosome is metabolically extremely active.

BRENNER: May I make another comment which arises from an earlier statement by Dr. Pontecorvo. If you take the haploid DNA, and calculate the number of nucleotide pairs, and then ask the reasonable question— assuming for the present that all we said about coding is correct—how many different enzymes could be made, you find you've got too many. For example, in a bacterium with about 10^7 nucleotide pairs, you should be able to make seven thousand enzymes. A mammalian cell, if we assume that there is one strand, should be able to make about two million enzymes. The DNA seems to contain too much information. If you try to enumerate enzymes it's possible to think of about a thousand or of that order, but these estimates go up to ten thousand or even a million.

WADDINGTON: Isn't that merely a tribute to the incompetence of bio-chemistry? If we look at differentiated tissues, it is clear that we know only a minute fraction of the chemical differences between them; the mere histology is enough to show that we are only scraping the edges of the real chemical distinctions that exist.

BRENNER: No. The point that I wanted to make is that there is a possibility that there is a lot of DNA that has no function.

WADDINGTON: But against that there is the genetic evidence of Demerec, that the vast majority of minute deficiencies are cell lethal even in the one particular tissue he studied. It looks as though you can't just get rid of a lot of DNA without doing any damage.

We have obviously not exhausted this subject but I think we shall have to stop here for this evening.

REFERENCES

1. CALLAN, H. G. (1955). Recent work on the structure of cell nuclei. In *Symposium on fine structure of cells.*—I.U.B.S. publication, series B, number 21, p. 89, Noordhoff, Groningen.
2. ALFERT, M. (1950) *J. Cell. Comp. Physiol.* **36**, 381;
   SWIFT, H. and R. KLEINFELD (1953) *Physiol. Zool.*, **26**, 301.
3. RIS, H. (1956) *J. Biophys. Biochem. Cytol.* Suppl. 2, 385.
4. GALL, J. F. (1954) *J. Morph.* **94**, 283.
5. LA COUR, L. F. and A. RUTISHAUSER (1953) *Nature, Lond.* **172**, 501; MARQUARDT, H. (1941) *Planta* **31**, 670; OSTERGREN, G. and T. WAKONIG (1954) *Bot. Notiser*, p. 357.
6. HUGHES-SCHRADER, S. and H. RIS (1941) *J. Exp. Zool.* **87**, 429.
7. FRIEDRICK-FRESKA, H. and F. KAUDEWITZ (1953) *Z. Naturf.* **8b**, 343.
8. BERNSTEIN, M. and D. MAZIA (1953) *Biophys. Biochim. Acta* **10**, 600.
9. DOTY, P. and G. ZUBAY (1956) *J. Amer. Chem. Soc.* **78**, 6207.

10. PLAUT, W. and D. MAZIA (1956) *J. Biophys. Biochem. Cytol.* **2**, 573.
11. TAYLOR, J. H., P. S. WOOD and W. L. HUGHES (1957) *Proc. Nat. Acad. Sci., Wash.* **43**, 122.
12. BEERMANN, W. (1952) *Chromosoma* **5**, 139.
13. BEERMANN, W. (1952) *Z. Naturf.* **7b**, 237.
14. BREUER, M. E. and C. PAVAN (1955) *Chromosoma* **7**, 371.
15. MECHELKE, F. (1953) *Chromosoma* **5**, 511.
16. FLEMMING, W. (1882) *Zellsubstanz, Kern und Zelltheilung*, Leipzig.
17. BEERMANN, W. (1956) *Cold Spr. Harb. Symp. Quant. Biol* **21**, 217.
18. RUDKIN, G. T. (1957) *Gordon Conference on Cell Structure and Metabolism*, In press.
19. FICQ, A. and C. PAVAN (1957) *Nature, Lond.* **180**, 983.
20. KOSSWIG, C. and A. SENGÜN (1947) *C. R. Soc. Turque Sci.* **13**, 94.
21. BERGER, C. A. (1940) *J. Hered.* **31**, 2.
22. SLIZYNSKI, B. M. (1950) *J. Genet.* **50**, 77.
23. PAVAN, C. and M. E. BREUER (1952) *J. Hered.* **43**, 152.
24. BEERMANN, W. (1950) *Naturwissanschaften*, **37**, 543.
25. BALBIANI, E. G. (1881) *Zool. Anz.* **4**, 367.
26. BAUER, H. (1953) *Zool. Anz.* Suppl. **17**, 252.
27. BEERMANN, W. (1957) *Annual Growth Symp.*, Princeton Univ. Press. In press.
28. BEERMANN, W. (1955) *Chromosoma* **7**, 198.
29. ACTON, A. B. (1958) *Am. Naturalist* **92**, 57.
30. BAUER, H. and T. CASPERSSON (1949) *Hereditas* Suppl. p. 533.
31. BEERMANN, W. and G. F. BAHR (1954) *Exp. Cell. Res.* **6**, 195.
32. BREUER, M. E. and C. PAVAN (1955) *Chromosoma* **7**, 371.
33. PAVAN C, and M. E. BREUER (1955) *Symposium on Cell Secretion* p. 90. Ed. G. SCHREIBER, Belo Horizonte. Brazil
34. FICQ, A. and C. PAVAN (1957) *Nature, Lond.* **180**, 983.
35. PAVAN, C. and A. FICQ (1958) *Proc. Int. Congr. Rad. Res.* Burlington Vermont.
36. BAYREUTHER, K. (1952) *Naturwissenschaften* **39**, 71.

CHAPTER IV

Functional Interactions of Nucleus and Cytoplasm

WADDINGTON: Yesterday we were talking about organisation at the level of the individual loci on the chromosomes. I think now we must go on to more general activities of the nucleus as a whole. The way I thought we'd arrange the material this morning is like this: I will start saying a bit about our autoradiographic work on general nuclear activities, and Jean Brachet will contribute to the same topic. Then we might go on to the enucleate cytoplasm; Plaut and Brachet I think largely agree on this, so perhaps it won't take us long to hear just what they agree about. Then we might have an example of activity in the cytoplasm of nucleate cells, if Holtzer would show us some of his material and bring out some of the points about the elaboration of proteins in the muscle cell. That will probably take us to coffee time. After coffee we might start on the electron microscopical studies on the cytoplasm, with perhaps Dr. Gay giving us a bridge between the nucleus and cytoplasm. I'm hoping that Sjöstrand will be here by that time, and Lehmann will probably also want to come in at that point.

Well, I will start with a very rapid account of some of our autoradiographic work. It's more a question of raising problems, I'm afraid, at this point, than of giving answers to them. Most of this work was done on relatively young amphibian or chick embryonic material. We start off at the stage when specificity is first appearing, which is more or less the time of gastrulation. At gastrulation you get an uptake of labelled amino acids into the nuclei which is particularly marked in the region around the blastopore lip. This is a very nice example, on the scale of whole nuclei, of the same kind of thing that the salivary chromosome people were talking about, namely differential activity of nuclear structures according to the particular tissue. In this case which is at the very beginning of differentiation, the only regional specificity which has yet appeared is between the region around the blastopore and the rest of the egg. But, in that region you do seem to have the nuclei activated, or at any rate beginning to engage in rapid uptake; presumably this is a response to the cytoplasmic condition in that region [1].

This raises a problem that I think we shall have to discuss. These differences in incorporation, that you see for instance in the salivary chromosomes, are they symptoms, or are they things with causative action? Personally, I don't think this is really a valid distinction in this sort of system. The appearances are both symptoms, in the sense that they are set off by cytoplasmic differences in the various regions, and they must also be causative, in that they will be followed by different consequences. When you are dealing with a long sequence of processes, no item is just a symptom or just a cause, but it will be both. By the time that you get to the end of differentiation, as perhaps you have done in the salivary chromosome story, then you might be able to make a distinction between a symptom and a cause. But in the early stages a phenomenon must be first a symptom of what precedes it and then a cause of what follows.

In Fig. 4.1 you see the nuclei, as a whole, being very active in the uptake of amino acids, and so they are for things like adenine. Now, a few more pictures in rather more detail. Figure 4.2a shows a nucleus with a nucleolus from the mesoderm of *Xenopus*; Fig. 4.2b shows the same section at a higher level of focus, focusing on to the silver grains. In the emulsion you can see a very high labelling of the nucleolus, after a 70 min exposure to methionine. Figure 4.3 is again methionine, but with a 4 hr 40 min labelling period, and you can see that not only is the nucleolus labelled but there is a great deal of label all round the whole nucleus and particularly round the nuclear membrane. That is the sort of general picture that we see. It raises quite a number of different problems. One which we are very interested in, and which Dr. Sirlin here is doing a lot of work on, is the question of what parts of the nucleolus are most active in this respect. In many cases you can see around these *Xenopus* nucleoli a sheath of DNA, or there may be DNA at one side of them—the so-called nucleolus-associated chromatin. I think there is no doubt that for such nucleic acid labels as adenine, the nucleolus-associated chromatin is certainly very active, possibly more active than the RNA main body of the nucleolus. Whether that is also true for the amino-acid labels is perhaps more doubtful, but on the whole it seems that the nucleolus-associated chromatin is at least as active as the RNA and possibly more so.

This type of nuclear labelling with a strong emphasis on the nucleolus occurs in the early stages of development when differentiation is just beginning. It is not consistently found throughout the whole of development. In later stages, when protein synthesis in particular cells must be very rapid, you find the cytoplasm being labelled as quickly as the nucleolus. Figure 4.4 shows early muscle fibres. A few nucleoli are labelled, but many of them are pretty well unlabelled, and there is a great deal more label in the cytoplasm than would be found in comparable tissue at earlier stages. This suggests that the pattern of protein synthesis —or at least the pattern of uptake of amino-acids—changes from stage to stage of differentiation. At the earlier stages the nucleus and nucleolar area are particularly active, but later on there is more activity in the cytoplasm.

That sort of change in the pattern of uptake can also be seen very clearly in oocytes, where you can follow it in a single type of cell. I will just show one or two pictures of oocytes from autoradiographs made by Pantelouris [2]. Figure 4.5 is a relatively early stage, with strongly labelled nucleoli. There is stronger activity in the cytoplasm than in the nuclear sap, and still more in the nucleoli themselves. Figure 4.6 is at a higher power; the bottom area is the nucleus with two nucleoli, and the cytoplasm lies above. This is at a later stage, when there is extremely active cytoplasm, comparatively inactive nuclear sap, and active nucleoli. Now it is quite a problem to put this on to a quantitative basis. Table 4.1 contains some of Pantelouris's data, in which he is beginning to quantify it. They are from a series of experiments in which there had been an exposure to methionine for an hour and a half, after which a dose of unlabelled methionine had been given to try to wash out the label, so that one can follow what happens to the already-incorporated tracer. Now, these figures show that in the more and more mature oocytes the situation after a short labelling changes. At the very early stages there are no nucleoli visible, and there is a very heavy labelling in the cytoplasm and less in the nuclear sap. By stage B the nucleoli are appearing, but initially the label is stronger in the cytoplasm although it is also appearing in the nucleolus. At later stages the nucleoli are fully functional, and you get a heavier label in them than in the cytoplasm after a short exposure. After a short exposure followed by dilution one might hope to get evidence about transfer of incorporated tracer from the nucleolus into the cytoplasm, or possibly vice versa. That is one of the things we are most interested in at present. But I should prefer to say that that is a problem we are studying than that it is something we have any answer to. We have in Table 4.1, for instance, a suggestion that after one and a half hours there is a moderate label in the nucleolus, and the label in the nucleolus goes up after you've left it another one and a half hours in unlabelled medium; this might be interpreted as a movement of material from the cytoplasm towards the nucleolar area. Whether that interpretation is really justified I should prefer to leave for a little; but that is the sort of problem which we are doing a lot of work on.

One of the other problems that this material raises is the distinction between rates of incorporation and concentration of incorporating material. What you see, crudely speaking, is a lot of label around a nucleolus. How much is that due to the nucleolar material being more active, and how much to its being more concentrated? One of the ways of studying this would be to make autoradiographs after 2 hr, 4, 6 and so on, and

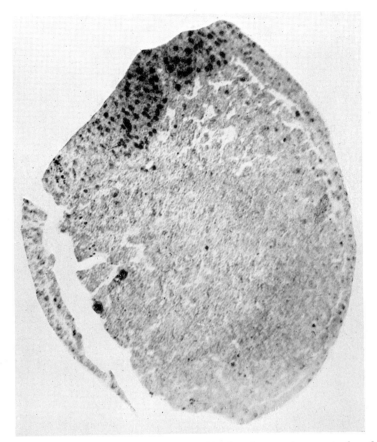

FIG. 4.1. Uptake of radioactive methionine into a late gastrula of *Triturus*. Autoradiograph showing concentration of label in nuclei of archenteron roof and presumptive neural plate. (From Sirlin, 1955.)

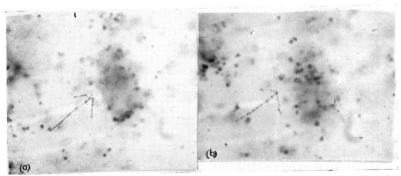

FIG. 4.2. A nucleus in early tailbud mesoderm of *Xenopus*, labelled by 70 min exposure to methionine-^{35}S. *a* is focused on the tissue, the arrow pointing to the nucleolus; *b*, focused on photographic emulsion, showing high activity of nucleolus.

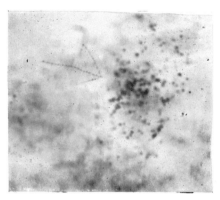

FIG. 4.3. *Xenopus* mesoderm nucleus after 4 hr 40 min labelling with methionine.

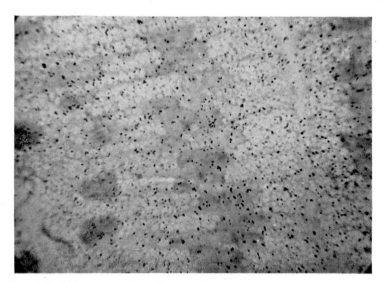

FIG. 4.4. *Triturus* muscle cells from late tailbud, labelled with phenyl-alanine. High activity in cytoplasm, some nucleoli labelled, others not.

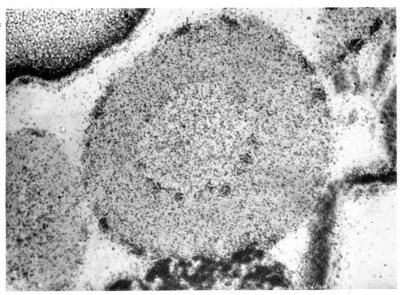

FIG. 4.5. Middle stage *Triturus* oocyte. High label in cytoplasm and especially in the ring of nucleoli just inside the membrane of the germinal vesicle. (From Pantelouris, 1958.)

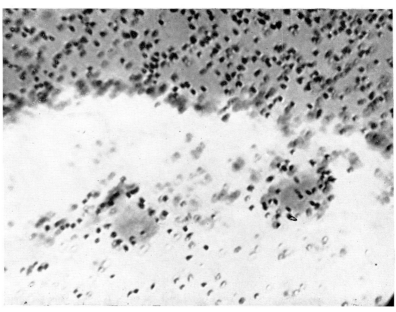

FIG. 4.6. *Triturus* oocyte. High activity in the dark-coloured cytoplasm, and on the two nucleoli, but low in the nuclear sap. From (Pantelouris, 1958.)

TABLE 4.1. MEAN GRAIN COUNTS PER $52\,\mu^2$

Exp. No. and fixation time in hours	STAGE A			STAGE B			STAGE C			STAGE D		
	Cyto-plasm	Nucleus	Nucle-olar area	Cyto-plasm	Nucleus	Nucle-olar area	Cyto-plasm	Nucleus	Nucle-olar area	Cyto-plasm	Nucleus	Nucle-olar area
7 (1·5)	62 ± 6	19 ± 2	—	60 ± 5	22 ± 2	38 ± 14	31 ± 8	24 ± 2	51 ± 16*	32 ± 7	18 ± 3	54 ± 10
8 (3)	43 ± 5	25 ± 1	—	61 ± 8	17 ± 3	86 ± 11	60 ± 7	18 ± 2	58 ± 16*			
9 (6)	36 ± 7	18 ± 1	—	60 ± 3	19 ± 3	49 ± 5	45 ± 4	19 ± 5	61 ± 7	41 ± 9	21 ± 2	51 ± 8
10 (9)	3 ± ·05	1·5 ± ·06	—	22 ± 4	13 ± 1	47 ± 30	13 ± 3	4 ± 2	10 ± 5*	9 ± 5	9 ± 2	18 ± 2
11 (19)	7 ± 2	2 ± ·05	—	7 ± 2	7 ± 1	39 ± 14	23 ± 1	5 ± 1	11 ± 4*	3 ± 1	5 ± 2	13 ± 2

* Note the considerable variability between nucleoli in these cases.

study the speed at which the incorporation increases. The preliminary results we've got—and they are still very preliminary—suggest that for labels like adenine the rates of incorporation are similar throughout the whole system of the cell. The label is more concentrated, of course, in certain regions of the cell, but the actual time course of incorporation goes up at the same rate everywhere. For labels like methionine, that may not be the case; it is quite likely that for them the material in the neighbourhood of the nucleolus is more active. The only comparisons we can make so far are per unit area of the squash or section, not taking account of the concentration of the material. One has to find how to distinguish between the rate of activity of the material and its concentration before one can get anything like a full understanding of what is happening.

But even if the rates of incorporation are the same for all the different structures, there is no doubt that the concentration of incorporation material is highest at the nucleolus, at least in the early stage. The total activity of the nucleolus at an early stage is about the same as the total activity of the whole nucleus, although of course the volume of the nucleolus is very much smaller. Of the activity of the cell as a whole, something like 20–30% is taking place in the nucleolus, so that a considerable fraction of the total uptake is spatially concentrated in that area. That seems to me slightly surprising. We have lots of evidence that nucleoli are formed at particular loci on chromosomes. Now other loci on chromosomes we consider to be sites of the synthesis of specific gene products. One can hardly imagine that in all the various different types of tissues which show high nucleolar activity those particular loci are always extremely active in manufacturing some specific substance, as we should assume for all the other loci on the chromosomes. That suggests that the nucleolus region is different from the other regions of the chromosome, and that we are not dealing with highly specific synthesis processes at that region. One of the possible interpretations is that the nucleolus is merely an assembly point, at which specific proteins synthesised at all sorts of points along the chromosome come together, and are kept together for some time before they go out into the cytoplasm, or whatever they do.

There is one piece of evidence which has recently been found here by Drs. Sirlin and Knight, which could be interpreted in support of that suggestion [3]. They have made a study of the sulphur-containing proteins of chromosomes, and from the type of extraction used they considered that these were the residual proteins of the chromosome. Now the distribution of sulphur taken up from methionine was rather peculiar. To simplify the picture, one can roughly put it that in most of the chromosomes about 50% of the methionine was more or less evenle scattered along the chromosomes, but about 50% of it seemed to by found in definite local concentrations, which were different in the chromosomes in different cells. Thus in ten or a dozen examples of one arm of a *Drosophila* salivary chromosome, 50% of the incorporated methionine seemed to be free in the sense that in one example it was concentrated in certain bands and in another example concentrated in other bands. There seem to be two major types of explanation. One could be dealing with a sort of sub-visible "puffing" phenomenon, with periodic release of the material, so that the chromosome is making something and every now and then squirting it out, so that you could sometimes watch it when it had just made but not yet released its product. That would give a possibility of getting variation from cell to cell. But another possibility is that we are dealing with proteins which are made at various sites along the chromosomes, and flow along the chromosome so as to come to the nucleolar area, where they then stick around for a bit.

These are the sort of questions which are coming out of our work at present; the question of the activity of the nucleolus-associated chromatin as compared with the RNA part of the nucleolus; the changing patterns of cellular activity, with sometimes the nucleolus the most active area and in other cases the cytoplasm; questions of the traffic of already incorporated material from nucleolus to cytoplasm and vice versa; and the general nature of the nuclear activity and why you so often find high rates of uptake in the region of the nucleolus.

GALL: Does the period when the label begins to appear more in the cytoplasm and less in the nucleus coincide with the period when yolk granules begin to be digested, which is about the neurula stage?

WADDINGTON: It is a bit later than that. We haven't actually got the whole series of stages, but we know that in the neurula stage the labelling is still very high in the nucleolus, and by the time you are getting elongated myofibrils, in the early movement stage, it is highly cytoplasmic. In between we haven't yet got the exact point of transition, but I should say it is somewhat later than the digestion of the yolk begins, and it is certainly before the digestion of yolk is complete.

LEHMANN: Are these amino acids being incorporated into proteins, so that this gives an indication of protein formation?

WADDINGTON: They have to be taken up into something which persists after the ordinary histological processing, and that means almost certainly that they are taken up into protein or RNA, or something of that kind.

BRACHET: Yes, I think so too. They have to be taken into something insoluble, but of course it is always a great problem to know if there is a net protein synthesis or if it is only a turnover which is giving incorporation; but in most cases where you have incorporation into these insoluble things there is probably real protein synthesis.

CALLAN: Could I make one remark about the oocyte nuclei you were speaking about? It's this; those nucleoli round the edge of the nuclear membrane—I think Gall would agree with me that we can't say for sure where they come from. There are these things which lie around here, and which have different shapes, and it was those which you were labelling. I'm not myself at all sure where they come from on the chromosomes, or indeed whether they perhaps don't come from the chromosones at all.

WEISS: You are speaking now of the very early ones; the later ones come from the chromosomes.

CALLAN: Yes, but I'm not sure at what stage they were.

WADDINGTON: The ones that were heavily labelled were from quite large sized oocytes.

CALLAN: One other point I think is worth mentioning. At this stage the oocyte is growing. It has laid down a tremendous lot of yolk, and has laid down a tremendous lot of nuclear sap which is going to become subsequently, in large part, the cytoplasm of the cells which form the embryo. It would not in fact surprise me in the least if you were to see labelling in the cytoplasm of material which then travels across the cytoplasm and accumulates in the nucleoli; that is, material which is destined to go in and stay in for some considerable time.

WADDINGTON: That is what Pantelouris thinks happens in the very earliest stage of oocyte formation. In this earliest stage, the label is mainly in the cytoplasm, and there was some evidence at a slightly later stage, after the dilution of the label, that the incorporated tracer might leave the cytoplasm and go into the nucleolar area.

BRACHET: I would like to add something, since we are talking about the oocyte. We have been, with Madame Ficq, working on newt oocytes on the incorporation of adenine and phenylalanine. [4] Of course, we get the same sort of pictures as Waddington has shown. One addition we can make is on the effect of centrifugation on these oocytes. You give the label by injecting into the animal, and after a certain time you remove the ovary and centrifuge it, after suspending it, if necessary, in sucrose. You then get the sedimentation of the denser material both in the nucleus and in the cytoplasm. The material that is sedimented in the nucleus is mainly the lampbrush chromosomes. If you stain with pyronin, you can detect the chromosomes at the centrifugal pole, and in the rest of the nucleus there is little chromosome material left. Now, if one studies the incorporation of adenine one gets enormous activity over the chromosomes, but almost none over the sap. In the cytoplasm you have, of course, a gradient. But if you study the incorporation of amino-acids into protein you have very little difference between the basophilic material and the rest, which doesn't contain much RNA. Thus you can get a sort of dissociation between the RNA and protein metabolisms. There is no doubt that you can get a good deal of incorporation in the nuclear sap.

I think that there is one other point that Dr. Waddington quite clearly said: In the autoradiographic technique all we are expressing is in terms of units of surface, and that does not mean much—it may even mean nothing—in chemical terms. What we really want to know is the specific activity of the compounds. However, in some cases we are willing to draw conclusions. For instance, in the nuclear sap you have no RNA metabolism to speak of, and you have very strong protein metabolism; but even here, we don't know at all what is the concentration of phenylalanine. We don't know even what amount of phenylalanine has penetrated into the oocytes, still less into the different parts of the egg. That can be found out to some extent if one compares the autoradiograph of freeze-dried material with that of the insoluble compounds. Madame Ficq mentioned that already in Cambridge; in the Spring she compared both the total amount of isotope and what had been incorporated in acid-insoluble substances [5]. But the same problem still remains; it is only quantitative cyto-chemical methods, which will have to be developed, which can give the answer. What we really don't know is how much of the various substances are in the different places. It is all very nice to use these autoradiographic methods, where you get a clear localisation, but we have to be extremely careful about the biochemical conclusions.

GALL: I would like to make one comment on RNA and the "nuclear sap". If you use the expression nuclear sap to mean everything outside of the chromosomes and the nucleoli, then there is RNA in the sap, although it is probably all in fairly large particulates. I've made some experiments similar to these, except that in addition to making sections I have also isolated the nuclear contents. In my experiments, using ^{14}C adenine, of course I get high incorporation into the nucleoli, but in addition there is quite a lot of activity in the chromosomes and in the non-chromosomal RNA, which for want of a better term I think of as being in the nuclear sap. This reminds me of Brown, Callan and Leaf's [6] original study of the composition of nuclear sap, in which they found no nucleic acid. They centrifuged their material before isolation and apparently brought down all the non-chromosomal RNA. In my experiments all the non-chromosomal material occurs as clumps of precipitation between the chromosomes and these are basophilic. So it depends on your definition of "sap" whether or not it contains RNA.

BEERMANN: I just wanted to make a comment on your suggestion that the nucleolus is nothing but an assembly point for material produced elsewhere in the nucleus. I have some cytological evidence for this.

WADDINGTON: Let me say, before you go on, that I didn't mean it was exclusively an assembly point. There is always this high activity of the nucleolus-associated chromatin which is presumably something different from an assembly point.

BEERMANN: Yes, I have some evidence on that point too. In *Chironomus* there is not only one nucleolus organiser but there are 2 or 3 nucleolus organiser regions. Of the two species I have been working with one has 2 nucleolus organisers which can be defined down to a single band of the chromosome. Actually the region itself seems to lie between 2 bands, although at this place between the two bands where the nucleolus is formed you find some vacuolised and Feulgen-positive material. This is something different from what you find in any other place in the chromosomes. Now the two species I have been working with do not have homologous nucleolus organising regions. These regions can be shown to be at different points within the chromosome set. If you make hybrids between the two species, they are heterozygous for the nucleolus-organising regions. Then, by making backcrosses, you can find that any combination of nucleolar-organising regions is viable. That is to say, one nucleolus-organising region can replace another one. The particular combination does not matter, so long as at least one nucleolus-organising region is present in the heterozygous region. As soon as you have no nucleolus-organising region the embryo does not develop normally; it is normal until the blastoderm stage but from then on it becomes abnormal.

I can show you some slides to illustrate this point. This is a Malpighian chromosome and this dark region between two bands is the nucleolar organiser region in chromosome 2R in *Chironomus pallidivittatus*. The next slide shows you a salivary in a hybrid where you have one nucleolus organiser at this point, but none here. The banding pattern is exactly the same in both partners, except that at this point is inserted the nucleolus-organising region. The next slide shows the same again, and here again the dark point is the nucleolus-organising region. It can be shown that no translocation, inversion, duplication or any normal kind of chromosome rearrangement, is involved in the difference between these species. It must be some sort of peculiar mutation at a specific point in the chromosome that gives them the ability to accumulate or produce nucleoli, and the reverse mutation must also occur sometimes. That can be concluded simply from the fact that the two sibling species, *C. tentans* and *C. palli-divittatus*, have different nucleolar organisers. Next slide shows some eggs of *Chironomus*. These are just beginning the segmentation, and these are the abnormal embryos containing no nucleolar organiser. I have made a lot of counts for segregation studies and it is found that these appear in the proper proportions. Also I have studied sections through these and found that the nuclei of these abnormal embryos indeed do not show any nucleolus.* The next slide shows that the development goes on and even eyes are formed but the development is abnormal and the condition is lethal.

WADDINGTON: This work on the nucleolus and the nucleolar-associated chromatin is done by Dr. Sirlin here. I do not know if he has anything he would particularly like to say.

SIRLIN: I think the question that is worrying us most now is relating the density of label to absolute concentrations, or as a first step to dry matter. We are thinking of interference microscopy to provide a background for the autoradiographic observations. Another thing is that we are trying to distinguish all the major sites in the cell; the nucleolus, the nucleolus-associated chromatin, the whole chromatin, the nuclear wall and the cytoplasm. That is quite a large range to consider. With respect to what Plaut has done to consider a transfer from the nucleolus to the cytoplasm, and what Pantelouris is doing now as regards the contrary, it seems to me they are simplifying the matter too much. They just take two points in a section, and draw conclusions about the whole system simply by seeing the variation over a long time in the labelling of these components. Now we have really got here the whole nucleus and the whole cytoplasm and we should consider the *percentage* of the label within the nucleus, and study the rate of labelling for a long time. It is quite true that we probably have some degree of concentration; the activity is first seen in the nucleolus-associated chromatin, but when you study the thing in terms of percentages, in the case of adenine, the whole cell is labelled at the same rate. With methionine it's different. There seems to be an increase of labelling in the nucleolar apparatus and it falls later in the cytoplasm something like this. Now in order to reach conclusions about transfers there is a very simple problem. It has to be accepted that here we work on sections; now there is a much greater percentage of a nucleus included in a section, than there is of a cytoplasm. You cannot directly compare what you see in a section of a little structure like the nucleus or nucleolus with what you see of a large structure like

---

* In studies of living embryonic nuclei, using phase contrast, the presence of small nucleolus-like granules in "nucleolus-less" nuclei has been demonstrated. This may be unorganised nucleolar material.

the cytoplasm. If you put it in absolute terms, it is probable that if you get three grains in a section of the nucleolus you have really ten in the nucleolus as a whole; for three in the cytoplasm you may have a thousand in the whole cytoplasm of the cell. I have been wondering about this point in the interpretation of autoradiographs, and I think a great deal of work has got to be done about it.

WADDINGTON: I don't think we could go into these details of the interpretation now, but I think you have raised the main points. An autoradiograph looks at first sight as though it gives one a great deal of information. The more you think about them the more doubtful it becomes.

WEISS: Might I ask a question about the resolution. Can you really resolve between the nucleolus-associated chromosome and the nucleolus itself?

WADDINGTON: That is getting to about the limit of resolution. I think we reckon that about 3 μ is the limit. Reliable interpretation at this size depends on comparing a large number of cells and finding regularities between them.

RIS: Aren't the nucleoli generally smaller than that?

BRENNER: I would like to make another suggestion about the nucleolus which I think can be put to an experimental test. Let us make the assumption that the nucleolar chromosome—and Beermann has shown very good evidence that the ability to make the nucleolus is genetically determined— let us assume that there is one site on the chromosome involved in making RNA which makes a protein in the nucleolus. In other words, you make the assumption that the nucleolus is a sort of super-puffed area. If we accept this, we should be driven to the conclusion that this would be active in almost every cell; that region would be making protein in almost every cell—although there are apparently a few cells which do not have a nucleolus.

WADDINGTON: You are assuming it is making some relatively non-specific protein, or some protein required for all nucleoli?

BRENNER: Yes. I want to suggest a definition of what this protein should be. Yesterday I mentioned the hypothesis that microsomal particles in the cytoplasm could be considered to be built up on an active RNA template, surrounded by a shell of inert protein which we assume to be the same for every microsomal particle, and to carry no information and to be merely part of the structure. Since the electron microscope photographs show that the nucleolus is packed full of granules about the same size as these microsomal particles in the cytoplasm, one could make the assumption that this is where the microsomal protein is being made in the cell. Since this is uniform for all cells, and shows no differentiated characters, the nucleolus would be uniform for all cells. I think this could be put to test in the following way. Suppose you isolated the microsomal fraction and made an antibody to it, one could then predict that the nucleolus would be specifically stained with the antibody to microsomal protein. It is possible, then, that the nucleolus has a dual function. That is, that in this region protein is made, and in addition RNA made all over the other parts of the chromosome is being assembled into these granules.

WADDINGTON: Yes, but would you not expect that in the absence of the nucleolus-organiser, there should be more trouble than Beermann found? His embryos developed eyes, and presumably a lot more than you could see. There was something wrong with them, but not so wrong that they could not make specific proteins at all. Your microsomal protein must be necessary for all specific protein synthesis, and if an animal hasn't got it, I should have expected it to die earlier.

BRENNER: I agree that that is the difficulty.

WEISS: But does not the embryo perhaps live from the prefabricated yolk protein up to that time, and only go to pieces when that runs out?

WADDINGTON: I am not clear whether it can live off prefabricated yolk protein. Work with antagonistic amino acids on embryonic cells has shown that an antagonist to one animo acid will suppress the uptake of most other amino acids [7]. This sort of evidence has been interpreted by the bacterial people as evidence that synthesis goes from an amino acid pool. There seems rather little evidence that embryos partially digest their yolk and use large fragments of it for their specific cellular proteins.

BRENNER: I agree with Professor Waddington that this is the difficulty. But of course one can use an *ad hoc* hypothesis to explain it away. I think it should be tested whether there is any serological relationship between the microsomal patricle protein and anything in the nucleolus. You might expect the nucleolus to be related to it.

NEW SPEAKER: I hope I can give you an answer to that in the next six months. I have got the fluorescent antibodies to the microsomes and very shortly propose to try it on the nuclei.

WADDINGTON: I think we ought to pass on. Jean, would you like to give us something about the activities of enucleated cytoplasm?

BRACHET: There are some things I should like to mention which have some importance and will make the picture more complete. The nucleoli themselves can be isolated from homogenates, and that is another method of studying them which might be useful to investigate the antigenic relationships between the microsomes and the nucleoli. But of course there you have the drawbacks of all homogenising techniques. We know that if you try to label the RNA with ^{32}P in the nucleoli which are isolated in that way, it is much less active than it is in autoradiographs of the whole cell. So it seems as though there is a good deal of soluble RNA which is lost, and which is metabolically more active than the other. But what I wanted to point out is that one can of course use these isolated nucleoli for enzyme studies. It has been found that there is exceedingly little enzyme activity in them, except for the enzymes which play a part in nucleotide metabolism. That fits in of course with the idea that their RNA metabolism is very high. For instance, nucleoside phosphorylase is very high there [8]. But what is also very highly concentrated there is the enzyme which synthesises the co-enzyme for glycolysis (i.e. DPN). In starfish oocytes about 70% of the enzyme is in the nucleoli fraction. So the nucleolus might have other functions besides RNA and protein metabolism, for instance, in the production of co-enzymes which are needed for energy producing reactions.

WADDINGTON: I understand that Plaut and Brachet now agree to a considerable extent on what goes on in enucleated cytoplasm, but we should like to know just what it is they agree on.

PLAUT: We would like to know what the cytoplasm can do without the nucleus. I am going to discuss possible answers to this question on the basis of experimental work with two unicellular organisms which can be readily studied as both anucleate as well as normal, nucleus-containing cells: *Acetabularia* and *Amoeba proteus*. It has been known for some time that anucleate fragments of *Acetabularia* can grow and synthesise protein [9]. In the anucleate amoeba there is incorporation of labelled amino acids [10, 11]. There is some disagreement on the extent of incorporation after given times of enucleation; however, this disagreement is minor, particularly in view of the fact that the two sets of available data were obtained with different amino acids. A more serious question concerns the acceptability of incorporation of a precursor as evidence for synthesis rather than some form of submolecular turnover or other. In general, one would like to be able to demonstrate a net increase in a specific substance before concluding that this substance is indeed synthesised under the conditions of the experiment.

Such a demonstration is, however, not possible in all experimental situations: the total amount of a substance present may be too small to be reliably measured or there may actually be a net loss of the substance in the course of the experiment. The proteins in the anucleate amoeba are a case in point: the anucleate amoeba, unlike an anucleate fragment of *Acetabularia*, does not grow; an increase of a general structural component, such as protein, cannot be expected. Incorporation evidence, then, is the best we can hope to get under such conditions. It should also be pointed out that even turnover, the exchange of one molecular constituent for another, similar one, involves some synthetic activity in a broad sense: one or more bonds must be broken and one or more bonds must be re-established. In order to simplify the discussion, then, I would like to suggest that we accept incorporation of precursors as a reasonable index of synthesis, a reasonable demonstration that the system is capable of making the particular substance under discussion. With respect to proteins in the anucleate amoeba we have some additional support for this operational conclusion: in one of the experiments which showed amino acid incorporation [11] the rate of incorporation ran reasonably parallel to the level of RNA present. To sum up, then: both *Acetabularia* and *Amoeba* are capable of synthesising at least some protein in the absence of the nucleus.

A second cellular constituent which has been analysed in this connection is RNA. In *Acetabularia*, one would expect that the capacity for growth and development of the anucleate fragment indicates its capability for RNA synthesis as well. Experimentally, one can demonstrate precursor incorporation [12] into the cytoplasmic RNA. Whether a net increase of RNA occurs is not certain at the present time. Two experiments [13, 14], utilising two different techniques, have led to contradictory conclusions. The difficulty appears to arise from the low concentration of RNA in the *Acetabularia* cytoplasm. Until this question is directly resolved, it is reasonable and consistent with the earlier discussion that we accept the incorporation evidence as an indication of RNA synthesis in the anucleate *Acetabularia* cytoplasm.

In *Amoeba* we presented evidence in the recent past which made it possible to suggest that there is a transfer of RNA from nucleus to cytoplasm [15, 16]. The experiments did not prove that nuclear RNA moved as such; it could be a fairly complex RNA precursor; it could also be an RNA-protein. This suggestion raised the question of whether the nucleus supplies all of the cytoplasm's RNA or whether there is a cyto-plasmically synthesised RNA as well. Experimentally, the question became: Can the *Amoeba* cytoplasm synthesise RNA in the absence of the nucleus? Again we have to deal with precursor incorporation data. The anucleate *Amoeba* not only fails to show an increase of RNA with time, it suffers a net loss. Several ^{14}C-labelled RNA precursors have been used on anucleate fragments of *Amoeba* in several laboratories [17–21]. There is general agreement on the incorporation of one of these: ^{14}C-adenine [19, 18, 20]. Prescott [21] failed to observe incorporation of ^{14}C-uracil and concluded that the anucleate *Amoeba* does not synthesise RNA, that the cytoplasmic

RNA is all of nuclear origin. In a more recent experiment we have obtained some uracil incorporation into the RNA of anucleate amoebae; it seems likely, therefore, that Prescott's negative results are attributable to experimental difficulties and not to the absence of RNA synthesis in the anucleate cytoplasm. Moreover, we have obtained very extensive incorporation of ^{14}C-orotic acid in recent experiments [19]. We can conclude, then, that the anucleate *Amoeba* is capable of RNA synthesis. Whether the cytoplasm does in fact synthesise RNA when a nucleus is present is quite another question. We assume, tentatively, that it does, without a better reason for this assumption than its simplicity. We can then ask about the relative magnitude of cytoplasmic synthesis, how much of the whole of the RNA found in the cytoplasm is made there and how much is of nuclear origin. At the present time we can only guess as to what the answer is likely to be. This guess is that the nuclear contribution is more likely to be small than large. The basis for this guess lies in the fact that with adenine, and even more so with orotic acid, as precursor, there is an appreciable number of anucleate cells whose total incorporation of labelled precursor into RNA equals that of the cytoplasms of nucleate cells. This will have to remain a guess until we have more information on the nature and extent of variability in uptake of labelled precursor from the medium, in the levels of RNA in nucleus and cytoplasm, and in the rates of RNA synthesis at different stages in the life cycle.

It is also of some interest to determine whether the transfer of RNA from nucleus to cytoplasm suggested for *Amoeba* can be postulated for other cells. If it is to be regarded as a general mechanism for the transfer of nuclear specificity to the cytoplasm it cannot be restricted to the *Amoeba*. We have approached this question of general applicability in *Acetabularia* [22] since this organism appears to be able to do more in the absence of a nucleus than any other which has been studied. By treating both nucleate and anucleate fragments of the alga with ribonuclease and then permitting their recovery in normal sea-water we were able to observe a very clear difference between the two types of fragments: the nucleate piece goes on to develop normally, the anucleate appears to have been incapacitated as far as growth, net protein synthesis, and differentiation are concerned. Ribonuclease treatment thus produces a situation in which the nucleus is immediately necessary in order that the normally relatively independent cytoplasmic machinery for protein synthesis and growth be restarted. It is permissible to postulate, as we have done, that the nuclear constituent which is instrumental in this process is nuclear RNA. This postulation hinges on the reasonable but unproven assumption that the operative effect of ribonuclease was the deactivation of RNA in the cytoplasm.

If our interpretation of the ribonuclease experiment on *Acetabularia* is correct, we may conclude that in both *Amoeba* and *Acetabularia* there is a transfer of RNA from nucleus to cytoplasm, that although both cytoplasms are capable of nucleus-independent RNA and protein synthesis, there is nuclear control through RNA or an RNA derivative. The differences between anucleate amoebae and anucleate *Acetabularia* fragments, such as morphogenetic capacity and capacity for growth, can be ascribed to the fact that the anucleate *Acetabularia* fragment is capable of photosynthesis while the anucleate *Amoeba* is starving.

WADDINGTON: After a certain length of time on this curve have you then cut off the nucleus so as to see how long it takes the nucleus to provide the cytoplasm with an adequate amount of RNA?

PLAUT: No, we have not done this. The other experiment one would love to do, of course, would be to take these enucleated halves and give them an injection of purified nuclear RNA.

LEHMANN: I should like to know where the incorporated adenine is located in the cytoplasm? We seem to overlook here the structural side. Our joint work with Bairati has shown a fibrillar network in the cytoplasm, containing fibrils and microsome-like bodies. This fibrous reticulum seems to be partially altered in enucleated amoebae [23]. This material might be the site of incorporation.

PLAUT: Chemically, we can be reasonably certain that the acid-insoluble label is in RNA: with ^{14}C-adenine and ^{14}C-orotic acid ribonuclease results in the complete or nearly complete removal of autoradiographically detectable label. ^{14}C-uracil is somewhat less completely removed by the enzyme.

The structural sites of this incorporation have not been investigated so far. With the exception of what are probably residual food vacuoles, the label appears to be fairly uniformly, or rather randomly distributed. Apparent inhomogeneities should probably not be regarded as significant in the present state of our knowledge.

BRACHET: I think that in our experiments with adenine, which were done on sections, the cytoplasm looks as though it is homogeneous. I do not mean it is absolutely homogeneous, because it is not, but it is pretty homogeneous. I think what you see is due to the squashes.

PLAUT: That would be my guess. It would, of course, be of extreme interest to try to associate structurally identifiable components of the cytoplasm with RNA synthesis or, for that matter, with the RNA postulated to come from the nucleus. We have to await the results of current electron microscope studies of the *Amoeba* before we can set up testable hypotheses along these lines.

GALL: One of the problems appears to be in the significance of autoradiographs of different grain density. Wouldn't it be fairly simple to strain these amoebae with Azure B and then make a rough estimate of specific activity by taking a plug and determining both amount and labelling of the RNA? One could then see if there are really differences between individuals or just differences in concentration.

PLAUT: What we really need to know is whether the amount of label incorporated is a valid index of the incorporation rate of a given cell or half cell. The amount of label incorporated can be related to the amount of RNA present, as you suggest, and we can get some idea of specific activity. However, differences in specific activity can arise from at least two causes: differences in the incorporation rate and differences in the amount of labelled precursor available for incorporation. With respect to adenine we know that the average anucleate takes up very much less than the average nucleate cell. This may mean that there is less available for incorporation; this could account for the lower *average* incorporation of anucleate cells. We also know that there is great variability between cells of all types in the amount incorporated. We do not know how much variability there is in uptake from cell to cell and to what extent this may contribute to the incorporation variability. We are currently attempting to obtain some data which will help resolve this problem.

BRACHET: I think there is a very great variability in the RNA content of amoebae, both nucleate and enucleate, but much greater in the enucleate than in the others. If you stain them with pyronin, you see that the population is very variable.

MITCHISON: I wonder if I could go back to one point which you raised at the very beginning, about the question of incorporation as an index of net synthesis of protein. I am not doubting this, but as the only evidence, I think, comes from Professor Brachet's experiments with *Acetabularia*, could I ask him perhaps for some details as to how you determine that there is really an increase in protein in the enucleated *Acetabularia*?

BRACHET: Well, we take equal lengths of the algae, from a fairly large batch of the algae coming from the same culture, and we follow the protein content, by precipitation with TCA and by Kjeldahls, from week to week.

MITCHISON: So you begin with a fairly large number of specimens, and you take one and weigh it and analyse it, and so go on in the following weeks, and you feel happy about the homogeneity of your sample to start with?

BRACHET: Yes, you can select algae which are very uniform. In the laboratory they are all very similar at the same age.

MITCHISON: Do you know what the order of the increase is?

BRACHET: Well, we got about 86%, but Hammerling tells me that one of his people got 250%. Of course, very much will depend on the illumination. You can show the same thing in another way, because the enucleate halves form a cap and these caps are quite big. So there is an increase in dry weight, and an increase in protein which is parallel to the general increase in substance. The amount of the protein synthesis, and the number of caps which will be formed, depends on the illumination conditions and on the stage at which you took your algae. If you took them at the time when they're going to make caps, they will all make a cap.

CALLAN: What happens with *Acetabularia* living in ribonuclease? Do you know what ribonuclease is in fact doing to them?

PLAUT: No. There is no development of any anomalies during this one-week period. We are assuming it is doing one thing, and that is getting rid of the local RNA. There is one test that should be made. That is, to take some protein molecule of about the same size as ribonuclease and see what that would do. It is conceivable that what we are giving is something quite independent of the ribonuclease specific effect.

BRACHET: If we are considering the effect of ribonuclease on cells we could go on talking for an hour. It is certainly very complex and very variable. You may have in some cases the RNA really degraded, and in others you just get a complex between RNA and RNAse, and the RNA is not broken down.

WADDINGTON: In the minute or two left before coffee time we might just have a few words about another system where we know something about the actions of the nucleus and cytoplasm. That is the nerve fibre, which Weiss would like to talk about.

WEISS: I would like to remind you of some quite old stuff. This dates back about 15 years, but it has not been picked up properly, and since we have laid off, that object hasn't been much discussed [24]. I should like to introduce the problem all over again. This is not a single-celled organism like *Amoeba* or *Acetabularia*, but is a highly differentiated cell of a vertebrate—a nerve cell or neurone—but otherwise it has exactly the same disposition as *Acetabularia*. It has a nucleus which is placed eccentrically at one end, and a very long cytoplasmic body, the axon. This is something like 4000 times the volume—in some cases much more—of the nucleated part. We studied the growth of this cell, and I will just summarise our observations in one diagram (Fig. 4.7), which tells the main story of six years' work.

The nucleus of the nerve cell is a very peculiar nucleus with a very large nucleolus; Hyden has described its properties rather fully. When you cut a nerve fibre (B), the peripheral part undergoes some degeneration —never mind the details—but after a while the stump begins to grow out and regenerate, much as the *Acetabularia* nucleated region will form a hat. Here the tip of the cell actually moves out (C), and eventually reconnects with the muscle (D). After reaching is terminal end-length, it fills up its substance by synthesising more and more protoplasm (E). While the original outgrowth is only about 1 μ across, the final fibre may be 10–15 μ.

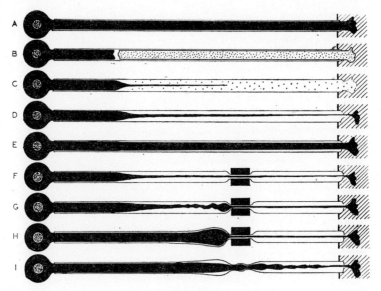

Fig. 4.7.

This means that the outgrowth has to grow, after reaching its terminal length, by a factor of about 100. This means there is an increase in the neuroplasm of about 100 times its original amount. Now when you place a bottle-neck—a little constriction—around such a nerve fibre (F) (never mind how it's done) the nerve fibre regenerates and it goes through the bottle-neck quite easily undisturbed. But, when the process of lateral expansion, which I mentioned, and the increase in mass of protoplasm begins, then you find that the mass of protoplasm becomes dammed up right in front of the bottle-neck (G), like traffic over a bridge on Sunday, while on the distal side of the bottle-neck, the axon remains thin. Now the essential thing is that this continues throughout life (H). The peripheral parts remain thin in proportion to the constriction, and the excess protoplasm piles up on the central side. This indicates that, as far as the synthesis of protoplasm is concerned there is a definite asymmetry between the part connected with the nucleus and the part which is indeed still connected with the nucleus but by a thinner supply line. The piling up of supplies on the proximal side must mean that the protoplasm is being supplied from the nuclear area.

We have investigated the process of supply. Little is known about protoplasm movement or cyclosis in general, but we know there is a sort of peristaltic wave on a micro scale which pushes the protoplasm from near the nucleus down the line all the time. You can do this experiment in tandem. You can have one constriction here, and the second constriction here, and after the protoplasm has gotten through the first, it piles up again in front of the second constriction; and you can do two or three in succession that way. Now, if you remove the constriction after three months, or even after a year, then you notice that the cytoplasm becomes squeezed down with a frontal wave here (I)—a sort of tidal wave moving down and gradually resorting the whole axon to its normal dimensions. If you use a normal axon—the one on top of this diagram—without disrupting it or cutting it, but put a constriction on it, then you see that the distal part emaciates or gets thinner throughout that part which is partially cut off from the nucleus: it is not fully cut off from the flow line, but the constriction restricts the flow. The rate of the movement of this wave, which gives you some idea of the rate of supply, is about 1–2 mm per day.

If you consider that much of this is used to replenish protein substances which are being used up at the periphery and if you assume that the very high ammonia production of nerve which has long been known, is due to complete deamination because there are too long distances to diffuse back to utilise components within the system, then one can calculate how much protein has to disappear to account for the ammonia production. On that assumption you can calculate that, in order to maintain a steady state in any part of the nerve fibre, you would have to have a replenishment from a localised source at the rate of about 1–2 mm per day. In general orders of magnitude these things jibe.

I do not see how we can explain any of these phenomena otherwise than by assuming that actual protoplasm, as a semi-viscous column—not in solution but as a physical body—is being constantly moved down the line to replace what is used up. There is probably no turnover in the peripheral part, and no synthesis. But this does indicate that some very essential component has to be supplied from the nucleated zone in the form of an organised system, not in solution.

A further indication of this comes when you cut the nerve. It has long been known that then the nucleated territory will show degeneration or gradual atrophy. The stages of that atrophy have been studied by Dr. Cavanaugh in my laboratory, and they are very characteristic. The loss of peripheral connections rebounds on the cell in the following order.

The first thing to shrink is the nucleolus. The next thing to shrink in dimensions is the nucleus. The next is the cell body, and the last thing to shrink, or to show the shrinkage, I should say, is the axon. There is then a primary action of the periphery on the nucleolus, nucleus and cell body. Regeneration after the recovery of the neuron goes in exactly the same way. The nucleolus recovers first, then the nucleus increases its size, and finally the cell body.

It's a very complicated system. It has been approached with isotopes by ourselves and also by Gerard's group. The results are not very convincing or conclusive and therefore I am not presenting them. The nerve as a whole is sheathed with Schwann cells, which have a very high metabolism, particularly in their mitochondrial portions around the nodes, and these obscure what is going on in the nerve fibres but Dr. Waelsch informs me that he has some isotope data that would seem to bear out my interpretation.

I have presented this material here because it is an ideal system for studying this type of problem we have been faced with; and perhaps a study on this different material will not only give us more basic information on the role of the nucleus and cytoplasm but also some light on differentiation.

WADDINGTON: I think we shall have to defer the discussion of this. Possibly we can take it up when we discuss the formation of myosin and actin in muscle cells, which is another example of cytoplasmic synthesis. But after coffee I am very anxious to get on to the electron microscopy work because I know Dr. Sjöstrand has got to leave. So I think we will take Dr. Gay first on the interactions between the nucleus and cytoplasm, and then ask Dr. Sjöstrand to give us something about the nature and structures of cytoplasmic materials.

REFERENCES

1. WADDINGTON, C. H. and J. L. SIRLIN (1954) *J. Embryol. Exp. Morphol.* 2, 340; J. L. SIRLIN (1955) *Experientia* 11, 112.
2. PANTELOURIS, E. M. (1958) *Exp. Cell. Res.* 14, 584.
3. SIRLIN, J. L. and G. R. KNIGHT (1958) *Chromosoma* 9, 119.
4. BRACHET, J. and A. FICQ (1956) *Arch. Biol.* (*Liége*) 67, 431.
5. FICQ, A. Meeting in Cambridge organised by *J. Embryol. Exptl. Morphol.* cf. FICQ and BRACHET *Exptl. Cell. Res.* (1956) 11, 146.
6. BROWN, G. L., H. G. CALLAN and G. LEAF, (1950) *Nature, Lond.* 165, 600.
7. WADDINGTON, C. H., M. FELDMAN and M. M. PERRY (1955) *Exp. Cell. Res.* Suppl. 3, 366; WADDINGTON, C. H. and M. M. PERRY (1958) *J. Embryol. Exp. Morphol.* 6, 365.
8. BALTUS, E. (1954) *Biochim. Biophys. Acta* 15, 263.

9. BRACHET, J., H. CHANTRENNE and F. VANDERHAEGHE (1955) *Biochim. Biophys. Acta* **18**, 544.
10. MAZIA, D. and D. M. PRESCOTT (1955) *Biochim. Biophys. Acta* **17**, 23.
11. FICQ, A. (1956) *Arch. Int. Physiol. Biochim.* **64**, 129.
12. BRACHET, J. (1957) *Biochemical Cytology*, Academic Press, New York.
13. VANDERHAEGHE, F. and D. SZAFARZ (1955) *Arch. Int. Physiol. Biochim.* **63**, 267.
14. RICHTER, G. (1957) *Naturwissenschaften*, **19**, 520.
15. GOLDSTEIN, L. and W. PLAUT (1955) *Proc. Nat. Acad. Sci., Wash.* **41**, 874.
16. RABINOVITCH, M. and W. PLAUT (1956) *Exp. Cell Res.* **10**, 120.
17. PLAUT, W. and R. C. RUSTAD (1957) *J. Biophys. Biochem. Cytol.* **3**, 625.
18. PLAUT, W. and R. C. RUSTAD (1956) *Nature, Lond.* **177**, 89.
19. PLAUT, W. and R. C. RUSTAD In preparation.
20. SKREB, cited by J. BRACHET and H. CHANTRENNE (1956) *Cold Spr. Harb. Symp. Quant. Biol.* **21**, 329.
21. PRESCOTT, D. M. (1957) *Exp. Cell Res.* **12**, 196.
22. STICH, H. and W. PLAUT (1958) *J. Biophys. Biochem. Cytol.* **4**, 119.
23. BAIRATI, A. and F. E. LEHMANN. Unpublished.
24. WEISS, P. and H. B. HISCOE (1948) *J. Exp. Zool.* **107**, 315.

CHAPTER V

Morphological Organisation of Nucleus and Cytoplasm

WADDINGTON: We will start this session with Dr. Gay talking about the relations between the nucleus and the cytoplasm.

GAY: I appreciate the opportunity Dr. Waddington has given me of speaking before Dr. Sjöstrand presents his material. Being a relative newcomer in the field of electron microscopy, I feel more comfortable if my electron micrographs are not evaluated in the light of Dr. Sjöstrand's beautiful photographs. I shall try to restrict my preliminary remarks to about ten minutes, only briefly reviewing some of the information which has been published, and use the remainder of the time to discuss the implications of these findings. By way of introduction, I should like to mention that the observations of nucleocytoplasmic transfer came about as a side line from a study on salivary-gland chromosome structure. I should therefore like to include in this discussion a little about chromosome structure, particularly in so far as it throws light on our conclusions about the mechanism of nucleocytoplasmic exchange.

The type of cell frequently used for the study of giant chromosome structure is from the salivary gland of a dipteran larva. The cells I studied were from salivary glands of mid-to-late third instar larvae of *Drosophila melanogaster*. In thin sections of this tissue fixed in buffered osmium tetroxide I discovered structural configurations which were suggestive of a mechanism of nucleocytoplasmic transfer. A lengthy series of tests modifying the preparative procedures—fixation, dehydration and imbedding—demonstrated that the observed structural phenomenon was not produced by the cytological techniques. This conclusion indicated that a more detailed study of the material should be undertaken. Several of my publications [1, 2, 3] include reproductions of electron micrographs of a typical cell of a mid-to-late third instar larval *D. melanogaster*. The polytene chromosomes occupy 80–90% of the volume of the nucleus. The nuclear membrane consists of two layers with "pores" and annuli, as has been described in many other types of cells [4]. The most prominent cytoplasmic structures are the ergastoplasmic lamellae and secretion granules and, in lesser numbers, the mitochondria.

Now, in studying this cell, we observed that the nuclear membrane did not always form a nice even outline, but in certain cases there were unevennesses which on closer examination looked like outpocketings or blebs. It was decided that this was worth further study because many of these outpocketings seemed to be associated with electron-dense chromosomal material (for illustrations, see [1, 2, 3]). In many cases the chromosomal fibres in the region of the nuclear-membrane bleb were thickened and denser than in the rest of the chromosome. In some cases the chromosomal threads seemed to be interspersed with dense granules, and sometimes this type of chromosomal material protruded from the chromosomes toward the nuclear membrane (see Fig. 6a [1]). The question was: is the association between chromosomal material and nuclear-membrane blebs a constant one? Since, in single ultra-thin sections we sometimes observed blebs that did not seem to show any direct connection to chromosomes, it was important to study these structural configurations by using serial sections to get a three-dimensional picture. In this way we could determine whether the chromosomal connection existed at a level of the cell which had not been traversed by the single microtome cut. In numerous instances we were able to obtain a long series of sections from one cell, something like 30–40 sections. In all of these cases analysed we found that every time a nuclear-membrane bleb was seen it could be traced to a chromosome, which in this particular region seemed to be very dense and highly differentiated. The next question raised was, what particular regions of the chromosomes were involved in these nuclear membrane associations? Unfortunately, in thin sections suitable for electron microscopy only very short segments of the giant chromosomes, which are wound about each other in the nucleus like a tangle of yarn, are available for identification. Usually this is not sufficient for a positive chromosome analysis. However, in several cases we have been able to identify tentatively the region of the chromosome associated with nuclear membrane blebs as a reverse repeat. Some reverse repeats, in *Drosophila*, have been shown to involve intercalary heterochromatin [5].

In all our observations, nuclear-membrane blebs were found quite consistently associated with chromosomes by means of dense chromosomal material. The question is, do these nuclear-membrane blebs occur throughout the development of the cell? In *Drosophila*, the salivary gland, with a definitive number of cells, is laid down during the first 12 hr of development, and after that there is no mitotic division. The increase in gland size occurs only through increase in cell size. It was decided to trace the development of the salivary-gland cells with both the light microscope and the electron microscope, in order to observe the condition of the nuclear membrane, to observe whether there were variations in the quantities of some of the cytoplasmic structures, and to determine if there were any detectable cytochemical changes. To those not familiar with *Drosophila*, let me point out that there are three larval instars. Our study dealt with the end of the second instar and the complete third-instar period. We studied seven different stages of development of the salivary gland, from the time just prior to the moult from second to third instar, through to pupation. I will now tell you about only three of these stages: the youngest stage that we studied, a larva which had just moulted to the third instar; a second stage, just at the midpoint of the third larval period; and, lastly, a larva just about to pupate. The appearance of the salivary-gland cell at these three different stages is sufficiently dissimilar to warrant description (see photographs in [3]). The important question, of course, was whether there were nuclear-membrane blebs at all stages? In the earliest stage studied, the outline of the nucleus was completely smooth; blebs appeared at about mid-third instar and could be seen in cells until slightly before pupation when there seemed to be some decrease in number. Our analysis of the changes in the numbers and kinds of cytoplasmic organelles during this same period indicated that there seemed to be a correlation between the appearance of nuclear-membrane blebs and the inception of secretion-granule formation. The cytoplasm of the salivary-gland cell contains no secretion granules until well into the third larval period—from the midpoint, on. The analysis of our light-microscope cytochemical preparations corroborated this point. The PAS test on very young glands produces only a very faint hue and this condition persists until after mid-third instar, when the cytoplasm becomes loaded with secretion granules which stain very brightly.

SOMEONE: What is PAS?

GAY: The periodic acid Schiff test, a colour reaction for polysaccharides. Testing to see whether the secretion granules also contained protein, we stained with the acid dye, fast green, both before and after pepsin digestion. The results of this cytochemical test exactly paralleled the results of the PAS test in showing that the granules contain a polysaccharide and a protein, both of which are formed simultaneously at mid-third instar. At pupation, the secretion granules are all passed into the lumen of the gland. This fact was observed in the electron micrographs, and confirmed by the cytochemical tests, which showed only a faint coloured cytoplasm, either with the PAS test or with the protein test, and a densely stained homogeneous material filling the lumen.

Our electron-microscope and cytochemical evidence, therefore, demonstrated that nuclear-membrane blebbing and the presence of secretion granules seem to go hand in hand. Both are particularly well seen at the middle of the third instar period. Now the question is raised whether this could have anything to do with function. Some of the aspects of the salivary glands of *Drosophila* have been in question until just recently. Poulson [6] and Sonnenblick [7] had shown that during early larval development the salivary gland is involved in producing a digestive juice. When the egg is hatched, the formed salivary gland already contains this substance. However, Fraenkel and Brookes [8] have indicated that digestion is not the sole function throughout the whole of larval life. They have observed that at pupation a puparial glue—used to stick the pupal case to the substrate—is ejected from the mouth of the larva. By chemical analysis, they have shown that this material originates from the lumen of the salivary gland. Our cytochemical tests indicate that the material within the lumen of the pupating larva stems from the secretion granules produced during the third instar. This evidence therefore led us to believe that the puparial glue and the secretion granules are one and the same thing. We therefore put our various lines of evidence together, that is, initiation of blebbing, initiation of secretion-granule formation during mid-third instar, and the beginning of a second functional aspect of the cell at this time, and we postulated that these things are related.

In a line drawing we indicate the mechanism of nucleocytoplasmic transport as postulated from these various lines of evidence (Fig. 5.1).

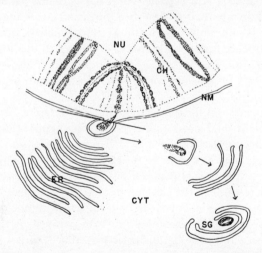

FIG. 5.1. Diagram of the proposed mechanism of nucleocytoplasmic transfer. The chromosome (CH) and associated dense material produce an outpocketing of the nuclear membrane (NM), which is detached from the nucleus (NU) into the cytoplasm (CYT) and contributes to the formation of the ergastoplasmic lamellae (ER). The ergastoplasm in turn appears to be involved in the production of secretion granules (SG).

The nuclear-membrane bleb, which is composed of the two layers of the nuclear membrane and contains material which apparently is "secreted" from the chromosome at regions that may be heterochromatic, is pinched off and lies free in the cytoplasm. In this transfer, there are two elements involved, both the material which is inside the bleb, and the portion of the nuclear membrane which forms the bleb. We have suggested [1, 2, 3] that the part of the membrane involved in the bleb may be converted to contribute to the ergastoplasmic lamellar system. We have proposed this possibility because the nuclear membrane and the ergastoplasmic lamellae, when viewed in the electron microscope both in cross-section and in tangential view, are very similar in structure. Also the accumulation of ergastoplasmic lamellae in the cytoplasm occurs most frequently in the vicinity of the blebs.

Now, what is the nature of the chromosomes that are involved in initiating this mechanism? I think it is pretty well agreed that the giant chromosomes of the dipteran larval salivary gland are polytene. Our own electron-microscope observations [2, 3] have shown that there are one to two thousand strands in the fully developed chromosome, each strand being a couple of hundred angstroms in width (some more recent evidence from our own laboratory [9] indicates that these strands may be as small as 125 Å). We would like to suggest that polyteny may favour a specific activity of these cells at a certain time; that is, when a chromosome has attained a certain number of strands a particular locus may make a substance which is not only visible to us but which occurs in sufficient quantity to influence functional activity. In regard to this, Painter [10] had earlier pointed out that polyteny may represent a device to facilitate functional activity in the secretion of the salivary gland, in both the honey bee and *Drosophila*.

Polyteny can account for the accumulation of different kinds of material. In combined light-microscope and electron-microscope studies [3] we have observed the accumulation of material at particular chromosomal regions (which I believe may be similar to the puffing observed by both Beermann and Pavan). Although this material has not been fully studied, we have been able to determine in the electron microscope that these accumulations of electron-dense material appear to be confluent with one or two chromosomal bands. In some instances in cytochemical preparations, this material has been found to be nucleolar-like, that is, it is basophilic when stained with Azure B and is Feulgen negative. We can determine that the material is not part of the nucleolus, however, since it is not connected with the heterochromatic region of the X chromosome. In still other cases, the chromosomal bodies are Feulgen positive and seem to be associated with particular chromosomal bands. I don't know what is the fate of these bodies but I think that in these cases we have evidence for the accumulation of basophilic material on the one hand and Feulgen-positive material on the other, at certain bands.

PAVAN: What is the structure of this?

GAY: Of this block? It looks like a nucleolus.

RIS: Does it have the same fibrils as the chromosome?

GAY: No, it does not.

RIS: Is it quite homogeneous?

GAY: Well, in the salivary-gland cell of *Drosophila* the nucleolus is a relatively dense and very compact structure. I know that in other types of nucleoli it has been reported that there are coiled fibrous strands and granules. In our material, the nucleolus is so compact and dense that we can only say that there are hints of fine structure.

WEISS: Aren't those fibrils there?

GAY: In some instances, we can see the chromosomal fibres project into these chromosomal bodies, but this is to be expected. In the ultimate analysis, the material of these "secreted" bodies may be very fine fibrils.

WEISS: What sort of fixation?

GAY: Buffered osmium tetroxide. We have modified the usual fixative by making it isotonic with *Drosophila* Ringer's solution.

I would like to digress a little and return to the question discussed yesterday, concerning multistrandedness of chromosomes. Dr. Ris's observations [11] that numerous kinds of chromosomes, both plant and animal, meiotic and mitotic, are composed of many fine chromosomal fibrils, has been corroborated in our laboratory by Kaufmann and De [12] on plant chromosomes. Yesterday Drs. Callan and Gall revived the older hypothesis of the unitary nature of the chromosome—a point of view which was debated extensively by light microscopists in the twenties and thirties and discarded after the bulk of observational evidence on mitotic and meiotic chromosomes of both plants and animals, and supplementary experimental studies [13] pointed in favour of the multistranded nature of chromosomes. I personally believe that a multistranded chromosome conforms most readily to the bulk of the light-microscope and electron-microscope observations. For this reason I would like to consider the possible implications of this type of chromosome structure in nucleo-cytoplasmic relations. I would like to suggest that multistrandedness might be a device for controlling different functional activities. If, in different types of cells there are different numbers of strands, the quantitative aspects involved in what the chromosome can produce might have some influence on the control of the function of the cell.

Now, to return to the nucleocytoplasmic transfer mechanism. As mentioned earlier, we have observed on several occasions that reverse repeats were involved in the phenomenon. This finding implicates intercalary heterochromatin, and would consequently be an extension of the Caspersson–Schultz hypothesis, which postulated that the nucleolus-organising heterochromatin was involved with protein synthesis. Our observations indicate that heterochromatin in general would be involved in protein synthesis and would also provide a structural mechanism for transfer of material from the nucleus to the cytoplasm. A nuclear-membrane bleb, if converted to ergastoplasmic lamellae, would then be involved in protein synthesis. There have been several reports recently (including some at the St. Andrews Congress) indicating that ergasto-plasmic lamellae are the site of the accumulation of protein material. There is evidence in *Drosophila* salivary-gland cells that secretion granules may originate in relation to ergastoplasmic lamellae [3]. It should also be kept in mind that some of Caspersson's original observations [14] on the relationship between basophilia (RNA) and protein synthesis were made on the cell which I have described to you today and the protein synthesised was that of the secretion granules.

In addition to our observations on blebbing in *Drosophila* salivary-gland cells, workers at the University of Chicago, Swift [15] and Rebhun [16], have summarised electron-microscope studies on oocytes of *Spisula otala* which led them to postulate that the nuclear membrane is involved in production of ergastoplasmic lamellae. They did not postulate production by the formation of blebs, but suggested a more elaborate synthetic mechanism, in which fine protein fibres penetrate the pores of the nuclear membrane and lay down lamellae parallel to the nuclear membrane. Stacks of such lamellae could be piled up on top of each other. This mechanism depends on the nucleus for the initiation of the formation of the lamellae, but the continuation is not dependent on nuclear contact. The suggestion is made, in fact, that aggregates of these membranous structures could break away from the nucleus into the cytoplasm and there continue to form lamellae. Rebhun has shown that these collections of lamellae constitute the basophilic yolk nuclei and that protein-containing yolk platelets are formed within them [17]. Thus, in this instance, the potentialities of the nuclear membrane for forming cytoplasmic lamellae are linked with protein synthesis. Afzelius [18] was one of the first to point out that fragments of the nuclear membrane occur in the cytoplasm of the sea urchin egg. More recently [19] he has found in the cytoplasm of the same material what he calls "heavy bodies", which are basophilic and are surrounded by membranes of exactly the same appearance as the nuclear membrane. He has observed these same types of particles at the nucleocytoplasmic border within outpouchings of the nuclear membrane. Although Afzelius does not care to draw the analogy to a nucleocytoplasmic transfer and although the mechanism proposed by Swift and Rebhun is different from that in *Drosophila* or the sea urchin, these observations do focus attention on the potentialities of the nuclear membrane for forming cytoplasmic lamellae which in turn may be involved in protein synthesis.

Schultz [20] several years ago suggested that the nuclear membrane may vary along its surface. This would depend on the contact with chromosomes when the nuclear membrane was formed. This is a very interesting idea because it would give differential regions throughout the membrane and would give many possibilities for differential nucleocytoplasmic activity. I would like to extend this idea to suggest that the properties of the chromosome in contact with the nuclear membrane at other times, even after its formation and subsequent enlargement, may be responsible for imparting some specificity to the nuclear membrane.

The mechanism for nuclear-cytoplasmic transfer which I have been discussing here does imply that the nuclear membrane is an active participant in the exchange. The view of nuclear-cytoplasmic transfer which has just been presented is not necessarily anything more than one of a possible series of alternative methods by which nucleo-cytoplasmic exchanges may occur. However, even though the blebbing of the nuclear membrane in *Drosophila* salivary glands may be unique, it does give evidence of a mechanism by which nucleocytoplasmic exchanges involving specific chromosomal regions may be effected.

WADDINGTON: I think it might be best to ask Dr. Sjöstrand to carry on the discussion next and for us to discuss both speeches together because it is obvious that the story of the nuclear membrane involves also the structure of the ergastoplasm and other cytoplasmic constituents and I think that with both the speakers together we shall have a better basis for a general discussion.

SJÖSTRAND: It is difficult to talk about electron microscopy in this connection because the electron microscopist is working at a level where structural details appear with sufficient clarity to leave less space for imaginative ideas regarding interactions and functional relations of various parts of the cell body. There are different opinions regarding the interpretation of the structural patterns that we see by means of the electron microscope, and I will keep to my way of interpreting and, as I find that I have joined a group that is violently speculative, I would like to follow that line and speculate a little about these patterns. I think these speculations should be taken with the same low degree of seriousness as many of the other speculations we have heard related so far.

To start with, I would like to display pictures of the structural components which are present in the cytoplasm. When we look at different kinds of cells we find a very remarkable repetition of a few kinds of patterns. With our present methods of preparing our specimens, these patterns seem mostly to consist of different kinds of membranes. That might well be due to our technical means. In Fig. 5.2, which is from a section through the retina of the perch eye, we see mitochondria accumulated in the inner segment of a cone cell. These mitochondria show the characteristic pattern which, however, can differ in different receptor cells of the same retina. We observe a pattern due to transversally cut membranes. A surface membrane bounds the mitochondrion, and a system of inner membranes is found inside this surface membrane. The inner membranes are separated by an homogeneous ground substance. Each membrane appears as a triple-layered component with two opaque layers separated by a less opaque interspace. Figure 5.3 shows mitochondria in another cone cell. A comparison between these two figures shows that there is a certain variation in the pattern but basically the same principle with a surface membrane and a system of inner membranes repeats itself. We are considering these membranes as metabolically active structures. They are interpreted as consisting of protein and lipid layers, and the protein layers are assumed to contain the enzyme systems of the mitochondria. The membranes are imagined as enzymatically active components. The organisation of enzyme molecules into such layers would make it possible to arrange the enzymes in certain well defined spatial relations. This, we think, would contribute to a co-ordination of the enzymatic activity in multi-enzyme systems. These ideas have to be tested by experiments, and such experiments are going on in several laboratories. So far, the experimental evidences support these assumptions.

In Fig. 5.4 a type of membrane is pictured which is present in most types of cells, and which is particularly abundant in protein secreting cells as, for instance, the exocrine pancreas cells. These membranes consist of a membranous component and of a great number of opaque particles fairly uniformly distributed over one side of the membrane. These particles show a fairly uniform size, and the work of Palade and Siekevitz [21] makes it obvious that they contain a high concentration of RNA. They are contained in the light microsome fraction and are responsible for the RNA content of this fraction. This type of cytoplasmic membrane we call the α-cytomembranes. They are frequently present in the ergastoplasmic regions of the cytoplasm, and the granules are then responsible for the basophilia of these regions. In other cases, the granules appear free in the basophilic cytoplasm.

Infoldings of the plasma membrane occur frequently in several cell types, for instance, the tubular epithelium of the kidney (Fig. 5.5), the ciliary epithelium of the eye and the epithelium of the choroid plexus. It is uncertain whether this duplication of the cell membrane is due to real infoldings or invaginations of the cell membrane or whether it merely

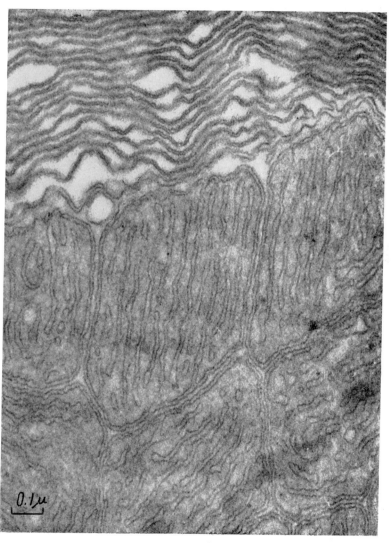

F<small>IG</small>. 5.2.

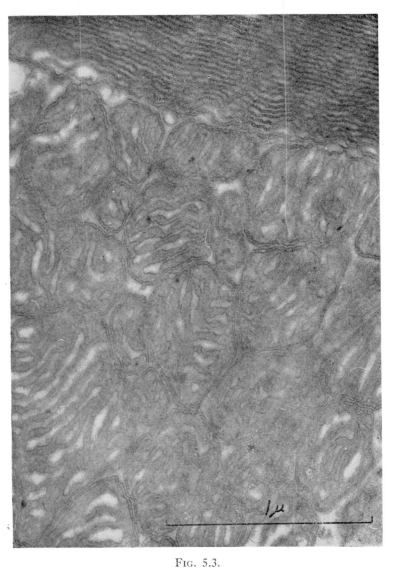

Fig. 5.3.

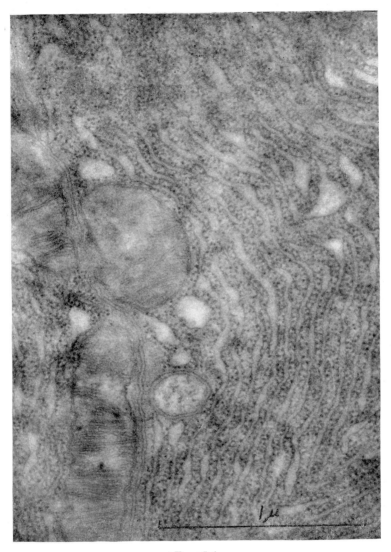

1 µ

F<small>IG</small>. 5.4.

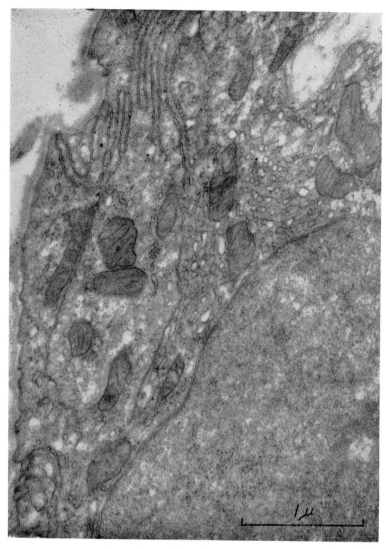

Fig. 5.5.

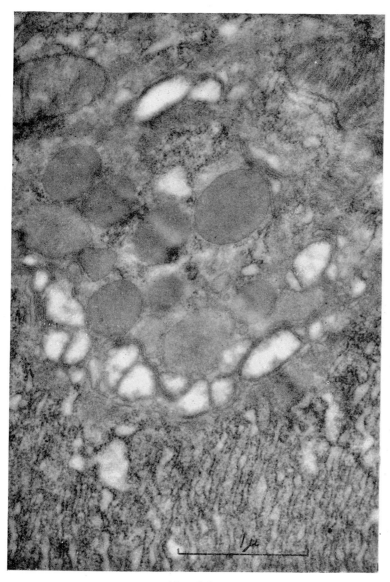

Fig. 5.6.

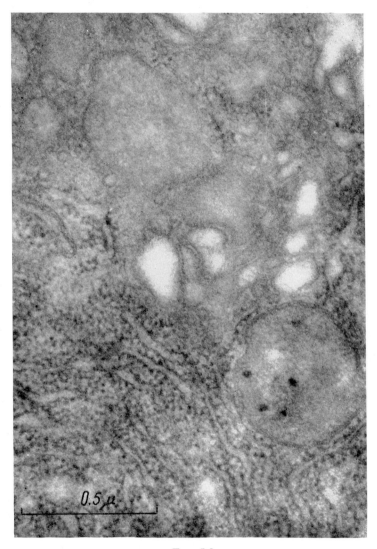

FIG. 5.8.

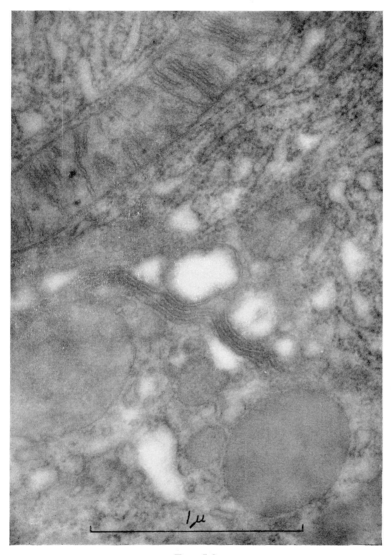

Fig. 5.9.

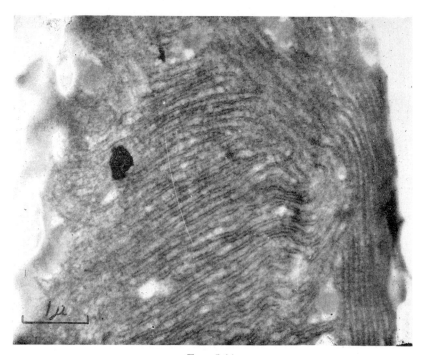

Fig. 5.11.

depends on a very complicated and extensive wrinkling of the cell surface of two adjacent cells. This type of membranes we call β-cytomembranes.

The Golgi apparatus of an exocrine pancreas cell is shown in Fig. 5.6. The main component of the Golgi apparatus is a system of membranes. These membranes frequently bound fairly large vacuolar spaces. Many of them seem to bound a narrow slit-shaped space, and appear then as pairs of membranes. This type of cytoplasmic membrane we refer to as γ-cytomembranes.

The α-, β- and γ-cytomembranes can easily be differentiated through their dimensions, their general appearance and their arrangement. Figure 5.7 shows the characteristic data for these types of membranes and, in

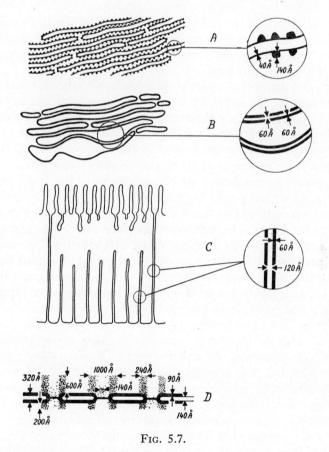

Fig. 5.7.

addition, the general scheme of the nuclear membrane is included. We have never been able to see any transition stages or to secure any continuity between these types of membranes or to find any indications that they would all represent different parts of one universal continuous system of membrane-bounded spaces as has been assumed by Porter and Palade as the background for the concept of their endoplasmic reticulum.

Let us now start the speculation that would make these pictures of the cytoplasm alive. On the one hand, we have the γ-cytomembranes with vacuolar spaces and, on the other, the zymogen granules containing the secretory products of the exocrine pancreas cells. In addition to the characteristic, fully developed zymogen granules, we observe a number of granules that are rather different in shape and opacity. These granules can be arranged in a sequence which shows all stages from small granules of low opacity through an intermediate size range of irregularly formed granules to the large opaque zymogen granules (Fig. 5.8). This would possibly indicate that these different types of granules in fact represent various stages during the formation of zymogen granules. The smaller, less opaque and irregularly formed granules would then represent precursors to the zymogen granules.

There is no doubt that a very close topographic relation exists between the first stages mentioned and the Golgi apparatus. In fact the presumed precursor granules are only observed in the Golgi apparatus, never outside the Golgi field. Therefore, it will here be assumed that the precursors to the zymogen granules are formed in the Golgi apparatus. The next problem will be to imagine how this takes place. However, let us first look at the α-cytomembranes which are closest to the Golgi apparatus. From Fig. 5.9 we can get the impression that the opaque particles attached to the α-cytomembranes on the side which faces the Golgi apparatus swell and fuse after being detached from the membrane. Some regions of the α-cytomembranes, which face the Golgi apparatus, are devoid of any opaque particles. It is now easy to conceive that elongated bodies are formed through fusion of these detached, swollen granules, and that these bodies become highly hydrated with the separation of a liquid phase confined to a vacuolar space bounded by the protein material contained in the granules and some lipids. The latter might have been admixed in connection with the transfer of these granules from the α-cytomembranes to the Golgi apparatus. What has been formed is a membrane from a granular material. The membranes formed in this way, we assume, are enzymatically active membranes consisting of a lipoprotein complex including enzyme molecules. The vacuoles formed collapse due to loss of water, and the collapsed sac disintegrates into membrane fragments which represent the first stages in the formation of the zymogen granules. These membrane fragments appear to fuse to form larger membrane-bounded granules. The surface membrane now synthesises or contributes to the final steps in the synthesis of the secretory products which are gradually becoming concentrated inside the zymogen granule. This would mean that the function of the Golgi apparatus would be to manufacture enzymatically active membranes from raw materials delivered by other parts of the cytoplasm including the α-cytomembranes. Figure 5.10 shows in a schematic way how this imagined mechanism works.

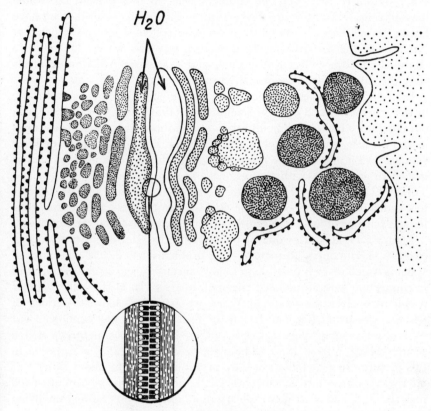

H_2O

FIG. 5.10.

When looking at the goblet cells of the mouse colon, this mechanism is even better illustrated. There we find the α-cytomembrane on one side of the Golgi apparatus. From the Golgi apparatus, vesicles are formed, these vesicles grow and we find all intermediate stages to the final secretory granules of the goblet cells along a line extending from the γ-cytomembranes of the Golgi apparatus to the free surface of the cell. In this case, there is almost a close packing of these granules, and there seems to be very little indication of any other kind of organised structural components which could take part in the formation of the granules.

This speculation gives an indication of a possible sequence of processes that may take place in the cytoplasm but there are great difficulties in proving that such a sequence is real. This is due to the very small field of view, which reveals only parts of a cell, to which we are restricted in high resolution electron microscopy. It would be useful to work with material where the activity of all the cells in a particular tissue had been synchronised so that each cell could be selected to represent the whole mass of cells. We are trying to synchronise the pancreas cells but we have not as yet succeeded. I think until we get a system where we are able to synchronise the activity of cells in such a way that we can introduce a stimulus and can collect the specimens at exactly defined time intervals after the stimulus, we cannot really prove anything.

In Fig. 5.7 a nuclear membrane is presented schematically according to the scheme worked out by Afzelius [18] (1955). A series of studies in our laboratory makes it difficult for us to join those who speak about pores in the nuclear membrane. I want to emphasise the membrane or layer which is extending over the presumed gap in the membrane. Our view is in fact in agreement with the original observations made by Callan and Tomlin [22] (1950) on the structure of the nuclear membrane. It is therefore difficult to accept holes in the nuclear membrane as a structural basis for an exchange of macromolecules between the nucleus and the cytoplasm.

Figure 5.11 illustrates one of the many serious technical problems in electron microscopy. The first of these problems is to devise experimental systems which make it possible to follow objectively any structural changes in connection with an induced change in the activity of the cell. Another problem involves the fixation. When we started to look at sections of tissue I was using freezing-drying for fixation. The first sections I cut were of frozen-dried pancreas cells. Figure 5.11 shows a picture of such a section which is from 1951. The cytoplasmic membranes are present in this picture. In fact I did not dare to publish anything about this result on the pancreas until I had checked this observation on osmium-fixed material and had also made polarisation optical observations on living pancreas cells *in situ* which revealed that the cytoplasm showed a birefringence which I analysed as negative with reference to a direction perpendicular to the cell surface. Since then, we have tried to improve the freezing-drying technique. This has been quite a problem and only recently we have succeeded in obtaining very good fixation by means of this technique [23]. In fact, freezing-drying preservation shows us a somewhat different picture of the structure of the cytoplasm as compared to osmium fixation. It is too early now to judge about these differences but we have the impression that what we see in osmium fixed material represents to a certain extent remnants of the real structure of the cytoplasm. I think it might be possible that we shall have to change the present fairly simple picture of the structure of the cytoplasm into a more complicated one. We have, so far, not been able to see the opaque RNA particles in the frozen-dried material. It may be that these particles are formed *post mortem* or during fixation by the aggregation of RNA-rich material.

I also would like to point out that it is very difficult, when looking at the cells, to decide what would constitute the microsome fraction or microsome particles. My impression is that the situation is like the one we would face if we homogenised Edinburgh and talked about the Edinburgh particles as represented by the remnants of the theatres of Edinburgh. I hope these remarks will provide some fuel for the discussion.

WADDINGTON: Would anyone like to take up something from that?

LEHMANN: I should like to answer Professor Waddington's question as to whether there are real submicroscopic differences in different cells. This is also an addition to Brachet's critical remarks concerning the unsatisfactory results of some fixation methods for electron microscopy. The pictures I am showing at this symposium are published elsewhere [24]. They were obtained with a new fixative.

We were especially interested to find cytoplasmic differences in the twenty-one-cell embryo of *Tubifex*. We know from the experiments of Penners [25] that some principal cells are different in their organ-forming potencies (Lehmann [26]). We have been doing mostly comparatively low-power electron microscopy with a magnification of 2000 or even 200. The pictures seem to give much more structural information than ordinary cytological sections because the power of resolution is much higher and the sections much thinner. It is very easy to identify the two large somatoblasts, the ectoblast 2d and the mesoblast 4d, as well as the entoblast 4D [27].

One of the most interesting components of all cells is the endoplasmic reticulum which is rather well preserved by our new fixative, in contrast to neutral osmic fixatives which destroy, as Brachet rightly remarks, a good deal of the reticulum and its particles. We must assume for *Amoeba* as for *Tubifex* that the reticulum is the primitive contractile system of the animal cell. At the St. Andrews Congress beautiful moving pictures have shown the activities of the endoplasmic reticulum in cellular movements.

Besides the endoplasmic reticulum we find more or less numerous mitochondria, lipid droplets with a delicate cytoplasmic coat, and yolk globules which are also coated by a cytoplasmic membrane. What is surprising, and I might remind you of what Dr. Sjöstrand said, is how monotonous this submicroscopic world looks. In our case we may distinguish two types of particulates: (a) particulates of "biosomatic character" mitochondria and the reticulum with its components as carriers of metabolism with anabolic and catabolic functions; (b) particulates with "nutrient" functions like lipid droplets and yolk grobules.

It is remarkable that the three cells 2d, 4d and 4D differ in their

particulate pattern. The ectoblast 2d contains a great amount of endoplasmic reticulum, a medium number of mitochondria, some lipid droplets
and few yolk globules. The mesoblast is very rich in mitochondria and
shows the greatest amount of lipid droplets, some yolk and a medium
amount of endoplasmic reticulum is present. The entoblast 4D being
poor in endoplasmic reticulum contains a group of perinuclear mitochondria (Weber), numerous lipid droplets and the greatest amount of
yolk globules. We see from this that the three cells 2d, 4d and 4D possess
a considerably different pattern of particulates. This also means essential
differences in metabolism. I do not want to say that this is the main
reason that these cells become different, also invisible differences might
be present. However, experimental embryology has discovered several
cases where quantitative differences produce a qualitatively different
course of development (gradients in sea urchin egg, sex determination and
sex differentiation). So I think that in the case of *Tubifex* primary purely
quantitative differences in metabolism might switch protein metabolism
and nuclear activities in qualitatively different ways in the three different
cells [26, 27].

WADDINGTON: I should like to give an example from a different system
of the differences in cytoplasmic and nuclear structure which may arise in
the cells of a differentiating organ. We are just starting here to examine
with the electron microscope the developing optic bud of *Drosophila*
larvae and pupae. In the late larva just before pupating the cells of this
imaginal bud all appear very similar. They are very closely packed
together and the cells are inter-digitated in a very complex manner (Fig.
5.12). The cell membranes show up very strongly in the electron microscope and the cells contain rather little cytoplasm but large nuclei, the
membranes of which appear thin and badly defined. Within the next few
hours the cells undergo very rapid processes of differentiation by which
a number of strongly distinct and different kinds of cells are produced.
Some become retinular cells; these form into groups of seven large cells,
the centre of each group being formed by the central transparent strand,
the rhabdomere, which has the structure of a honeycomb arrangement of
small tubules and vesicles (Fig. 5.13). The cytoplasm of these cells is
heavily loaded with mitochondria and also contains many small vesicles.
The nucleus is large with a well-defined double membrane. It contains
a nucleolus which is always placed very near the nuclear membrane and
usually towards the outer side of the cell, that is away from the rhabdomere. The other side of the nucleus, nearest the rhabdomere, is frequently lobulated. The appearances suggest that vesicles are appearing
in the cytoplasm near this region of the nuclear membrane and then move
towards the rhabdomere with which they eventually form part. Above the

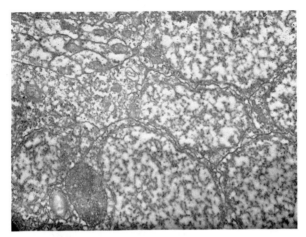

FIG. 5.12. Radial section through the basal part of the optic disk in the mature larva of *Drosophila melanogaster*. Well marked cell membranes, scanty cytoplasm, ill-defined nuclear membranes. ($\times$ 18,000)

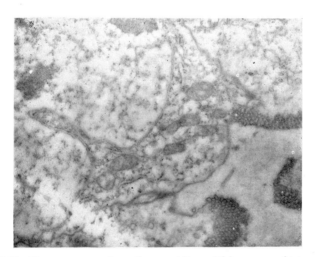

FIG. 5.13. Transverse section of ommatidium, 72 hr pupa. At top left a nucleus, with deeply infolded membrane. In the cytoplasm mitochondria and vesicles which join up in a meshwork to form the rhabdomeres. ($\times$ 15,000)

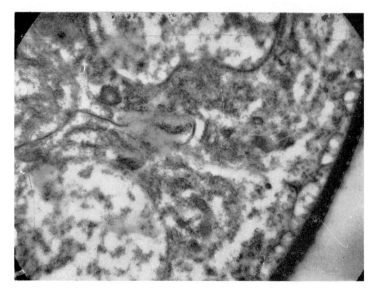

Fig. 5.14. Radical section of pseudocone cells, which are secreting the cornea at the bottom right, 48 hr pupa. ($\times$ 12,000)

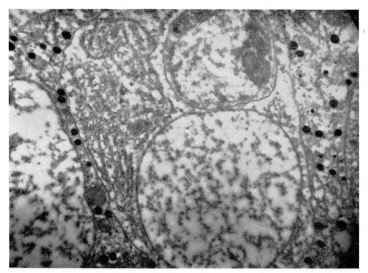

Fig. 5.15. Cells associated with the sensory hairs, with well developed endoplasmic reticulum, 48 hr pupa. ($\times$ 12,000)

retinular cells are a group of four pseudocene cells (Fig. 5.14). These have a different and quite characteristic type of cytoplasmic structure. Between the ommatidia there are, in the first place, at least two different varieties of pigment-forming cells. The types of endoplasmic reticulum and mitochondria which are seen in these are again recognisably different from those found in the retinular or pseudocene cells. Finally, one may mention the group of cells associated with the nerves which lead to the hairs on the outer surface. These cells have, in the first place, characteristically well-defined endoplasmic reticula, and on the other they have nuclei whose appearance suggests that intense activity is proceeding all over their surface (Fig. 5.15).

We have here an example in which there are quite clear differences in cytoplasmic structure between cells which lie in immediate contact with one another. Again, there are considerable differences in the structure of the nucleus and the nuclear membrane in the various types of cells and this suggests to me that the mechanism by which nuclear activity is carried out may vary widely from one type of cell to another. This may bring us back perhaps to Dr. Gay's paper. Would anyone like to take up the question of the form which may be taken by the activities of the nucleus?

WEISS: I would like to ask Dr. Gay whether she thinks that the Swift and Rebhun scheme, of fibres penetrating the nuclear membrane and then originating some of these membrane systems, is realistic in view of the fact that there is constant shifting of the nucleus in relation to the surrounding cytoplasm? Can you visualise any fibrous structure across there maintaining its orientation?

GAY: I do not know how long these fibrous structures would have to be maintained or how long the process would take. One could perhaps visualise the origin of these things in rather a short length of time, and then the shifting could occur.

WEISS: But why should these membranes be orientated parallel to the nucleus? What has led me to this question is that that is extremely striking. In amphibians we have seen something that looks like a shed nuclear membrane; you get in some cells a membrane that looks as though this process of shedding had gone over the whole nucleus, just like a snake sheds its skin. It does not look like local centres of production.

LEHMANN: Is it certain that all nuclei move? That seems to be the first question. I have seen moving nuclei in living tissues, but that does not imply that all nuclei move.

WEISS: All the nuclei we have seen move. They do not necessarily all revolve, but they are buffeted around, and since the nucleus is a gel and the cytoplasm loose, this would tend to be so.

WADDINGTON: This movement of the nucleus causes little difficulty when the membranes are parallel to the nucleus. The difficulty is when the membrane is at an angle to it.

WEISS: Yes, that's right.

PLAUT: How far out from the nucleus do these fibres extend?

SJÖSTRAND: I think electron microscopists should always have access to movie films of living cells and should look at these films and thus try to get away from a too static idea of structure. I think the orientations of the membranes around the nuclei might well be secondary to forces due to the movement of the nuclei and not have anything to do with shedding of the nuclear membrane.

WADDINGTON: What then moves the nucleus? If the movement of the nucleus orientates the membranes, something has got to push the nucleus around.

TOIVONEN: Yamada has taken some electron microscope pictures of amphibian cells from the amphibian neurula. There were there such out-pocketings from the nuclear membranes, like those described by Dr. Gay, and these outpocketings seemed to break free and eventually disappeared. Yamada was of the opinion that these outpocketings appear just when the cells are being activated.

GAY: This is exactly the point in the *Drosophila* salivary gland. At this stage it is definite that the cell has to put out a great deal of material. In my opinion, the outpocketing is very visible at this stage just because it is a sort of stress mechanism.

WADDINGTON: Has Dr. Gay any idea how many outpocketings there are per nucleus? Presumably each outpocketing corresponds to one region of a chromosome. That would seem to mean that some particular gene is active at the point in connection with the synthesis of the secretion. Are there very many genes concerned with making this secretion, or are there only one or two?

GAY: This question was asked of me at the Cold Spring Harbor Symposium and in the published discussion of this paper [3]. I presented some calculations. Of course, these can only represent a very rough estimate because we cannot tell at what level our series of sections passes through the nucleus.

WADDINGTON: You can't cut serial sections through the whole nucleus?

GAY: Well, I suppose it would be possible but a very monumental task. I've got several long series of sections in several nuclei—about 35 sections. The diameter of the nucleus is about 20 μ and the average thickness of each section is about 500 Å, so we have sampled less than one tenth of the nucleus; but on this basis we could calculate that there are anywhere between 20 and 200 blebs per nucleus.

WEISS: It would seem to depend on how fast they are extruded. If they extruded very fast the opportunity of catching one would be much lower. I think one would have to know that.

WADDINGTON: I was taking it that the bleb would take quite a long time to form and then come off.

WEISS: It might go quite fast.

GAY: Well, it may really be something like that under normal conditions in my material. I have grown my larvae under the usual cultural conditions for good larval development and for good chromosome preparations, that is at a lower temperature, about 17°C. I believe that other people who have looked at salivary-gland cells have grown their cultures at about 25° or 26°C, the usual temperature for raising the adult flies. Of course, if blebbing occurred very rapidly it might be more difficult to detect at the higher temperature. I haven't checked this point myself.

WADDINGTON: Have you ever been able to identify the same region of chromosome forming a bleb in two different nuclei?

GAY: Well, the nearest we can get is the reverse repeat story. Salivary-gland chromosomes in *Drosophila* are very long and are very much intertwined, and one section cuts through only a very small part, so that it's almost impossible to identify what chromosome you are dealing with. I believe this is a problem we must tackle now, to be able to identify particular regions, and we hope to do it.

LEHMANN: Are these blebs visible also in the phase contrast microscope?

GAY: Although I have looked at the *Drosophila* salivary-gland cells with the phase contrast microscope, I have not made any serious attempt to study these cells for the presence of blebs. However, I have had a recent communication from a Japanese worker, Dr. Yoshikazu Kimoto from Kobe University, concerning his phase contrast microscope studies of living salivary-gland cells of larvae of *Chironomus dorsalis*. He says he found it was important to make the phase contrast microscope observation within 15 min of dissection, to avoid chromosomal vesiculation. He found that chromosomal bands were frequently attached to the nuclear

10

membrane and that at the points of contact there frequently seemed to protrude from the nucleus a strongly "phase-negative" droplet. I have seen his excellent phase contrast pictures and some of them look quite similar to the electron micrographs which I have demonstrated here.

PONTECORVO: Does this blebbing occur in tissues other than the salivary gland?

GAY: I have not made a thorough study of other tissues in *Drosophila*, and have not studied any other animal. I made one brief attempt to study the nuclei of the Malpighian tubule cells of the third-instar larva of *Drosophila* and found no blebs there; but if our experience with the salivary gland means anything, it probably would be necessary to study different stages of development of the Malpighian tubule cell before any definite conclusion could be reached about that tissue.

WILDE: In this connection some observations we have made on cine-matographic film may be important. I have no way of knowing whether this particular phenomenon that we have observed is an equivalent of blebbing, but in phase contrast movies of differentiating striated muscle cells in the amphibian we discovered, much to our surprise, a short section of film in which a nucleus travels through the myoplasm and leaves its nucleolus behind. As far as we can identify this particular dense round structure, that is what it is. The frame-by-frame analysis of this bit of film is such that the nucleolus is within the nucleus in one frame and in the cytoplasm in the next frame. The frames are 4 sec apart. This may give some idea of the rate of extrusion.

WADDINGTON: You are certain it's not passing over just the top of the nucleolus?

WILDE: We can be pretty certain of that.

PLAUT: Is there any deformation of the nuclear membrane or the nucleolus in the second exposure?

WILDE: There is no evidence of it.

GAY: In this connection I might mention some observations of Dr. T. C. Hsu of Houston, Texas. He has some moving picture records of tissue-culture cells which show blebbing of the nucleus and the detachment of the bleb into the cytoplasm. He has told me that he looked specifically to see if there was any spilling out of nuclear contents or other deformation which one might expect in such an "injury", but that immediately after the bleb was pinched off the nuclear outline seemed to be intact, and he has seen a cell like this go on through a further mitotic division.

NEW SPEAKER: Do the blebs become PAS positive directly, or do you get the intervention of the Golgi apparatus such as Dr. Sjöstrand mentioned?

GAY: In some paraffin sections of *Drosophila* salivary-gland cells, we saw on one occasion very, very faint pink droplets just at the outside of the nucleus. However, these structures have been observed so rarely that we have not been able to do any cytochemical analysis.

WADDINGTON: One thing I was hoping Dr. Sjöstrand would stick his neck out about was the reality of the existence of microsomes as individual particles within the cell. He mentioned that in the freeze-dried material you do not get these dark lumps on the alpha membranes, which seems to raise the suspicion that microsomes may have less reality within the cell than at the bottom of the centrifuge tube. I don't know whether he would like to comment on that.

SJÖSTRAND: I think that the original concept of microsomes was quite different from what has come out now from electron microscopy about the nature of these particles. About microsomes in the cell, I think it is possible that the material is more diffusely spread in the cytoplasm and that one thing that takes place when homogenising or fixing the cell is the aggregation of this material into the particles. I think we should use the phrase "microsomal particles" to refer to definite particles in the intact cell. Microsomal particles should refer to what is in the microsome fraction.

BRACHET: After the cell has been homogenised.

WADDINGTON: What happens if you homogenise a fixed cell?

WEISS: You can't. It's too tough.
I should like to show you four slides which are relevant to some of the questions we've been discussing. This is material which has a bearing on almost everything we've been discussing. The epidermal cell of amphibian larvae is attached to its substratum by bobbin-shaped organelles which we have dissected chemically. They are not RNA and not connected with the nucleus and this may extend a little our discussion. They rest on a thin layer of about 600 Å, which contains lipid–protein granules and separates the epidermis from a fibrous basement lamella. These bobbins consist of two electron-dense plates after osmium fixation, with a lighter neck in between. They are about 1500 Å high and about 1200 Å in diameter. Originally we thought these were merely condensations of the osmic acid and so on. Now, in formalin fixation, they appear grey instead of black, so there was suspicion that the osmic acid was forming a compound in here. We put the whole skin in living conditions into pancreas lipase, leave it for half an hour in 1% lipase, and then it is osmicated. After that the basement membrane and everything else is pretty well

preserved but the bobbin plates have lost their osmophilia as compared with controls. So we find these plates are apparently pretty heavily loaded with lipid. The neck is hydrophilic because we can break the neck with distilled water, and then the two plates snap apart. Now, how real are these things? Are they just deposits on the surface? With salivary amylase we can dissolve the cementing film, which is apparently rich in carbohydrate. The cell loses its foothold on the basement lamella, but the bobbins remain rigidly in existence, even though the whole cell has been eroded by the penetration of the amylase into the cell. It eats out the cell but these bodies retain their integrity. So in that case we can be sure that they correspond to something which has physical stability in real life. This combination of enzymatic digestion before fixation for electron microscopy promises very well for further exploitation.

SJÖSTRAND: One difficulty with this is that if you have a microscopic structure and you dissolve the lipids and so ruin the structure, you will also destroy the orientation of the proteins.

WEISS: That isn't quite true of these structures. They show afterwards essentially the same gross structure as they did before the lipase treatment. There is no change in general dimensions. It's just that they become less electron-absorbing, although they still show some electron structure. They have a protein backbone.

WADDINGTON: I should like to ask Dr. Sjöstrand if he has any ideas about mitochondrial precursors, or mitochondrial division. Even in the old films of tissue culture made in the 1930s by Canti, one could see elongated mitochondria breaking up into shorter strands. As well as that problem of the breakage of mitochondria, there is the problem of their origin. Mitochondria are presumably generated from something else. Cells which at one time have few mitochondria may at a later stage have many more. Where do these mitochondria come from? Do they always arise from previous mitochondria, or can the lamellar structures of the ergastoplasm sometimes condense in some way to give mitochondria? What have you to say about this general problem?

SJÖSTRAND: We have been working on that problem recently but it is difficult to give any definite statement. There are two possibilities. We have the initiation and development of the heavy mitochondrial populations in the elements of the visual receptors. There you find in chicken embryos of about 18 days a tremendous increase in the number of mitochondria. At that time, we have fairly opaque particles appearing among the mitochondria. It might be that these opaque particles are transformed into mitochondria by the appearance of a surface and of the inner membranes. The first mitochondria seem to be very simple. They have just one inner membrane and are very small. That is one possibility, but at the same time there is this too. It may be that mitochondria derive from vesicular structures. In the kidney Rhodin [28] has certain evidence that the granules which he calls microbodies, which are medium dense and which are lined by a single membrane, may be transformed into mitochondria. He has observed this in connection with the injection of albumen and the destruction of the mitochondria in connection with this. Yes, there are possibilities that we have the formation of mitochondria from vesicular granules.

The division of mitochondria is of course very difficult to see in the electron microscope but we have some pictures of mitochondria in electron micrograms that may correspond to what you see in tissue cultures. You can see the mitochondria apparently pinching in two, and you can see that the internal structures are intact. If you take this picture in conjunction with the pictures of living cells you get the impression of the mitochondrial structure being very labile, and it may be that it is very easily reformed, but in these cases you always have the intact internal structure.

WADDINGTON: Now, I know that Dr. Gustafson has discussed the changes of the particle populations in cells in relation to development, and the changing relation between mitochondria and microsomes. I think we will come on to that more fully on Monday, but I don't know whether he has done any electron microscope work on it?

GUSTAFSON: No.

WADDINGTON: Well, we ought not to spend very much longer this afternoon, so perhaps we had better stick to the EM side of things.

BRENNER: Could I make a comment? I think that Dr. Sjöstrand has been questioning the existence of the microsomal particles, and of course I take his speculations very seriously because they underlay my speculations. I think, however, that one has to take all the evidence at the same time. At the outset, one must make a very clear distinction between what the biochemists called microsomes and the idea of microsomal particles. Essentially microsomes are a mess. That is to say, in homogenates they are all of different sizes, according to their sedimentation properties, and they have tremendously heterogeneous chemical properties. Different fractions have different enzyme activities. They have considerable lipid content and they have considerable enzyme activity apart from their RNA content. If the microsomal fraction, which we would like to think of as the disrupted alpha cytomembrane in Sjöstrand's terminology, with the attached particles, is first sedimented, Palade [29] has shown that centrifugation of the supernate at $105,000\,g$ for 18 hr will sediment a fraction which, on fixation with osmic acid and sectioning, shows only the presence of these microsomal particles which are electron dense and extremely regular in size. They are, in fact, very similar to small viruses.

The other evidence for the existence of particles apart from the membranes is that the membranes can be treated with deoxycholate, whereupon most of the enzymes, nearly all the lipids, and a considerable fraction of the protein become soluble. From this material you can sediment a small-particle fraction which seems to be very similar in properties to the microsomal particles [30]. Littlefield [31] in Zamecnik's laboratory has shown that it is the particle fraction which has everything to do with the incorporation of amino acids. Similarly, from *Ascites* tumour cells, which apparently have very little membranous material, a very homogeneous particle fraction with a sedimentation content of about 70 S, can be prepared [32]. These particles will incorporate amino acids into protein when supplemented with the usual supernatant enzymes. Finally, in bacteria, in which I think the electron microscopists will agree there is no evidence of any reticulum at all, or any membrane structure within the cell, particles of the same size can be isolated. Electron micrographs of sectioned bacteria show that the cytoplasm is densely packed with these particles. Kellenberger [33] has exploded a cell directly on the microscope grid and his pictures show the presence of regular grains, as he calls them, of between 200 and 300 Å units. Finally, extracts of bacteria run in an ultracentrifuge show a very well defined peak with a sedimentation constant of 40 S [34]. The particles making up this peak are extremely regular in size when spread on to an electron microscope grid and shadowed, as also are particles isolated from pea seedlings. These particles contain exclusively RNA and protein, and have no enzyme activity. Similar particles can also be isolated from the rabbit appendix. These are electrophoretically homogeneous and are also homogeneous in the ultracentrifuge. All this evidence strongly suggests that the particles are not only real but also universally distributed.

There is one other point that I think I should raise now. One way of looking at cells, which is not an uninteresting way, is to ask what are the uniform properties of all cells. We have heard of looking at cells to see what are the differentiating properties. I should like to draw your attention to the following remarkable fact. It is well known that from mitochondria, as the Wisconsin school have shown, one can isolate a small particle, which Green has called the electron transferring particle. This has a defined constitution, that is, there is a definite ratio of flavin to haem to copper, and the cytochromes are present in these particles. These particles will carry out all the steps of oxidation of succinic acid. Now, rather remarkably, a particle almost identical in properties can be isolated from *Azotobacter*. These particles are differentiated from the microsomal particles. For one thing, one third of their weight is lipid, while the microsomal particles have no demonstrative lipids. It is well known that you can see nothing in bacteria that looks like mitochondria, and in fact recent evidence suggests that the analogous structure to mitochondria in bacteria may have something to do with the cell membrane; for example, the ghost which is left after osmotic lysis of the protoplast can carry out all the respiratory functions of the intact protoplast. It seems, therefore, that the electron transferring particle, in bacteria is in the cell membrane or attached to it, while in mammalian cells, the same particle is packed into a different sort of larger structure, namely a mitochondrion. This suggests that there are unifying properties of all kinds of cells.

RIS: It has been shown that in mitochondria the electron transport system is contained in the membranes. You can take these membranes off the mitochondria and break them up into smaller and smaller vesicles. Apparently the broken membranes re-fuse again into vesicles of various sizes which retain the enzymatic properties of the intact mitochondria. This is an example of the great mobility of these membranes. So long as you have the membranes you can put them together in many ways, or break them up into very minute units, without changing the enzymatic properties.

BRENNER: What are the dimensions of the small vesicles? Are they about 100 Å?

RIS: Bigger than that. Perhaps two or three hundred.

SJÖSTRAND: I think this is a very peculiar situation and unexpected. As a morphologist I am usually accused of complicating things by biochemists and physiologists, but I notice that these pictures that we demonstrate, even if we know that they are definitely artifacts, if they fit in and suit the physiologists and biochemists they will be accepted; and the morphologist who knows about the mobility and difficulty of the material has to remember that his attitude should be critical about his material and not be taken in. What I want to do is to see if we can get any further in our ideas about the microsomes by improving our technique and getting more and more complete data about the cell. There is no reason to question that you get in your microsome fraction particles with specific properties. The point is, do these particles look exactly as they do in the cell when they may be attached to the membrane? Or are they perhaps the vesicles? Or are they aggregated on to these membranes? Because when they first appear freely in the embryonic cells we do not have these membranes but we have the free particles. This I think shows that with a fuller study of how these particles appear in the intact cell we will get more interesting ideas about their functioning.

WADDINGTON: I think, from some of the things we have heard about the mitochondria, that the actual morphology of these particles—the shape they assume under different circumstances—may not really be so very important. The enzymatic and metabolic activities may go on in a rather similar way whether the particle is packed together tightly or is expanded into a vesicle. Probably the activity proceeds on the surfaces, and perhaps these may be tightly crumpled together, or be expanded, without making very much difference. If so the morphology may possibly turn out to be less crucial from the biochemical point of view.

I think now we shall have to bring this session to an end.

REFERENCES

1. GAY, H. (1955) *Proc. Nat. Acad. Sci., Wash.* **41**, 370.
2. GAY, H. (1956a) *J. Biophys. Biochem. Cytol.* Suppl. **2**, 407.
3. GAY, H. (1956b) *Cold Spr. Harb. Symp. Quant. Biol.* **21**, 257.
4. WATSON, M. L. (1955) *J. Biophys. Biochem. Cytol.* **1**, 257.
5. HANNAH, A. (1951) *Advanc. Genet.* **4**, 87.
6. POULSON, D. F. (1950) *Biology of Drosophila*, Chap. 3, John Wiley, New York.
7. SONNENBLICK, B. P. (1950) *Biology of Drosophila*, Chap. 2, John Wiley, New York.
8. FRAENKEL, G. and V. J. BROOKES (1953) *Biol. Bull.* **150**, 442.
9. KAUFMANN, B. P. and M. R. MCDONALD (1956) *Cold Spr. Harb. Symp. Quant. Biol.* **21**, 233.
10. PAINTER, T. S. (1945) *J. Exp. Zool.* **100**, 523.
11. RIS, H. (1957) In *Chemical Basis of Heredity* (Ed. by W. D. MCELROY and B. GLASS), Johns Hopkins Press, Baltimore.
12. KAUFMANN, B. P. and D. N. DE (1956) *J. Biophys. Biochem. Cytol.* Suppl. **2**, 419.
13. KAUFMANN, B. P. (1948) *Bot. Rev.* **14**, 57.
14. CASPERSSON, T. (1950) *Cell Growth and Cell Function*, Salmon Lectures, New York.
15. SWIFT, H. (1956) *J. Biophys. Biochem. Cytol.* Suppl. **2**, 415.
16. REBHUN, L. I. (1956a) *J. Biophys. Biochem. Cytol.* **2**, 93.
17. REBHUN, L. I. (1956b) *J. Biophys. Biochem. Cytol.* **2**, 159.
18. AFZELIUS, B. A. (1955) *Exp. Cell Res.* **8**, 147.
19. AFZELIUS, B. A. (1956) *Proc. Stockholm Conference on Electron Microscopy*, 147.
20. SCHULTZ, J. (1952) *Exp. Cell Res.*, Suppl. **2**, 17.
21. PALADE, G. E. and P. SIEKEVITZ (1956) *J. Biophys. Biochem. Cytol.* **2**, 171.
22. CALLAN, H. G. and S. G. TOMLIN (1950) *Proc. Roy. Soc.* B137, 367.
23. SJÖSTRAND, F. S. and R. F. BAKER (1958) *J. Ultrastruct. Res.* **1**, 239.
24. LEHMANN, F. E. and U. MANCUSO, (1958) *Exp. Cell Res.*
25. PENNERS, A. (1934) *Z. Zool.* **145**, 86.
26. LEHMANN, F. E. (1956) *Naturwissenschaften* **43**, 289; (1958) *The Chemical Basis of Development*, MacCollum-Pratt Symp. In press.
27. LEHMANN, F. E. and V. MANCUSO (1957) *Arb. J. Klaus Stfit.* **32**, in press.

28. RHODIN, J. (1954) *Correlation of Ultrastructural Organisation and Function in . . . Mouse kidney.* Karolinska Inst., Stockholm (Aktieb. Godvil): see also ROUILLER, C. and W. BERNHARD (1956) *J. Biophys. Biochem. Cytol.* **2**, Suppl. 355.
29. PALADE, G. E. and SIEKEVITZ (1956) *J. Biophys. Biochem. Cytol.* **2**, 671.
30. PALADE, G. E. and SIEKEVITZ (1956) *J. Biophys. Biochem. Cytol.* **2**, 171.
31. LITTLEFIELD, J. W., E. B. KELLER, J. GROSS and P. C. ZAMECNIK (1955) *J. Biol. Chem.* **217**, 111.
32. LITTLEFIELD, J. W. and E. B. KELLER (1957) *J. Biol. Chem.* **224**, 13.
33. KELLENBERGER, G. and E. KELLENBERGER (1957) *Virology* **3**, 275.
34. SCACHMAN, H. K., A. B. PARDEE and R. Y. STANIER (1952) *Acta Biochem. Biophys.* **38**, 245.

CHAPTER VI

Activities of the Cytoplasm

WADDINGTON: This morning we shall start with organisation within the cytoplasm and we have some rather different points of view to be put forward. Perhaps it would be best to begin with Beale talking about some of the evidence for permanent self-replicating units within the cytoplasm in *Paramecium*; and I think he can tell us something about how far he feels this can be generalised to apply to the cells of higher organisms. After that perhaps it would be best to ask Holtzer to show us some of his stuff on the formation of specific proteins mainly in the cytoplasm. Then I think there is Gustafson with a story of considerable fluctuations in the particle populations in the cytoplasm during development. It will be interesting to consider particles which are not permanent but which change as development proceeds. So would Beale start us off with these alleged plasmagenes?

BEALE: These plasmagenes are very much "alleged". And as for the question of generalisation from particular examples of cytoplasmic particles or cytoplasmic inheritance, it seems to me that it is at present very difficult to make such generalisations, because the particles that have been analysed most carefully seem to be extremely heterogeneous. They vary amongst themselves and do not possess any essential common features. I shall try to show you this when I discuss details about two of them. These are cytoplasmic determinants in *Paramecium aurelia*, namely, the determinants of the antigen system and of the killer system. In both of these systems we have a situation where the properties of the cell may vary on account of variations in the cytoplasm even when the nuclei remain constant. The details of the cytoplasmic particles concerned are utterly different in the two systems, however. In the antigen system the cytoplasmic materials are extremely obscure—in fact, one might even think that they are not there at all. You can't identify these materials in any particle present in the cytoplasm of a paramecium. There is no visible difference in the cytoplasmic particles of the different antigenic types, although we know that the cytoplasm must be different in these different types. So in the antigen system the material nature of the cytoplasmic factors is entirely obscure—unknown in fact. By contrast, in the second

136

system, the killer system, the cytoplasmic particles are extremely clear, in fact, so clear that one might feel that this example is almost irrelevant to the general problem of cytoplasmic differences between cells undergoing normal development.

Now, I'd like to give a few details about each of these systems: first of all about the antigen system (described in detail elsewhere [1, 2]). The end product here, the immobilisation antigen, is something liberated on the outside of the paramecium. Figure 6.1. shows a paramecium treated while still living, with a preparation containing homologous antibody and examined under phase contrast, and here you see the clumping of the cilia at their tips and accumulation of some "sticky" material there and in a mass around the posterior of the animal. Without going into further details, which Dr. Kacser and I have described elsewhere [3], we can say that the immobilisation antigen accumulates on the outside of the animal: it appears to coat the surface structures. We have no evidence for the presence of this antigen in the interior of the cell, though it is possible that the methods so far may not be sensitive enough to show that, if it does exist.

Now it has been known for some years [4, 5] that these antigens are controlled in a very precise way by certain genes in the nucleus. We have the familiar 1:1 gene–antigen relationship, that is, there is a determination of the specificity of a particular antigen by a particular gene in the nucleus. So something has to come from the nucleus and form the antigen on the surface, but we don't yet know of any intermediate materials between the initial gene and the final antigen.

We do however know from genetical evidence that there is present in the cytoplasm some substance which allows a given gene (or gene product) to operate and bring about the formation of a given antigen on the surface, and prevents other antigen-determining genes at other loci from coming to expression. This situation is shown diagrammatically in Fig. 6.2. Unfortunately, as I mentioned, the material basis of this cytoplasmic factor is still unknown. We therefore refer to it by speaking of the "state" of the cytoplasm. There isn't any other information I can give about it now. We can, however, get some information about the cytoplasmic substance indirectly by studying its response to various sorts of changes either in the external environment or in the nucleus. It is undoubtedly affected by the environment. We can change the state of the cytoplasm by altering the temperature, for instance, or the salt content of the medium. These have definite predictable effects on the cytoplasmic material. Similarly, substitution of one allele by another in the nucleus will bring about characteristic alterations in the properties of the cytoplasmic states controlling antigen production. The details of these effects are exceedingly complicated, and I don't think I need give them now; but it is interesting to point out one thing, namely, that the particular gene which controls specificity of an antigen is itself known to have an effect on the properties of the cytoplasmic state. There is thus a peculiar mutual effect of gene on the cytoplasm and of the cytoplasm on the gene (or possibly a product of the gene).

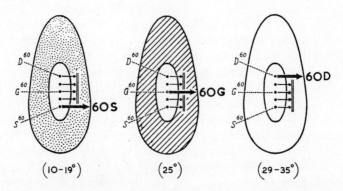

FIG. 6.2. Interaction of cytoplasmic states and antigen determining genes in *P. aurelia* (after Beale, 1954). The three antigen-determining genes,—S^{60}, G^{60}, D^{60}—come to expression in combination with the three cytoplasmic states indicated by different shading, and formed at different temperatures.

A number of hypothetical schemes have been proposed to account for the operation of this system [1, 2, 7], but none of them are satisfactory, and in any case critical evidence is lacking, and I therefore don't think it is profitable to discuss such models at the present time.

I would now like to contrast the antigen system with the killer system. As you know, the killer paramecia were discovered some 15 years ago by Sonneborn [8], and there was a good deal of excitement about the nature of the particles in the cytoplasm which make a paramecium a killer. They were called plasmagenes and a good many other names. Recently, we have obtained some new evidence on the structure of these particles and I thought it would be interesting for you to hear it. The material I am going to describe is *P. aurelia*, variety 1, stock 540, which is a mate-killer [9], i.e. when caused to conjugate with a normal, sensitive animal of any other stock of variety 1, the ex-conjugants which receive cytoplasm from the sensitive parent die, while the ex-conjugants which receive cytoplasm from the mate-killer parent survive. The mate-killer pheno-menon was discovered in *P. aurelia*, variety 8, by Siegel [10]. Like the variety 4 killers, described by Sonneborn [11], mate-killers of variety 1 contain at least one essential dominant gene (*M*), and a large number of cytoplasmic particles.

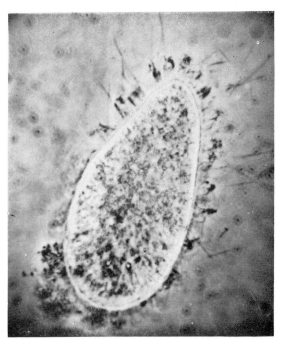

Fig. 6.1. Living *Paramecium* treated with homologous antiserum and examined by phase-contrast.

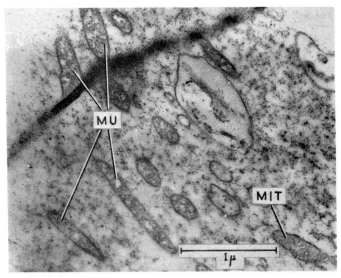

FIG. 6.3. Ultra-thin section through cytoplasm of a mate-killer *Paramecium* (stock 540, variety 1, *P. aurelia*). Fixed in osmic acid and embedded in methacrylate. mu = mu particles, mi = mitochondrion.

When you squash a paramecium with a cover-slip, by the method devised by Preer, Siegel and Stark [12] and allow the contents to flow out and look at it under phase-contrast, you see a large number of rod-like particles. In length they vary from about 1 to some 10 μ, and the long ones appear to be made up of sequences of the short ones. Many thousands of these particles come from one squashed cell. They are Feulgen positive like the original kappa particles, as first stained by Preer [13]. When stained with Feulgen and examined with ordinary transmitted light, they appear as uniformly stained particles. No internal details can be seen at all. In that one respect they differ from bacteria (as pointed out by Preer for kappa particles). From this it might appear that the particles contain only DNA but I don't think such a conclusion is warranted merely from the appearance after staining by the Feulgen technique.

With the aid of Dr. K. Deutsch, and Dr. Jurand*, we have made some EM sections of these particles. In Fig. 6.3, you see a section through the cytoplasm of a paramecium containing a number of mu particles. It is now quite clear that they are not homogeneous but have a definite and complex structure. There is a double membrane on the outside, and inside there is electron-dense material (denser than that of the cytoplasm of the paramecia). Embedded in the dense material are several clear areas, which may in their turn contain further condensed material. The particles have a structure quite different from that of the mitochondria which exist side by side with the mu particles in the same cytoplasm.

These pictures are extraordinarily like some of the sections of bacteria which have been looked at with the EM, and some bacteriologists when they see these things say they are "undoubtedly bacteria".

Now, even if they do turn out to be bacteria, and we have something like a bacterial infection, the mu or kappa particles are still of great interest, because they are extremely intimately ensconced in the cytoplasm, and are very well adapted to living there. They seem to be almost a part of the paramecium and are incredibly well adapted to the genotype of the paramecium.

What I have said is intended to convey to you some idea of the great difference between two examples of "cytoplasmic inheritance" in *Paramecium*.

WADDINGTON: Presumably the thing which you say can't be generalised is the function of particles in the cytoplasm. Surely the general system of cytoplasmic states activating or setting going particular alleles which control antigens—that, it seems to me, possibly could be generalised.

---

* Dippell [14] has independently obtained EM sections of kappa particles from other varieties of *P. aurelia*.

BEALE: Yes, I agree, but it seems to me there may be many different types of system on which to base the generalisation. These are just two of the possible systems. I think that if one started analysing some other cell, if it were possible, by the techniques which have been used in *Paramecium*, it might turn out that every single example was different. For instance, Ephrussi's system in yeast. He has cytoplasmic particles which are visible but which are quite different from the kappa particles and have different properties. I imagine that the same might apply in other systems, and that is why I do not think there is one system at all. I think there are very many.

PONTECORVO: You cannot grow these bacterium-like particles which have a genetic effect by themselves, can you?

BEALE: Nobody has succeeded yet, but it is possible they will do so in the future.

PONTECORVO: I didn't catch the situation there. You meant that the mate-killer strain had these particles and then it mates with one which doesn't have them and only one ex-conjugant gets them?

BEALE: Yes, one ex-conjugant dies. The ex-conjugant which is descended cytoplasmically from the one which has the particles survives and the one descended cytoplasmically from the one without the particles dies.

PONTECORVO: When you do the conjugation further on (i.e. between two F_1s) and get the nucleus homozygous for the ordinary situation (i.e. *mm*), what happens then?

BEALE: The particles disappear.

WADDINGTON: By treating a mate-killer, can you change the cytoplasm so that the animal becomes sensitive?

BEALE: Yes, you can do that by changing the environment (e.g. by heating) so that all the particles are killed. You then have the same genes in the nucleus, but no particles.

WADDINGTON: Well, the difficulty now seems to be that you say the one without particles always dies when it conjugates with one which has particles. How then do you ever get particles in the first place?

BEALE: Well, that's one of those mysteries that I wouldn't like to say anything about. I was formerly very definite about this. I thought the particles were undoubtedly foreign bodies which had got themselves into the cell, but I sometimes have doubts about that now.

WADDINGTON: But some of the cells are resistant and can maintain particles in their cytoplasm and live quite happily?

BEALE: It does no harm to the paramecia to have the particles if they have got the right genetic make-up.

PONTECORVO: They must have one *M*.

BEALE: They must have one *M*, and at least one particle there to start with.

WADDINGTON: But you've never been able to find a cell without particles and infect it with particles and find it remains alive and allows the particles to multiply?

BEALE: I haven't done that, but it has been done by others with kappa particles. If you take a cell of suitable genotype and inject it—well, not inject it but treat it in various ways—you can get kappa particles to go in and maintain themselves in the cytoplasm. But this is a very unusual procedure which would be very unlikely to occur in nature, I think. The main problem, as I see it, in the origin of this situation is the extraordinary adaptation between the particles and the cell they are in. The particles don't survive unless the "medium" (i.e. the paramecium cell) contains the right genes.

WILDE: Could not the paramecia be segregating, for some other purpose, a genetic system which accidentally was acceptable to these bacteria? Once a suitable internal condition was found, you would then have a most favoured constitution to maintain the bacteria.

BEALE: Yes, that's feasible. This material is one particular strain (stock 540) of one variety (variety 1). I have got about 50 other strains caught in nature of the same variety. None of these contain the particles. It is obviously a rare occurrence in this variety. We know another thing; there are enormous numbers of these particles. When you stain the cell with Feulgen it is quite clear that it is almost solid with DNA in the cytoplasm, and yet this "foreign" DNA doesn't seem to hurt the cell at all. The only thing it seems to do is to make them rather heavier, so that they sit down at the bottom, owing to their weight, perhaps! But it doesn't do what, for instance, phage particles do in bacteria. It doesn't divert the general DNA metabolism or bust the cell up. You have this enormous mass of DNA present with really no harmful effect at all. It is really most curious.

BRENNER: Isn't this completely analogous to rickettsia symbiosis where, if I remember my parasitology correctly, the rickettsia are transmitted through generations of ticks by symbiosis in the ovum? That would have been a case, if you didn't know about it, of cytoplasmic inheritance.

WILDE: Aren't there certain insects which have mycetocytes in the ovary which pass on fungal hyphae into the egg so that the same cells in the offspring are equipped with the correct symbionts?

WEISS: Yes.

WADDINGTON: Of course, there are many insects which pass on bacteria through their eggs. It does seem as though in the killer system we are dealing with something which can be considered a parasitic organism, or next door to it; whereas in the antigen system we have a rather pretty parallel with what one imagines must be happening in development, with different cytoplasmic states setting off particular genes, but there you can't see any cytoplasmic particles involved in the process.

BRACHET: As regards the antigen system, there seem to be quite a number of examples where the nucleus exerts a strong influence on the cytoplasmic membrane. Beale seems to have a case of that sort and of course Danielli [15] in his experiments on transplantation in amoeba gets the same sort of thing. He seems to have specific antigens which appear to be on the membrane when he transplants nuclei. In many cases when the nucleus is modified or altered, as in lethal hybrids, or if you fertilise the egg with nitrogen-mustard-treated sperm, which amounts to the same thing, you get great changes in permeability [16]. The uptake of ^{23}P, and the uptake of other labels, is completely changed; and it is a well-known fact that almost all of these lethal hybrids die by swelling, which seems to indicate that their ion permeability is modified.

WADDINGTON: Perhaps Holtzer would now give us his story.

HOLTZER: As a morphologist I find it rather difficult to keep a straight face when talking about protein synthesis. However, owing to the happy circumstances of collaborating with Dr. J. Marshall, we have been attempting to learn something about myogenesis by means of fluorescent antibodies. And anyone using this technique of Coons [17] sooner or later succumbs to the illusion that he might have something to contribute to the problems of protein synthesis.

But before discussing our findings on the intracellular elaboration of the structural proteins in developing muscle, it might be advisable to set the background by relating our findings on the localisation of different labelled antibodies in mature muscle. Rabbit antibodies against several muscle antigens of the chicken have been labelled with fluorescein and used to "stain" glycerol extracted mature muscle myofibrils. In reasonably relaxed sarcomeres antibody staining is found primarily in the following regions: (1) anti-myosin, thoughout the A band; (2) anti-H meromyosin, in the H band; (3) anti-L meromyosin, along the lateral aspects of the A band; (4) anti-actin, in the I and M band; (5) anti-tropomyosin, in the I band. These patterns of localisation vary depending upon the degree of isometric or isotonic contraction. It is also worth stressing that until this material is more carefully examined the terms A, I and H band only indicate the general area of the sarcomere binding the antibodies. It should also be stressed at this point that a great deal more work has to be done before we can even begin to claim that our antisera actually reveal where in the sarcomere the respective antigens are located. The homogeneity of our antibody solutions has yet to be determined, the problem of *in situ* masking of antigen, the question of the sensitivity of the technique, etc., are problems still to be analysed. Nevertheless, I hope you will agree with me that to the extent that these different antibodies localise in different areas within the sarcomere, and to the extent that they do not react with other cell types (e.g. liver, kidney, cartilage, nerve skin), to that extent we have a tool with which to follow the synthesis of these several muscle antigens which are present in the mature cell.

When the entire trunk of a 4 day chick embryo is treated with labelled antimyosin, only those areas engaged in myogenesis (i.e. the segmented myotomes) bind the antibody. When such material is examined under higher magnification it is observed that the fluorescent antibody does not stain the entire myoblast. Rather, the antimyosin is bound only by those segments of the embryonic myofibril that correspond to A bands as determined under the phase microscope. These fluorescent segments have the same longitudinal dimension as the A bands of a mature muscle myofibril. Neither the nucleus nor the sarcoplasm of the myoblast bind the antibody.

Figure 6.4 is a diagrammatic representation of the changes observed with antimyosin treated material as a 3 day mono-nucleated myoblast differentiates into a 7 day multi-nucleated myotube. The fluorescent antibody is confined to A band-like segments along the very fine myofibril of the 3 day myoblast. In cross-section the myofibril, or myofibrillar sheet as I would prefer to call it, occupies only a small sector along the circumference of the cell. In our material the myofibrillar sheet cannot be distinguished from the sarcolemma. In a matter of 48 hr the over-all length of the still mono-nucleated cell has increased from approximately 90 to about 500 μ though there has been little change in cell width. The most prominent difference between the 3 and 5 day myoblast is that the myofibrillar sheet occupies a larger sector of the circumference of the cell—the myofibril is wider laterally. The longitudinal dimensions of the individual A bands have not changed. It is important to note that the embryonic myofibril in any given myoblast is remarkably uniform in width from one end of the cell to the other.

WADDINGTON: So they've increased in number?

11

HOLTZER: Yes, the number of individual A bands have increased in number from the 3rd to 5th day. From the 5th to the 7th day the major changes involve further lateral extension of the myofibrillar sheet and the fusion of mono-nucleated cells to form the multi-nucleated myotubes. That mono-nucleated cells fuse with, or are incorporated into, the growing muscle fibre has recently been observed in tissue cultures of suspended embryonic cells [18] and deduced from microspectrophotometric determinations of DNA in regenerating muscle [19]. To demonstrate further

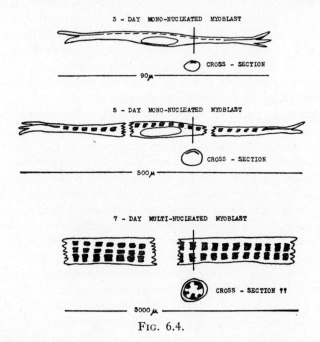

FIG. 6.4.

this general type of cell fusion we have grown mouse and chick myoblasts together in the same culture and attempted to demonstrate mouse and chick nuclei in the same fibre. However, as yet we cannot convince ourselves that individual chick and mouse nuclei can be clearly distinguished, as has been shown for other tissues. Be that as it may, as illustrated in Fig. 6.4, in the 7 day multi-nucleated myotube, the myofibrillar sheet is deployed as a thin cylinder just under the sarcolemma.

Well now, if we speculate from these findings with respect to the formation of the myofibril, several things strike one. To begin with, the work of Hanson and Huxley [20] and others shows that the myofibril is a complex structure made up of at least three major proteins—myosin, actin and tropomyosin. It is even possible, without going into details here, that myosin is in turn compounded of at least two other proteins—L- and

H-meromyosin. Each of these several proteins, as mentioned earlier, is localised in a restricted region of the sarcomere. Now what is the nature of the intra-cellular mechanisms that can fabricate a myofibril consisting of several different proteins each with a specific location along the fibril? There is no evidence that the antimyosin is bound by elements in or around the nucleus or in the sarcoplasm. Moreover, the fact that throughout the developmental period the myofibril in a given cell is of uniform width could be interpreted to indicate that A band material (myosin?) adds to preformed A band, I band material (actin? tropomyosin?) adds to pre-formed I band, H band material (H-meromyosin?) adds to preformed H band and so on. In short, the myofibril may grow by apposition and the first formed sarcomeres function as primers or templates for the further synthesis of the muscle proteins. We think it possibly significant that there is no indication that the sarcomeres closest to the nucleus are larger or more differentiated than those sarcomeres several hundred microns away. If a precursor to myosin or other protein were synthesised in or around the nucleus one might expect a gradient such that those sarcomeres closest to the nucleus were more advanced, and that, due to the time required for such nuclear precursors to diffuse to the end of the cell, those sarcomeres farthest away from the nucleus might be expected to be least developed. The absence of such a gradient leads us to consider that the nucleus is not directly and immediately involved in the synthesis of these muscle proteins. It strikes us, at least as a working hypothesis, that in this case we are not dealing with protein synthesis in the sarco-plasm at large either, with protein molecules being ferried into their proper place along the myofibril. Rather it may be that all the different proteins making up the myofibril are synthesised simultaneously and in a spatially organised way right on the surface of the myofibril. And that is the contribution of a morphologist to the problems of protein synthesis in embryonic muscle cells (see [21] for further details).

BRACHET: I should like to ask what you get at earlier stages. Can one see anything before one can see the cross striations? I was wondering whether in these large cells, for instance, when they have grown to full length you get these things, but perhaps at an earlier stage you might get something in the nucleus?

HOLTZER: I deliberately avoided discussing the earlier stages for in some respects the cytology is more difficult to interpret and the problem of the sensitivity of the technique becomes more prominent. In the trunks of 2 day chick embryos there are no elongate cells that can be identified as myoblasts and there are no cells in the presumptive myotome or else-where in the trunk that bind the antimyosin. Neither in the earlier nor later stages is there evidence for the binding of the antibody by the nucleus.

The earliest indications of antibody deposition is found in cells which are already somewhat oval in shape. In these early stages the antibody combines with a non-striated filament that is closely associated with the sarcolemma; but again, there is no fluorescence in the sarcoplasm or nucleus. As I have attempted to indicate in Fig. 6.4 in the early myoblast, even when it has a myofibril with clearly distinguishable A bands, the tip of the myofibril which extends out into the pseudopodinal ends of the myoblast is not resolvable into distinct segments. This suggests that perhaps two mechanisms are involved in the synthesis and organisation of these proteins, and we don't really know where to separate them. To begin with, we believe that the first sarcomeres are laid down in a meristematic manner from the growth tips at the ends of the cell. The growth in number of the sarcomeres could be attributed to this type of activity. The growth laterally we attribute to the kind of appositional protein synthesis I've described before. I think it is also worth mentioning that the amount of protein synthesised even in a 7 day muscle fibre is but an exceedingly small fraction of the amount of protein that will be present in the adult fibre. Though the synthesis of these muscle proteins commences during the 3rd day, it continues for months.

This problem of whether or not there is a brief stage when the myofibril is not cross-striated is a puzzling one, and one difficult to approach experimentally. For example, cross-striations cannot be observed in living myoblasts until they are 96 hr old, though a non-striated myofibril can be observed in living material from about the 72nd hour onwards. With some of the trichome stains non-striated filaments can be observed from about the 96th hour onwards, but cross-striations are not observed until maybe the 5th day. With a good iron hematoxylin preparation sectioned at one micron cross-striations can be observed by the 70th hour, whereas similarly prepared material reveals a non-striated stage beginning around the 60th hour. Cross-striations are found with the fluorescent antibody at about the 52nd hour, but there is a brief preceding stage of maybe 6–8 hr when the fibril appears non-striated. This simply demonstrates that the problem of resolution comes in here, and that by using different techniques you get different answers.

BRACHET: But, when you have apparently continuous fibres under the best stains will they react with the antibody?

HOLTZER: Yes, for no conventional stain can reveal a myofibril, cross-striated or not, as early as it can be revealed by the antibody procedure.

CALLAN: Am I right in thinking that if you look at the cell at that stage with a polarising microscope you would get the same sort of picture as you do with the fluorescent antibodies?

HOLTZER: We haven't used a polarising microscope, but Baud [22] has on developing cardiac muscle. Extrapolating from his data we can say that the skeletal antimyosin stain reveals non-striated and striated fibrils earlier than the polarising microscope [21].

WEISS: Did not Ebert get earlier reactions with an antimyosin antibody? Is there something wrong with his technique or what?

HOLTZER: I can't speak for Ebert's work other than to say it was his findings that encouraged us to undertake this investigation in the first place.

WEISS: Well, he did report, didn't he, that positive reactions occur at an earlier stage?

HOLTZER: Yes, but he was working with a different system. He was analysing for myosin and actin in the developing heart. For a variety of reasons (e.g. the heart starts beating around the 36th hour) we know that the cardiac musculature develops earlier than the trunk musculature (see also [21, 27]) so the fact that Ebert [23] reports cardiac myosin as present earlier than when we find skeletal myosin is to be expected. The major issue is not *when* Ebert obtained a positive test for myosin, but *where* and *in what kind of cells*. For example, I referred to the fact that our skeletal antimyosin reacts with 36 hr heart muscle in the same way it reacts with 72 hr trunk skeletal muscle—the A bands are stained, but not the nuclei nor the sarcoplasm. I think the major difference between Ebert's work and ours is that Ebert's suggests or at least lends itself to the suggestion, that cells not destined to form muscle cells are synthesising myosin, whereas we find evidence for myosin only in cells actively engaged in myogenesis. This of course is a very fundamental point—are embryonic cells, not destined to form muscle, actively synthesising such specialised proteins as myosin, actin, etc.? This being, at least to my mind, one of the major problems in cell differentiation it requires a great deal more experimentation before the matter is cleared up. However, pertinent to this point is the recent work of DeHann [24] on the appearance of myosin in regenerating salamander limbs. Using methods similar to Ebert's he was not able to detect myosin in blastema cells until the time when he could observe non-striated myofibrils with conventionally stained material. In short, in DeHann's work, as well as our own, the presence of myosin is to be correlated with, so to speak, the cell's commitment to go on and form a muscle cell. Until blastema or embryonic cells are committed to myogenesis, they are not synthesising myosin; so-called undifferentiated cells do not synthesise muscle proteins.

WEISS: Is it possible, in the light of what you said before, that in the case of Ebert, who used of course the whole tissue in bulk and did not make a cytological examination, the things simply didn't go into the cell?

HOLTZER: Again, I can't comment on Ebert's procedures, although as I recall he both homogenised and extracted his material. As far as our own work is concerned in addition to glycerol extracted material we have used freeze-dried sectioned material stained on the slide and formalin fixed sectioned material stained on the slide. With all three techniques the reaction to the antibody is the same.

WEISS: No, but he hadn't done this. I mean that in his case there might have been a barrier against the penetration of antibody.

WADDINGTON: Yes, but he got the antibody–antigen reaction earlier than Holtzer did. If he had a barrier there you'd expect him to get it later.

WEISS: No, if you use the whole tissue the thing may be between the cells, so to speak. There might first be a surface reaction of a different nature, and later on a specific reaction inside the cell. I am just trying to reconcile two sets of facts.

BRENNER: In one of your pictures of a single fibre there was a cloud of fluorescent material which appeared to be in the cytoplasm near the fibre. Was this in the myoblast stage before the appearance of the fibril?

HOLTZER: No, there was a well formed cross-striated fibril in that myoblast. The cloud in that slide was probably due to incomplete washing or from reflected light. Recall that was a teased, single, whole myoblast, maybe 20 μ in width and over 200 μ in length. In sectioned material such clouds are not observed.

ZWILLING: Is it possible that this absence is due to too complete washing?

HOLTZER: No, I don't think so. If in our washing procedures we were dislodging either the antigen or the antigen–antibody complex, we should expect a good deal of "false" localisation particularly around surfaces, such as the nucleus and the sarcolemma. Indeed we can produce just such staining artifacts—fluorescent nuclei, cell membranes and staining in the connective tissues—by washing the nuclei in salt solutions of high ionic strength. You will recall strong salt solutions solubilise myosin and so permit it to diffuse throughout the tissue.

ZWILLING: But are you getting rid of actual cytoplasmic particles which in fact bind your antibody, but nor being parts of the fibre are not fixed?

HOLTZER: This is, I guess, possible but unlikely. Remember in the case of the formalin fixed material, the cell is fixed before we actually wash.

ZWILLING: But this is very critical in regard to whether or not you have the appearance of any myosin or myosin-like material in a myoblast.

HOLTZER: What you say is very true. However, we can detect what might be called a more "soluble" myosin in the sarcoplasm, by simply injuring a muscle cell. When either a mature or embryonic muscle fibre is injured, the myofibrils are rapidly broken down and when conventional stains are used the muscle appears as a tube of eosinophilic cytoplasm [32]. If such a fibre is treated with the antimyosin there is a general diffuse fluorescent throughout the area in which the myofibrils underwent dissolution. In the preparative steps you do not wash out such dispersed myosin.

WADDINGTON: Is it possible that your antibody is specific for the myosin only when it is arranged in its final organisation in the myofibril, and that the early embryonic cells may have their cytoplasm full of pre-myosin, very like the final myosin but different in some final detail of arrangement which in fact carries the antigenic specificity? Have you ever made antibodies against embryonic somite material, say, to see if you can find evidence of myosin precursors in the cytoplasm?

HOLTZER: Yes, that is quite possible. In so far as nothing is known about the synthesis of myosin there is no reason to suspect that there is or is not a pre-myosin molecule. A little more promising, according to the work of Szent–Gyorgyi [25] and Velick [26], is the notion that the meromyosins are synthesised separately and that they are the precursors of myosin. This notion was tested by using labelled anti-H and anti-L meromyosin antibodies on our embryonic material. The results were precisely what we found for the antimyosin. The antimeromyosin antibodies were bound to their appropriate regions along the myofibril, but there was no staining of the sarcoplasm or nucleus. The meromyosins could not be detected at stages earlier than we could detect the whole myosin molecule. From this we are inclined to doubt that the meromyosins are precursors, at least in any simple sense, to the myosin molecule. Right now, we are impressed with the evidence that proteins are built directly from amino acids, and we tend to feel that is what is happening here.

As for making antibodies against somite material, I'm not sure that would help in tracing hypothetical myosin precursors. Matters are complicated enough when one starts with an antibody against a so-called pure antigen, like myosin or actin. I suspect antibodies prepared against such a complex of antigens as would be present in the somites would yield data that just couldn't be interpreted.

PLAUT: Could you attempt to prepare an antigen, and therefore an antibody, against a postulated precursor by taking myosin from the earliest possible stage as your initial source, and making antibodies against it?

HOLTZER: If embryologists want to take advantage of the specificity and sensitivity of immunological procedures, then they must be very concerned about the purity of the initial antigen and the homogeneity of the resulting antibody. If you prepare your antibodies against a complex mixture of antigens your antisera will react with a variety of antigens and the specificity of the immune reaction is lost. The problem of what myosin is in mature muscle and how pure the myosin is when using well established procedures for its isolation is still far from settled. What kind of product you would get starting from embryonic material would be a major problem in itself. Off hand I suspect you would get a good deal of nucleoprotein contamination that would foul up your results.

WADDINGTON: You can't do anything about degenerating your myosin? Take adult myosin, and break it up slightly before making the antibody?

HOLTZER: This we must have done unintentionally. Myosin is not a particularly stable protein and it is quite likely that by the time it acted on the antibody-producing system of the rabbits it has undergone some degree of denaturation.

POLLOCK: Can you titrate your antibody?

HOLTZER: Yes.

POLLOCK: Well, couldn't you get at the possibility of precursors by absorbing the antibody with preparations of cells in various early stages and titrate them to see if they contain things like myosin which combine with the antibody?

HOLTZER: Yes, I daresay that could be done. However, to the extent that the amount of myosin per mass of protein or nucleic acid in embryonic cells is quite different from the ratios found in mature muscle, this might get a bit tricky. All we can say so far is that we have found no definite difference in the myosin of embryonic myoblasts and the myosin of mature muscle, nor have we found a difference between the myosin of skeletal muscle and that found in cardiac muscle. For example, when skeletal antimyosin is absorbed against cardiac myosin, it no longer "stains" skeletal myofibrils—presumably the cardiac myosin has removed all the skeletal antimyosin molecules. Now coming back to Ebert's work, he absorbed his cardiac antimyosin against skeletal muscle before analysing his embryos. It is possible, judging from our results, that by this step he actually removed all antimyosin antibodies and so was not assaying for myosin at all.

WEISS: To my way of thinking you are touching a very fundamental issue here. In the light of what I have said about collagen, this seems quite a different story. There with collagen the production site is diffuse, and then you get the thing condensed to certain patterns. I am perfectly willing to accept either solution, because we know so little about it, but we ought to realise that we face that problem. Please let me ask you again: Would it be possible to detect by fluorescent microscopy a molecular dispersion of myosin in the cytoplasm, or can you only detect it if it has become condensed in such high concentrations locally that they appear by this particular technique? Because after all, in the whole cell body one could calculate—perhaps one should calculate—how many molecules you have in the A bands and see what would happen if they were dispersed in the much larger volume: Would they be detectable?

HOLTZER: All I can say to that is, "Amen". We have tried to point out before that we have no idea what the sensitivity of this technique is (see pp. 716–718 in [21]). I can quote some theoretical considerations which suggest that this is a mighty sensitive technique, but that would be but a paper exercise. Until experiments are performed directed to this question we just can't discuss it, and at the same time we can't talk of things we cannot see.

WEISS: Now, wait a minute. You said that you could pick up these segments in regenerating muscle. Do you find then that the cytoplasm lights up a little diffusely?

HOLTZER: In early stages of muscle regeneration—two to four days after a mouse muscle is injured, and while the injured myofibrils are *degenerating* and before new myofibrils appear— myosin exists in a dispersed form in the sarcoplasm. The sarcoplasm "lights up" when treated with the antibody. We believe that this dispersed myosin is due to the break up of the myofibrils incident to the injury. We have no idea of what happens to this dispersed myosin. Beginning around the 5th day the *regenerating* myofibrils appear. From this, all we conclude is that myosin molecules not packed into an A band, but distributed throughout the cytoplasm, can be detected with our technique. This however is all indirect and I certainly agree that we will have to do quantitative work on the problem of whether small numbers or dispersed molecules can be detected.

WADDINGTON: You never centrifuged the cells to see if you can drive down any particles, and get them concentrated enough to show up?

HOLTZER: No, this is one of the things we are planning to do.

CALLAN: What about the distribution of some of the other components in the embryonic cells?

HOLTZER: What components other than the structural proteins?

CALLAN: Actin, for example.

HOLTZER: It's precisely the same. A diagram of myogenesis based on anti-actin "staining" would follow that shown in Fig. 6.4, with the difference being that instead of broad A bands being fluorescent, the I and M bands would fluoresce. Neither the nucleus nor the sarcoplasm would bind the antibody, nor would there be a period when the myosin was present, but not the actin. It is, I think, of some interest that both appear at the same time. Furthermore, even by the 3rd day, the myoblasts respond to ATP by contracting just as mature fibres contract [21, 27]. In addition, when stained with antibody, these myoblasts are as reactive to ATP as are mature fibres. So that from a physiological, morphological and serological point of view these very early myoblasts have some of the properties associated with the mature myofibril.

WEISS: Another interesting point is that it always starts from one single centre of aggregation. You never find two such centres in one cell?

HOLTZER: If I understand Dr. Weiss rightly, he is referring to the problem of how from one myofibril we get to several. This is currently being studied, our technique so far is a cytological one, and hence provides a final, static picture of events. What is needed is to adapt it to actually following the event. For what it is worth, and more for its aesthetic appeal than anything else, we like to think of new myofibrils as arising from the splitting of pre-existing ones and that maybe it is not too dissimilar from chromosome duplication.

WADDINGTON: Well, I don't know if anyone would like to call that myofibril a plasmagene or not?

HOLTZER: I am rather surprised Dr. Weiss didn't mention some observations he made some time ago [28]. This was the case when in certain experimental animals he observed a second myofibrillar sheet running at right angles to the main ones. If we could dislodge, say, a twenty sarcomere length of myofibril, so that it came to lie at an angle to the longitudinal axis of the cell, would that fragment expand laterally? In short, would it act as a surface for the further growth of the sarcomeres?

WADDINGTON: Well, if no one wants to answer that, perhaps Gustafson would now tell us about his work on cytoplasmic particles.

GUSTAFSON: I will try to give you a review of the work we have done on the mitochondria in the developing sea-urchin egg. During our studies on enzyme formation in the sea-urchin egg we found that a long series of enzymes had a rather constant activity during the cleavage stages; then there was a sharp increase in activity starting at the onset of gastrulation.

Some of these enzymes were mitochondrial enzymes, and this suggested that there is a strong multiplication in the number of mitochondria when the primary mesenchyme cells are formed and the invagination starts. This hypothesis is in agreement with the observation of Hultin [33] that the acetate metabolism is greatly intensified at that time. In order to test our hypotheses, we tried to count the mitochondria. We were able to do so by the aid of phase contrast microscopy and vital stains, and we obtained the same type of curves from our mitochondrial counts as for the mitochondrial enzymes. These results have later been confirmed in our laboratory, and similar results have also been obtained by counts on homogenised material by Shaver [34]. So I think that the rise in mitochondrial number is fairly well established.

During the embryonic development, the distribution of the mitochondria in the larva is not uniform. We found that the mitochondrial concentration is highest in the animal region, lowest at the vegetative pole at the time of onset of gastrulation. This means that there is a gradient in mitochondrial formation along the animal-vegetal axis. After the implantation of micromeres into an animal half in early cleavage stages, the animal half develops a gradient which is similar to that in the intact larva. The conclusion can be drawn that the micromeres act as a kind of inhibitor against formation of mitochondria.

The distribution of the first population of mitochondria is not stable. After about 2 hr there is a slow decrease in the number of mitochondria, but when it decreases it is succeeded by new populations which develop in various parts of the ectoderm, in the area which we call the oral field, in the arms, and so on. Summarising, the mitochondrial populations appear and disappear, and are followed by new transitory populations in other parts of the larva. Each area of the larva has a mitochondrial maximum at a characteristic time.

Studies on coenzyme A (CoA), which is generally supposed to be confined to the mitochondria, are in agreement with these observations. After some peculiar cycles during the cleavage stages which may correspond to the mitotic cycles described by Agrell [43], there is one important peak in CoA content, which closely corresponds to the first mitochondrial peak, then we have a second peak and peaks of higher order.

It is not my intention to try to explain the whole of development from a "mitochondrial angle". I think, however, that the development of the mitochondrial populations may play a rather essential role in the differentiation of the sea-urchin egg. One reason for this is, of course, that the mitochondria are seats of the production of energy. One can suggest that when and where the mitochondrial populations are dense, much energy is produced and transferred to the "microsomal" elements, which to a large extent carry out protein synthesis. Another reason why I feel attracted to the idea that mitochondria play an important role is that the peaks of the mitochondria can be correlated in time with visible processes of differentiations of the cells in various areas. The peaks thus correspond to the disappearance of yolk and to the time of the transformation of the more of less cylindrical embryonic cells into cells characteristic for more advanced larval stages.

We may ask which are the factors which regulate the formation and disappearance of mitochondria. If we treat the eggs during early cleavage stages with lithium, the first major peak in mitochondrial number is very much diminished. This may indicate that lithium inhibits the formation of mitochondrial precursors in the cleavage stages, but this reduction in the mitochondrial number might also be explained in other terms. The peaks in mitochondria and in co-enzyme A seem to occur during periods when we have a large number of interphase nuclei. Perhaps we can look upon these peaks as the result of a nuclear production of co-enzymes, e.g. co-enzyme A during the interphases. Nuclei are evidently not necessary for the enzymatic activity of mitochondria in the ameoba, as shown by the enucleation experiments of Brachet, but maybe nuclei are necessary, e.g. as producers of co-enzymes, for the formation of new mitochondrial populations. The pattern of mitochondrial formation may thus reflect the pattern of mitotic activity in the larva. We can also discuss the formation and disappearances of mitochondria in terms of yolk utilisation. It is to be noticed that the yolk breakdown goes on at the same time as more mito-chondria appear, and by the time they disappear the yolk is more or less consumed. We could therefore consider the mitochondrial formation as an expression of enzyme adaptation, a response to the mobilisation of the yolk reserve. Analogously, the reduction in mitochondria could be looked on as an example of enzyme de-adaptation, a consequence of the exhaustion in yolk.

LEHMANN: I should like to ask Dr. Gustafson two questions. The first one is this. I am still quite uncertain whether the mitochondria are formed *de novo*, or whether they are in some way self reproducing units. Because apparently mitochondria are always present in eggs, as we know from sections. And the other point is that the mitochondria may some-times break up, giving smaller units during mitosis, and then fuse together again after mitosis (Frédericq [36]). So it seems a quite open question whether the mitochondria are formed as new units—I think I got that impression from your work—or whether they are growing in numbers by division. I should like to know what Dr. Gustafson thinks about that.

GUSTAFSON: We have studied the behaviour of mitochondria during these changes and we have found that the mitochondria do divide; and we have also found pieces fusing together, perhaps with other mitochondrial halves. But we do not yet know whether the mitochondrial pieces can grow into complete mitochondria. It is, however, not essential for my interpretation of our results whether the mitochondria are formed in this or that way. The essential thing is that differentiation can be correlated with a changing mitochondrial pattern, and that agents inducing changes in that pattern also change the morphological differentiation so that it is reasonable to guess that differentiation is dependent upon the mitochondrial distribution.

WEISS: It seems to me that there is a crucial experiment in the literature to answer that question; and that is Mrs. Harvey's centrifuged eggs [37]. She found that the half that is free from mitochondria—or is supposed to be . . .

LEHMANN: That is not critical; I think we can be sure of that. Nobody ever followed that experiment with the electron microscope, and we know now that there are some mitochondria sticking so fast to the cortex that unless one controls that with the electron microscope one could never be sure that the half was free of them.

CALLAN: But the animal quarter of, I think it was, *Arbacia*, which according to Ethel Brown Harvey's description lacked mitochondria, is also incapable of division, and some very peculiar things happen to the nucleus in those animal quarters. The animal half-eggs still have mitochondria, but the animal quarters according to Ethel Brown Harvey, have none; and at the time they should start dividing in fact the nucleus blows up into a great sphere and that is as far as they get, and then they die.

WADDINGTON: Is there any evidence from the electron microscope of different internal structures in the mitochondria? If they are being formed *de novo*, one would expect to find different kinds of mitochondria corresponding to the stages of their formation.

GUSTAFSON: We do not know.

LEHMANN: There is such evidence in amphibia. Yamada [38] showed a few pictures in Cambridge, and Eakin [39] has now found more evidence that the mitochondria in the young gastrula look very different from those in the neurula, and these are again different from those in the tail-bud stage. This fits very well with observations of Boell and Weber [40] about the activation of cytochrome c oxidase; that is, the properties of mitochondria are different in the earlier stages from the ones in the later ones.

WADDINGTON: Yes, we have done a little work on EM studies of amphibia also. I think the crucial point is whether at any given stage the population is homogeneous or heterogeneous. If it is homogeneous at any given stage, but changes from stage to stage, then the change would simply be transformation of the original population of mitochondria, which might also be multiplying by division. If, as is my own impression, at any given stage you find three or four different types of mitochondria within a single cell then, it's more plausible to suggest that some of these may have arisen *de novo*, or from some non-mitochondrial structure.

LEHMANN: You might also be able to detect differences by differential centrifugation. But the question of qualitative differences of mitochondria is not yet decided.

CALLAN: What is very puzzling is to reconcile with all of this the fact that the *Arbacia* egg, strongly centrifuged and stratified, so that the mitochondria all form one layer and are then in effect rigidified in this position by fertilisation, can still develop normal larvae.

WADDINGTON: How long does it take them to re-assort?

CALLAN: Virtually they don't re-assort; or at least if the re-assortment takes place it is at some time after cleavage; but they cleave prior to re-assortment.

WEISS: How much mitochondrial material is brought in with the sperm?

WADDINGTON: I think Lehmann's point is more helpful, that there are mitochondria fixed on to the cortex.

WEISS: And also some in the sperm, though that is not normally considered very seriously.

CALLAN: But, I believe I am right in saying that they can also be parthenogenetically activated, and still develop normally.

WADDINGTON: Yes, I think you are.

WEISS: But not the quarters.

CALLAN: No, I'm talking about the entire egg, simply stratified and then either fertilised or parthenogenetically activated.

LEHMANN: But, of course, it has never been studied by the electron microscope.

BRACHET: I should like to know if Dr. Gustafson could satisfy me about the specificity of his staining technique; and I wonder if he would tell us something further about the behaviour of cytochrome oxidase—exactly what he found with that.

GUSTAFSON: For the determination of cytochrome oxidase activity we used a technique which was based on that of Smith and Stotz [41]. We found a peculiar decrease in cytochrome oxidase activity, similar to that which has been found in amphibian material by Spiegelman, instead of an increase (Deutsch and Gustafson [42]). I don't know how to explain that, but the method of homogenisation may be an important factor, as cytochrome oxidase is sensitive to structural derangements.

Then, about the stain specificity. When we looked for a suitable stain we first tried Janus green. This stained the mitochondria in the ciliated bands excellently, but it was difficult to use the stain in earlier stages of development especially as the stain bleached under the anaerobic conditions which developed beneath the cover slip during the counting. The unsuitability of Janus green has been confirmed by other authors with similar material. Thus we tried to find another stain which stained the mitochondria quite as well as Janus green does in the advanced stages. We found that Dahlia, which has earlier been used for mitochondria, stained the mitochondria, and so did Nile blue sulphate. We decided to use Nile blue sulphate after comparing our results with those obtained with phase microscopy. As a confirmation of the specificity in our counts, we are now using time-lapse cinematography. We can see the mitochondria very well in our films. It is quite clear that the dynamic behaviour of the stained bodies counted by us and that of the mitochondria on the films is the same. Finally, there is an agreement between the mitochondrical number and the co-enzyme A activity, which makes the specificity of our counts still more convincing.

BRACHET: You didn't have any difficulty with globules of the kind described by Shaver?

GUSTAFSON: We can recognise fat globules and follow how they accumulate during development.

BRACHET: And you can differentiate them from other granules?

GUSTAFSON: Yes, fat globules are quite transparent and do not accumulate stain to the same extent as the mitochondria do. The results of Shaver on the other hand may be explained by the kind of material he had chosen for his investigation. He used the highly pigmented *Strongylocentrotus*, and that material is not only pigmented but also opaque. I use a completely unpigmented and very transparent sea-urchin egg.

POLLOCK: I wasn't quite clear about the time relationship of your fluctuations of co-enzyme A and the mitochondria.

GUSTAFSON: Of course, these CoA estimations have not been made on the same material as the mitochondrial counts, so that we can only say that at a certain time there is a rise in the number of particles, and in other material, at a comparable stage, a similar rise in the co-enzyme A.

POLLOCK: Quite. But when you have the fluctuations, in either mitochondrial number or enzyme, what is the time scale in terms of cell generations, or hours?

GUSTAFSON: The first strong increase starts after about 9 hr. That is about the time the mesenchyme cells are formed. I can't say very much about the number of cell generations, because the rate of cleavage is variable, and has decreased quite considerably by that time, but, there are still quite a number of mitoses, especially in the vegetal region, according to Agrell [43].

POLLOCK: I'm only asking because you had suggested, as a possible explanation, an enzyme adaptation or "de-adaptation"; and, in microorganisms at least, adaptation or reversion—as "de-adaptation" is sometimes called—is usually a slow process. It isn't something that happens rapidly, and it may involve a lot of protein breakdown, or a high protein turn-over rate. Would you expect to lose previously induced enzymes quickly? That's what I was driving at.

GUSTAFSON: I don't think it's very easy to make clear comparisons between these observations on mitochondria and the situation in microorganisms. The essential question is probably not the number of cell divisions but the intensity of the protein synthesis. This process is not proportional to the mitotic rate, but is very intense, as indicated, for example, by the rapid disappearance of yolk granules, raw material for protein synthesis.

BRENNER: How about the fusion of mitochondria? How do you count them? Do you count them as individual particles?

GUSTAFSON: Yes.

BRENNER: Are they all of the same size?

GUSTAFSON: Well, not exactly, of course, there are rods, and some rather dumb-bell shaped.

BRENNER: When they are dumb-bells do you count them as one or as two?

GUSTAFSON: As one.

BRENNER: So if the population decreased by a half in numbers you could have the same mitochondrial mass but joined together in pairs.

GUSTAFSON: Well, yes.

WADDINGTON: But, presumably it would be fairly easy to see that, if at one time they were all rods and at the next time all dumb-bells. Surely you would be able to notice that?

BRENNER: Well, that's a simplification of the situation; there might be an asynchrony.

LEHMANN: But you could make a homogenate and take a sample of the mitochondria and count it.

BRENNER: Yes.

GUSTAFSON: Yes, that has been done by Shaver. In fact he confirmed the total fluctuations we had demonstrated by counting *in vivo* on vital stained material.

REFERENCES

1. BEALE, G. H. (1954) *The Genetics of Paramecium Aurelia*, Cambridge University Press.
2. BEALE, G. H. (1957) *Int. Rev. Cytol.* **6**, 1.
3. BEALE, G. H. and H. KACSER (1957) *J. Gen. Microbiol.* **17**, 68.
4. SONNEBORN, T. M. (1948) *Proc. Nat. Acad. Sci., Wash.* **34**, 413.
5. BEALE, G. H. (1952) *Genetics* **37**, 62.
6. BEALE, G. H. (1958) *Proc. Roy. Soc.* **B148**, 308.
7. DELBRÜCK, M. (1949) discussion to SONNEBORN and BEALE in *Unités biologiques douées de continuité génétique*, Paris.
8. SONNEBORN, T. M. (1938) *Science* **88**, 503.
9. BEALE, G. H. (1957) *Proc. Roy. Phys. Soc., Edinb.* **26**, 11.
10. SIEGEL, R. W. (1953) *Genetics* **38**, 550.
11. SONNEBORN, T. M. (1943) *Proc. Nat. Acad. Sci., Wash.* **29**, 329.
12. PREER, J. R., R. W. SIEGEL and P. S. STARK (1953) *Proc. Nat. Acad. Sci. Wash.* **39**, 1228.
13. PREER, J. R. (1950) *Genetics* **36**, 344.
14. DIPPELL, R. (1958) *J. Biophys. Biochem. Cytol.* **3**,
15. DANIELLI, J. F. (1955) *Exp. Cell Res.* Suppl. **3**, 98.
16. BRACHET, J. (1954) *Arch. Biol.* **65**, 1.
17. COONS, A. H. (1956) *Int. Rev. Cytol.* **5**, 1.
18. HOLTZER, H. and J. ABBOT. In press.
19. LASH, J., H. HOLTZER and H. SWIFT (1957) *Anat. Rec.* **128**, 679.
20. HANSON, J. and H. HUXLEY (1955) in *Symp. Soc. Exptl. Biol.* **IX**, Academic Press, New York.
21. HOLTZER, H., J. MARSHALL and H. FINCK (1957) *J. Biophys. Biochem. Cytol.* **3**, 705.
22. BAUD, C. A. (1955) in *Fine Structure of Cells*, Interscience Publishers, New York.
23. EBERT, J. D. (1954) in *Aspects of Synthesis and Order in Growth*, Princeton University Press.
24. DEHANN, R. L. (1956) *J. Exp. Zool.* **133**, 73.
25. SZENT-GYORGYI, A. G. (1953) *Arch. Biochem. Biophys.* **42**, 305.
26. VELICK, S. F. (1956) *Biochem. Biophys. Acta* **20**, 228.
27. HOLTZER, H. and J. ABBOT (1958) *Anat. Rec.*
28. WEISS, P. and R. JAMES (1955) *J. Exp. Zool.* **129**, 607.
29. STONE, L. S. and H. STEINITZ (1953) *J. Exp. Zool.* **124**, 435.
30. FRITSCH, C. (1911) *Zool. Jb.* **30**, 377.

12

31. WEISS, P. (1925) *Arch. f. Ent.-Mech.* **104**, 359.
32. HOLTZER, S. (1956) *J. Morphol.* **99**, 1.
33. HULTIN, T. (1954) *Ark. Kemi.* **6**, 195.
34. SHAVER, J. R. (1956) *Exp. Cell Res.* **11**, 548.
35. SMITH, F. G. and E. STOTZ (1949) *J. Biol. Chem.* **179**, 881.
36. FREDERICQ, J. (1958) *Arch. Biol. (Liége)* **69**, 167.
37. HARVEY, E. B. (1940) *Biol. Bull.* **79**, 166; (1946) *J. Exp. Zool.* **102**, 253.
38. YAMADA, T. Unpublished.
39. EAKIN, R. M. and F. E. LEHMANN (1957) *Roux Arch.* **150**, 177.
40. BOELL, E. J. and R. WEBER (1955) *Exp. Cell Res.* **9**, 559.
41. SMITH, F. G. and E. STOTZ (1949) *J. Biol. Chem.* **179**, 881.
42. DEUTSCH, H. F. and T. GUSTAFSON (1952) *Ark. Kemi* **4**, 221.
43. AGRELL, I. (1957) *Ark. Zool.* **6**, 213.

CHAPTER VII

The Chemical Organisation
of the Cell

WADDINGTON: In this session we are going to discuss the organisation of the cell as a chemical kinetic system. For the time being we shall be leaving rather on one side the structural considerations which we were dealing with earlier this morning, but we shall be tackling the same fundamental problems from a rather more theoretical point of view. It will be interesting to see how far we can go in getting a general understanding of them from this more general method of approach. I should like to start the session by giving you some ideas of my own on the subject.

Suppose that we have a cell; and let us consider it from the point of view of differentiation and the formation of certain specific substances. We shall have, of course, materials of various kinds coming into it, and others possibly going out of it, and we shall have various products being formed within the cell. It is clear that the equations expressing the rate of formation of any given product will involve functions of the quantities of raw materials which are available. Many of the substances formed in the cell will certainly be enzymatically active, and will therefore influence the rates of the various reactions, so that the equation will involve their concentrations also. The whole synthetic metabolism of the cell will therefore involve a more or less complicated series of simultaneous differential equations.

In considering development we are interested in the changing composition of the cell with respect to a number of different substances and there will be an equivalent number of equations. The equation which gives the rate of formation of substance a may involve the quantity of various of the other substances b, c, d, etc. Now, such a set of mutual interdependent equations will lead towards an end steady-state at which the rate of change of the variables disappears. There will in fact be a series of such steady-states, which can be found by equating the rates of change to zero. This will give a set of ordinary simultaneous equations, and any such set determines a number of alternative solutions, that is, alternative steady-states. The number of these alternative solutions depends on the number of variables, and their powers. Some of the solutions will be of no biological interest because they may involve negative or imaginary values of particular variables, but some of the alternative solutions will involve only real and positive values of the constituents, and will represent states which could actually occur. Which out of these alternatives the system will actually choose may depend on the initial conditions or on the amounts of the various raw materials which are coming into the cells. However, the solutions of such a set of equations are not always very sensitive to the initial conditions or to the amounts of material coming in. In some systems of equations each end-state is arrived at from quite a large variety of initial conditions or rates of entry, but if the initial conditions are made still more different the system may click over into one of the other alternative end-states. Now, that sort of system provides us with a close analogy of differentiation, where we find that a number of alternative types of adult differentiated tissue are produced.

The general theory of such systems has been very little investigated, and is very difficult to study explicity in mathematical terms. We are hoping here to rig up an analogue computer into which we can feed different electrical charges representing different rates of inflow of material, and with this we shall try to investigate what types of equations do lead to real alternative steady-states, and how resistant these end-states are to changes in the supply of raw materials, and other similar problems. Unfortunately it has taken longer to get this analogue computer working than we hoped, and we are therefore not yet able to discuss these systems any further than one can do by common sense. By common sense I think one could guess that the degree to which an end-state is independent of initial conditions, and is resistant to changes in the inflow of material during the course of development, would probably depend, firstly, on the complexity of the situation, that is, on the number of variables and rate constants. The more complex the system, the more resistant any given end-state is likely to be. Secondly, an important factor would be the degree to which the different equations interlock. The more often the concentration of one substance, say X, occurs in the equations for the formation of other substances, Y, Z, etc., the more one would expect the end-states to be relatively invariant.

I have recently been discussing these subjects in a book called the *Strategy of the Genes* which I have been writing, and I have discovered to my surprise that there seems to be no word to mean the course of change of a polyphasic system. If you take a system whose behaviour is defined by such a set of simultaneous differential equations, the whole system will change along some definite course in time, towards one or other of its alternative end-states. The course could be plotted as a line in a multi-dimensional space, if one wanted to. There seems to be no word for such a course of a change. As I have not been able to discover a word which is used for such a course, I have invented one, which I will put before you. I have called it a "creode". This is derived from the Greek words χρη, meaning fate or necessity, and ὁδος meaning a path. It is supposed to indicate the necessary pathway of change which the system has built into it.

It is difficult enough to investigate in what way different systems of equations behave in relation to their final steady-states. It's still more difficult to investigate how they behave on the way to an end-state and therefore what the nature of the creode is. However, it is frequently the case, in such systems of equations, that the solutions are periodic in time, so that the system goes through periodic fluctuations on its way to the final state. I am mentioning this because of its possible relevance to the rather remarkable periodic fluctuations which the echinoderm workers have found both in free amino acids, and, as Gustafson was telling us this morning, in mitochondria. At first I thought it was most improbable that any developmental system would be found to follow a creode that was periodic. One would expect it to be monotonic, so that the concentration of any substance either went steadily down or steadily up. But, in fact, systems of equations of this kind can very easily generate periodic phenomena, and we do seem to find some in the biological world.

Now, just interpolating for a minute, I have said that it sounds very likely that firmly defined end-states involve very many interacting components in the system, with a lot of cross-reacting or interlocking. Well, we have a lot of evidence that that sort of system occurs in biological organisms which have been subjected to natural selection for a long time. If you take an organism which develops in a certain way to a definite end-state, and if you try to push it away from its normal end-state by altering the environmental conditions—which in general terms amounts to altering the rates at which substances come into the system—you usually find that you can push it away from its end-state if you push hard enough. You can then select for the capacity to be moved away from the end-state, and you will find that there is a genetic variability in the resistance to the system to change. This genetic variability usually involves a very large number of genes. This is shown by the fact that the response to selection is relatively slow, and goes on for many generations. This shows that you are in fact dealing with a system which involves very many variables, since each gene must correspond to one variable.

That opens up a subject which is not really appropriate at this meeting, since it concerns organisation not on a cellular and sub-cellular level, but on what I should call a supra-organismal level; that is, organisation in relation to evolution. We are here discussing questions of gene action which have somewhat the position of nuclear physics, say. Evolutionary theory has a place in biology which in physics is held by cosmological theory or the theory of general relativity. Gene theory and evolutionary theory are both aspects of theoretical biology, but from rather opposite ends of the spectrum. The kind of approach I have been talking about is relevant to organisation on the supra-organismal level because one has to conclude that natural selection is working on the genetic variability which affects the stability of the systems against environmental variations. A genotype formed under natural selection would be selected for its ability to resist influences from the environment which tend to make the organism less fit, and to respond easily in an appropriate manner to other environmental stresses which elicit a response which makes the animal more fit. There will be built into the genetic system, which fixes the rate constants in the set of equations, certain tendencies to be resistant and certain tendencies to be labile in a manner appropriate to the environmental stresses which the animal tends to meet. So the developmental system will be tuned in to respond to the environment in a suitable manner. That, of course, has a bearing on one's general picture of evolution. For instance, new gene mutations will operate on this stage which has been set by natural selection. Their phenotypic effect will be dependent on the way the developmental system is stable or unstable. In this way you will reach, rather at second-hand, a relation between the organism and the environment which is rather more close than one has usually envisaged. We reach the view that the environmental stresses impinging on an organism do in fact have something to say about the nature of the phenotypic variation that will be submitted to natural selection, not at first hand but at second hand, by building-in these stabilities and instabilities of the developmental system, and in that way influencing the type of phenotypic effects which random changes in the nuclear proteins of the chromosomes may produce.

Returning to the cellular and sub-cellular level, I want to mention two of the main problems which arise from this very general theoretical type of approach. One is the problem of the dynamic mechanism of these creodes, or paths of development towards an end-state. They must be influenced by a great deal which is going on all through the cell, and by the whole complex set of interactions which underly a large series of equations. But, although all these things must be influencing the creode, is it the case that there are certain key substances in differentiation, around which all the rest can be regarded as secondary modifications? In the development of the myoblast into a muscle cell, for instance, is it the case that once the cell starts making myosin that as it were pulls all the rest of the metabolic system of the cell into a path organised around myosin formation, so that the myosin acts as one might call a "histogenetic key substance", really defining that path of development and dragging everything else along with it? That seems to me a possible way in which the cell system could be organised, and one could now perhaps begin to get at it experimentally.

The second problem I should like to mention is a very fundamental one from the developmental point of view. Does such a picture as this provide one with a stable enough type of cell organisation? It's an essential part of this picture that there are alternative end-states, and that the system can under some circumstances go to one or the other of these: but, is the system sufficiently irreversible? It is clearly going to be hard to reverse such a path of differentiation once you've got into it; it's going to be moderately irreversible, simply because of the complexity and number of the processes involved in it. But we have to account for the phenomena which are usually referred to as embryonic determination. Now, I don't want to commit myself to the view that there is an absolute distinction between the determination of the cell and modifications of its character which are more easily reversible. I don't think there is a sharp distinction between determination and what Weiss would call modulation, that is to say, a more or less reversible response of the cell to the environment. I think these two categories are matters of degree, but they lie at the opposite ends of a fairly longish spectrum. There are some characters of the cell which can be changed fairly easily, for instance, by changing the type of interface they're sitting on, or the type of medium they're growing in, and those are typical modulations. But, there are other characters which are pretty resistant to change, and in fact there are, of course, many which no one has yet succeeded in changing. The question is, does such a set of interlocking synthetic processes give one a system which is stable enough to account for the relatively firm determination of things like kidney cells, which may be grown in tissue culture for a long time during which they look nothing like kidney cells but when they again have a chance of tubule formation they completely reassume their kidney appearance again and start to secrete.

Now, we have been considering the systems of equations as applying to substances in solution, but there is no reason why in general terms it should not apply to more complicated systems. And, it is perfectly clear that in cells we are not dealing only with substances in solution. We are dealing with solid structures as well. As soon as you imagine the system as containing solid materials you can picture it as having much greater irreversibility. In the actual biological system we have genes, mitochondria, microsomal particles and so on, and one can therefore add to the picture the possibility that certain genes, for instance, may at some stage be totally destroyed or completely inactivated, or that some other things may be precipitated out of the system and effectively lost to it, and so on. I think one of the great problems in embryology at present is to decide how far structural alterations, in which I include the total loss of genes, have got to be invoked over and above the more elementary considerations that would apply to substances in solution. We know of course the recent beautiful experiments of Briggs and King [1], which is the main evidence one produces nowadays for the suggestion that certain nuclei have definitely lost certain properties. Personally I should like to see the evidence on a considerably wider basis than it is at present. The nuclei for which Briggs and King had the best evidence for this loss of capacity are nuclei from the endoderm, where we know that many of the cells are destined to die off in normal development; many of these cells will disappear during the normal differentiation of the gut. So the fact that certain of them have lost the capacity to support complete differentiation might perhaps be related simply to changes preparatory to this eventual disappearance, and it is not perfectly clear that one can generalise it to all other tissues. Again, even if one supposes that one is justifiable in generalising this loss of capacity to other types of tissue, the question still arises, what kind of loss is it? It is pretty clear that a salivary gland nucleus, if injected into the egg, would not be able to support complete development, for purely mechanical reasons. If a nucleus cannot support complete development, one explanation is that it has lost certain genes which are necessary, but other explanations might be possible; the loss of capacity might not be due to a direct loss of a gene or genes. So it is still an absolutely open question, to my mind, how far we have to suppose that changes in the content of genes in the cell have got to be added on to this picture of competing or interacting kinetic processes.

LEHMANN: May I say that I like very much what Waddington was stating because without being an expert mathematician, you can arrive at very similar conclusions just by analysing the variability of developing systems. There you find that, if you change one factor continuously the reactions of certain systems give you a continuous range of end results (especially in growing systems), but there are other systems with a differentiating pattern which produce a discontinuous series of realisation grades (Lehmann [2], Grüneberg [3]). Some are frequent and seem to be very likely whereas others are rare and seem to be rather unlikely. From these results also you reach the conclusion that the underlying system must have some dynamic states which are stable and other dynamic states which are quite unstable. Another point is this. If, for example, a regenerating system is treated with one metabolic antagonist, it is always surprising that you don't usually find a key substance which suppresses regeneration entirely (Lehmann [4]), but you find mostly a quantitatively reduced reaction of the whole system [5]. And I also should like to envisage at least for the higher organisms, pathways of developmental change of this kind which you call a creode which I think is a very useful term, at least to get further in the discussion.

WEISS: Some time during this discussion I think I should like to ask for the privilege of extending your mathematical formulation here, by a concrete mathematical treatment of a case which introduces in each one of your equations a feedback function. This actually is concerned with the pattern which the cells of a complex community assume, but resides within each cell. So again it refers to the build-up of organisation by individual cell activities so I think it may be pertinent here and if you want me I shall be glad later on to present some of the actual mathematics.

WADDINGTON: I think undoubtedly these systems involve feedback. The fact that the same variable occurs in different equations will already give you some degree of feedback. Particular types of feedback would take the form of the way they are involved. For instance, in Delbrück's type where Y acts as an inhibitor on the formation of X, you get functions involving XY.

WEISS: We have the actual solution for concrete cases.

WADDINGTON: It will be very interesting to hear that but I think we should leave it till a bit later. Probably now we should go on to some of the other general discussions and I think the next speaker should be Dean.

DEAN: First of all, I should like to compliment Professor Waddington on his attempt to apply chemical kinetic theory to these very complicated systems where of course the mathematics cannot be fully developed. In what I am going to say you will see what I think is a much simpler system.

As many of you know, Sir Cyril Hinshelwood's group in Oxford has been interested for the last 18 years or so in seeing how far the laws of chemical kinetics could be applied to some aspects of the behaviour of the bacterial cell, and it is on this topic that I went to make a few remarks this morning. There are many things in common between the chemical kinetics of non-living substances and some of the reactions carried out by the bacterial cell. For example, the bacterial cell can often synthesise all its complex proteins, nucleic acids, etc., from very simple substances such as glucose, ammonia and a few inorganic salts, and it follows that this synthesis of complex molecules must take place by a large number of stages each of a very simple nature—a situation which is quite common in the chemical kinetics of non-living material. Moreover, some of these reactions will be accompanied by a loss of entropy, and hence if increase in cell material is to take place at all, it follows that they must be linked to others in which there is an even greater increase in entropy, and in many cases the raw materials available to the cell will not be present in a very reactive state and hence the operation of catalytic cycles would appear to be necessary.

Let us consider now some of these kinetic aspects. First of all the bacterial cell in the logarithmic state of growth in a constant environment reproduces its parts in accordance with the autosynthetic law, $dx/dt = Kx$ or $x = x_0 e^{Kt}$. This increase in living matter results from the co-operation of the many enzyme systems in the cell and yet enzymes in isolation do not increase autocatalytically. However, one can show by mathematical methods using simple models that, in a system in which the constituents are formed in such a way that the increase of each depends on the catalytic action of the others, these constituents behave as if they were autocatalytic, and this applies no matter how many constituents are involved.

That is to say, although enzymes, proteins, nucleic acids, etc., are not autosynthetic in isolation, they do when part of a linked system, even when that system is complex and has branching sequences, increase with time in accordance with the autosynthetic law (once a steady-state has been reached) and thus we can formulate

$$\text{enzyme} + \text{metabolite (1)} \rightarrow \frac{\text{more}}{\text{enzyme}} + \text{metabolite (2)}$$

This has been called the first kinetic principle [6].

If cells in which the stable proportions of the various constituents have been established are introduced into a new medium such that the velocity constants are altered, it further follows that the proportions will also change. This is the second kinetic principle.

Cell division moreover takes place from time to time and the important point in the hypothesis is that it takes place when the amount of some cell component has reached a critical value. This is the third kinetic principle and we can write $y/n = \beta$ where n is the number of cells, y is the total amount of the key substance in all the cells, and β is a constant. Using this relationship cell number as well as ratios of components can be introduced into the equations.

From these three principles a fourth can be derived and it states that in systems such as have been described the proportions of constituents tend towards those which give a maximum rate of growth in the given environment. That is to say, under new conditions a new quantitative scheme of reactions will gradually replace other quantitative schemes with smaller resultant reaction rates. In this way adaptive changes in response to the environment are possible.

Since growth depends on a long series of linked reactions, time will be necessary before the steady-state is reached and the longer and more complex the reactions the longer the time required. This is the lag phase which bacterial cultures pass through before growth begins. In this non-steady-state theory predicts complex and erratic behaviour, which is found in practice.

It is often found that more than one route is possible to a given product.

The kinetic considerations mentioned earlier have been shown to apply to systems in which alternative routes exist. In general, the route chosen will be the one leading to the optimum rate of growth in the given environment although considerable time may elapse before this condition is fulfilled since the route leading to the best rate of growth may be inhibited by the operation of a less effective alternative route already in operation.

A kinetic scheme has been outlined whereby bacterial adaptations may take place as an automatic adjustment in response to the environment. Examples in which we think that this sort of mechanism explains the observed experimental results better than does a theory involving mutation and selection have been published by us from time to time and references are given in my earlier summary.

The question is often asked whether these adaptations represent stable heritable changes. It is our experience that in general the longer the training process has been continued the more stable does the adaptation become until eventually it appears to a cursory sort of test to be stable. But the stability is never absolute and so what we are dealing with are not stable heritable changes but sluggishly reversible adaptations. Kinetic theory in its simplest form predicts easy and complete reversibility on removal of the inducing agent but there are good physico-chemical reasons why reversibility may on occasion be slow. The more important of these are:

1. Enzymes may become saturated with their substrates and in this condition the rates of the reactions they cause are insensitive to the concentration changes which in other conditions would provoke reversion.

2. The establishment of a new and more efficient mechanism may be actively hindered if an established one consumes active intermediates which are needed by the new one.

3. The establishment of a more efficient mechanism may show a lag phase during which the operation of a less efficient one may continue.

That is a very simplified picture of the kinetic system of the bacterial cell as we see it. I have kept the application of the principles out of the discussion. I have a lot of the detailed equations here for anyone who would like to see them. The point I would like to stress is that one cannot generalise; even in the bacterial cell one has to examine each particular example on its own merits. Some adaptations may arise by the selection of mutations and others by kinetic adjustment and I certainly would not like to extend what I have been saying without question to cells of higher organisms. We do have quite a large number of examples which we think can be explained on this system more simply than by the hypothesis involving mutation followed by selection. I could give you details of these later on if required.

POLLOCK: I don't quite understand your hesitation about applying these principles to higher organisms.

DEAN: The only thing is that we haven't actually done it and from the experience we've had with a number of different bacterial systems, we feel that generalisation is dangerous until you have actually done the experiments. In any case, I imagine you would have to complicate the kinetic equations considerably.

WADDINGTON: Well, Weiss, won't you perhaps present your case in the higher organisms?

WEISS: Well, that might complicate the issue still more, because you might find that you might not be able to generalise from some of the things found in higher organisms to the cases of homogeneous populations of cells that you are dealing with.

I would like to show the way in which these things can be calculated to a higher degree of approximation than that attained heretofore. I have never been quite happy with the formulation, going back to Brailsford Robertson, of an autocatalytic growth curve. In studies with different cell clones in the organism we have had to recognise the great difference between the different types, which in your case would be called different species perhaps of bacteria. We have made a bold attempt in the last two years. I have been sitting down to this with my collaborator, Lee Kavanau. By combining our mathematical and biological information we came out with a rather remarkable result, which I want to present to you in a summary. We tackled the subject of growth with the sort of approach which Professor Waddington has suggested. The real situation turned out to be a rather complicated one as compared to the ordinary autocatalytic reaction.

Let the outer circle (Fig. 7.1.) be the outline of an organism or a culture

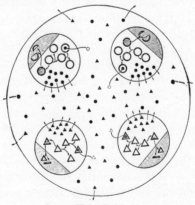

FIG. 7.1.

medium, or whatnot—a closed system. The inner circles represent the outline of cells, and I'm not going into the further subdivisions of the cell. The cells are inside an organism with a dilution space between them, the dilution space in an organism being the intercellular fluid and of course the other cells. You get the following situation: We have in each cell-type a system—I don't say a substance because it isn't a single substance, it's a system—which is symbolised here by double rings and double triangles; and this system we might consider as capable of reduplication, of producing more of the same. Let's say this is a kidney cell (rings), for instance, and this is another kidney cell (rings), and here is a liver cell (triangles) and here another liver cell. Whether we consider these as specific catalysts or as templates, is irrelevant in the present case. They are the generative systems of the cell. Just call them the generative substances. They are liver specific or kidney specific. As to how these differences come about, we shall hear more about that from other speakers, and I am not going into it here. Part of this reproductive system serves to produce the differentiated mass, which is indicated here by stippling, and this is different from the reproductive mass in that it is sterile. It is simply ballast from here on, which can no longer produce more of the same except through the mediation of the generative system. The rate of reproduction of the generative system is now diminished by the drainage of the reproductive mass into sterile differentiated mass, and I indicate this by the broken symbols. Now, while these macromolecular systems remain locked up within the cell, and the liver specific and kidney specific systems are not found outside the cell, there are complementary systems which are produced by each cell, and are indicated here by solid circles and solid triangles as symbols, which can diffuse out of the cell into the surrounding medium. These have the property when combining with the original cell-specific systems of sterilising them, so that they can no longer participate in their own reproduction. This is indicated here by some of these little symbols going in to some of the corresponding large ones by steric conformance, combining with them and thereby effectively eliminating them from further participation in reproduction. All of the little ones can go into the cells indiscriminately but only the conforming one has this blocking or eliminating action. However, as you noticed, they can go out of the cell of origin and can go into any other cell and any cell of the like character will be inhibited. Now, a scheme of this kind implies differential equations of the following sorts. First, there is the rate of reproductive activity of the generating mass. Second, the rate of drainage of this mass into differentiated mass. Third, the rate of production of the specific inhibitors. Fourth, the rate of diffusion out, of the specific inhibitors, due to their differential concentration in the cell space as compared to the pool. Fifth, the rate of catabolism of all these cellular systems, of the generative mass, the differentiated mass, and the inhibitors; this may be due to excretion or breakdown or in any other way. Now, the differential equations for these processes have been set up and solved [7]. Their main components are two feedback terms, the main one referring to the progressive sterilisation of their production source by the inhibitor molecules —if you want to regard them as molecules which they probably are—in proportion to their rate of reproduction and release. Now this looks very simple here, but it took two years of concentrated mathematical work to get these things down to a mathematical formulation. Of course, it involves a lot of simplification, but it is not as much simplification as the earlier simple autocatalytic formulae. In applying our formula to the growth curve of the chick plotted from data from Landauer and Schmalhausen, there resulted a very close fit between calculation and observation. A kink appeared at the time of hatching, and this is real, due to the change in volume of blood and so on at the time the yolk sac disappears. This is an ideal case, so far as we can see, and hasn't been dealt with by any other formulation. But this formulation can be used not only for description— you can of course fit a formula to the skyline of New York if you are free to use a sufficient number of parameters—but we could now work out with electronic computers what would happen if we remove part of the system; how will the rest of the system react? If you remove one kidney we know that the other kidney hypertrophies. If we remove one lobe of the liver, the other lobe starts to regenerate. All these spontaneous steady-state reactions leading back to the final equilibrium point are not merely part of the formulae as Dr. Waddington first put them out, but are the growth fomulae with the inclusion of the feed back circuits. I will show you that on two examples, so that you can see what one can do on paper and then experimentally test the results. The next slide shows you, for example, what happens when a mass of 100 is reduced to 50 or 25%. What will the rest of the system do? It will not know that you have reduced something of its mass, but the inhibitor concentration gradually goes down because their source has been diminished, and it is that change of inhibitor concentration in the medium which then becomes perceptible to the remaining tissue and automatically starts the compensatory growth reaction. The computer showed that after about 25 days the organ is back at about its normal volume but it doesn't stop there. The calculation tells us that it must overshoot, and comes back in an oscillatory, damped wave to its equilibrium value, as many feedback systems do. This oscillation has actually been observed if you look through the literature, but it has mostly been attributed to experimental error. What I mean to say is that by combining this technique of mathematical analysis with actual empirical tests of the material, we may find the answer instead of going to very generalised and over-simplified mathematical assumptions on the one hand, or being purely empirical and studying only how liver regenerates or a kidney hypertrophies. This calculation, then, presents us with a concrete problem involving at least 5 parameters—possibly more, but at least 5—which can be experimentally isolated, instead of working with one single generative system depleting itself. Now I suppose that tissue culture, the growth of populations of cells and bacteria, protozoa, and so on, would be amenable to similar treatment, showing an influence on the total mass by inhibition through homologous inhibitor systems. So, in summary, the point I want to make is that the organism reproduces, along with its reproductive apparatus, its own specific inhibitor systems, and

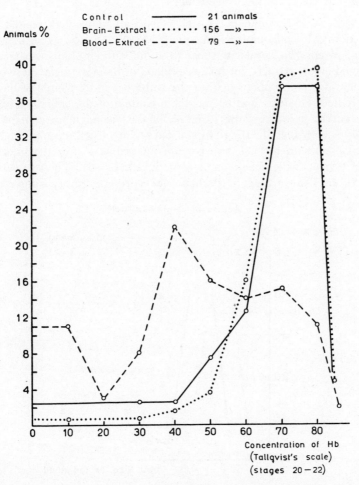

FIG. 7.2.

that this feedback system is the one which places a ceiling on the total mass of a cellular population which self-regulates in this way. I think that fits in with the story we have been hearing before.

CALLAN: This is right outside my field but at the Gatty Laboratory at St. Andrews, there has been some very amusing work done by Dodd with *Xenopus* recently which fits extremely well with your formulation. If you take out the thyroid gland in *Xenopus*, the larvae develop goitres. That sounds absurd, but what in fact happens is that after taking out the thyroid the feedback mechanism with TSH from the pituitary is affected, and a few isolated thyroid cells then become exceptionally stimulated with TSH. These start dividing like mad, and form a goitre, and at least one has got as far as the big over-swing.

GUSTAFSON: I should like to tell you about some work related to this question. My collaborator Lenicque [8] has made some experiments with the chick embryo, similar to those Rose did with amphibian material. He injected organ extracts, for instance, blood or brain extracts, close beneath the one-day embryonic shield of the embryos, and a couple of days later he studied the shape and haemoglobin content of the embryos (Fig. 7.2). The curves here show the variation in the haemoglobin content of the embryos with age. To the right you can see the distribution of the haemo-globin values in normal embryos and in embryos after the injection of brain extract (which contains no or very little blood). The two curves are identical. The third curve (dashed line) represents embryos injected with

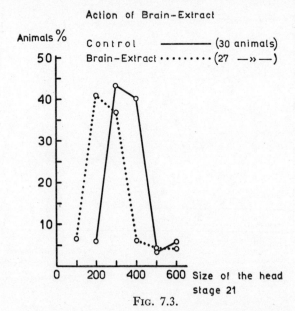

FIG. 7.3.

blood. You can see that the distribution curve in the third case is shifted to lower haemoglobin values. Lenicque has also made several experiments with brain extracts. This curve (Fig. 7.3) only represents some preliminary, small experiments. One curve represents the distribution of the brain size in the controls, the other curve the brain size after brain extract injection. The curve is shifted towards lower values in the brain extract series. Blood extracts have no action on the brain size. The results of the experiments support the hypothesis that the production of various tissue components in an embryo is controlled by a feed-back mechanism, each cell-type producing substances which inhibit the growth of corresponding cells.

WEISS: I should like to add a cautionary remark. Rose did similar experiments. I think the thing we ought to keep in mind is that we are dealing with two systems operating in opposite directions. The net effect may be either facilitation, or it may be inhibition, depending on the proportions of the two. In the ambient medium, you have only inhibitors. If you put crushed cells into it you release something which can combine with the inhibitors and inactivate them. Whether we have a surplus of inhibitors left depends entirely on the proportions of the two components. One can get positive or negative effects. The main thing is that a specificity has been demonstrated. The rest is still a matter for the future. Perhaps we can, from the superposition of a lot of those experiments, eventually decide how many inhibitors and how many original templates, if you want, are present.

LEHMANN: I should like to mention that Tardent [9] in *Tubularia* has been able to separate such inhibitory substances by chromatography. These substances are extracted from differentiated hydranths. In this case, there is a distinct inhibitor present which is clearly phase-specific in its action.

POLLOCK: I would like to put the biochemical point of view in relation to Gustafson's experiments. There seems to be a close analogy here with the phenomenon of specific enzyme inhibition. In studies on microorganisms there are quite a number of cases now where the product of a chain of reactions will inhibit the production of one or more of the enzymes concerned in the formation of this product [10]. That would, I think, be quite a fair analogy with your results on the effects of blood extracts or brain extracts on the formation of the organ from which the extract is obtained.

WADDINGTON: I think perhaps, Pollock, the time has come for you to give us a longer exposition about enzyme formation and its relation to general kinetics.

13

WEISS: Perhaps I might say that this mathematical treatment will appear next month in the *Journal of General Physiology* for those of you who might like to look it up.

POLLOCK: I should like to say something about the phenomenon of enzyme induction, which, as you know, has mostly been studied in lower organisms, although there are one or two cases in higher organisms also. I think today I should confine my remarks to the way in which a biochemical study of enzyme induction can possibly be applied to the problems we are faced with in embryonic differentiation of higher organisms. I will begin by reminding you of a few of the basic facts of enzyme induction. Figure 7.4 simply gives an example of enzyme induction in *B*.

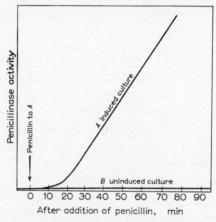

FIG. 7.4. Penicillinase induction in a logarithmically growing culture of *B. cereus*.

cereus: the formation of penicillinase [11]. There are one or two points I should like to draw your attention to, which are basically true for all cases of enzyme induction. The first point is that it is a very rapid process. In the space of a few minutes after addition of penicillin the cells have changed from a very low rate of penicillinase formation to a very high rate, which may involve an increase of up to a thousand fold. If it was *E. coli*—galactosidase [12]—I had been talking about, the lag phase before the switch-over takes place would be only a matter of a minute or two, or not even as long as that.

The second point is that the reaction is highly specific. It is only substances very closely related to the normal substrate of the enzyme which exert this inducing action. Thirdly, it is a transitory process, in the sense that when you remove the inducer the cells return fairly rapidly—I will discuss a little later how rapidly—to the original rate of forming the enzyme. Thus, it cannot be regarded as a strictly inherited form of change.

Another point I might refer to is that in most cases there is a small amount of the enzyme formed before the addition of the inducer. This so-called "basal enzyme" production seems to be a pretty general phenomenon. Where it is carefully looked for, there are traces of the enzyme—and I would emphasise that we know now pretty definitely that it is the same enzyme [13]—i.e. the same protein—as that produced after induction, always being formed at a very low rate. The enzyme induction, therefore, is only a quantitative increase in the rate of production of, so far as we know, a single enzymically-active protein. Finally, a point which is essential to some of the remarks which I shall make later. The concentration of the inducer, up to saturation point, will determine the new rate of formation of the enzyme. The more inducer you add, the faster will be the rate of formation of the enzyme, up to saturation level, beyond which no further increase occurs.

Now, the specificity to which I have referred is a very high one. The only point which I should like to stress in relation to that, at the moment, is that it isn't necessarily only the substrate of the enzyme which can evoke the formation of the enzyme. It must be some substance very closely related, but it need not necessarily be one which is acted on by the enzyme itself. I think it is important to bear that particular fact in mind in relation to what I'm going to say later.

Now, although the phenomenon has been studied in micro-organisms almost exclusively, I am going to extrapolate most of the considerations I shall be dealing with to higher organisms. These are what we are concerned with mainly in this meeting. The best-known instance of enzyme induction in higher organisms is, I think, that of tryptophane peroxidase in rat liver which has been studied by W. E. Knox and his colleagues [16]. The concentration of this enzyme increases about 10-fold during a period of 4–10 hr after the injection of l-tryptophane into rats. It is a slower process than in micro-organisms and the percentage increase much less. But it appears to be pretty specific, and I do not think there is much doubt that this is, in fact, a true switchover from a low rate of production of one particular enzyme to a relatively high rate.

Having very briefly presented the facts of enzyme induction, I want to talk particularly about the phenomenon which we now refer to as enzyme reversion. This is the question of how rapidly, when the inducer is removed, do the cells lose the enzyme which has been induced [17]. Now, on the whole, enzymes in micro-organisms are rather stable, though that is not always so. There are different grades of speed with which enzymes are lost after the inducer is removed. In some instances the enzyme is very unstable, and as soon as the substrate is removed the enzyme may be metabolised, or inactivated in some way, and the activity will be lost very quickly (Type 1). Usually, however, it is a fairly stable protein, and what often happens is that when you remove the inducer you switch off the induction mechanism and the cells revert to the original rate of forming the enzyme. The already formed enzyme then dilutes out as the cells grow (Type 2). The rate at which the cells lose their acquired character will simply be a function of the rate at which they grow. Finally —and this applies to the penicillinase induction case which I have been mainly studying—the reversion may be much slower. It would appear here (Type 3) that what is induced is not just the enzyme, but an apparatus for forming the enzyme. Then, assuming that the induced apparatus for forming the enzyme is stable (as indeed appears to be so), what happens is that when you remove the inducer, the enzyme goes on being formed at the same rate as when the inducer was removed; and the loss of the enzyme, as the cells grow, is very much slower.

I'll just refer to purely theoretical curves to begin with. Figure 7.5

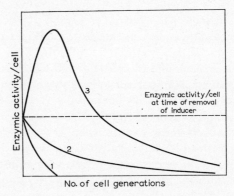

Fig. 7.5. Three types of enzymic reversion following withdrawal of the inducer in a logarithmically growing cell population.

shows the three types of enzyme reversion. The enzyme activity of an organism or population of cells, or, if you like, an individual cell is plotted against the number of generations which the cells have grown through in the absence of the inducer. Type 1 is where you get very rapid loss because the enzyme is intrinsically unstable. In Type 2, you get an exponential loss of the enzyme, because, although the enzyme itself is stable, as soon as you remove the inducer you switch off the apparatus which is producing it. In Type 3 when you remove the inducer you switch off the formation of the apparatus for producing the enzyme, and in this case it can be shown that you get an increase before you get a decrease in the enzyme activity per cell. Figure 7.6 shows that what we actually found in penicillinase is of this Type 3. If total penicillinase is plotted against time increase is linear. Growth, however, is exponential and if you plot the penicillinase per cell against time, or against cell generations, you first get

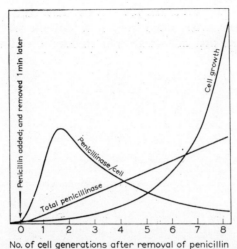

No. of cell generations after removal of penicillin

FIG. 7.6. Enzymic reversion in penicillinase synthesis by *B. cereus* following transient exposure of cells to the inducer (penicillin).

an increase and then a very slow dying away. The point is that even after eight cell generations of exponential growth in the absence of the inducer, you still have a very much higher enzyme content per cell than the basal amount you had before you actually induced the formation of the enzyme.

An interesting thing to me about enzyme induction is the reciprocal relation between the substrate or inducer and the enzyme which is formed. Normally, one thinks of an enzymically catalysed reaction as substrate I going to substrate II under the catalytic activity of the enzyme. Now, in enzyme induction you have the additional reaction that substrate I (i.e. the inducer) normally catalyses the formation of the enzyme. You have therefore a substance which is a catalyst itself, and is catalytically formed under the influence of the substance which is normally regarded as an ordinary substrate, but which in this case is functioning also as a catalyst. A particular case of this would be where a product itself, and not the substrate, acts as an inducer of the enzyme which forms it. This in fact does sometimes occur [15]. In such a case you have got an autocatalytic system, and will expect that under those conditions the enzyme will increase autocatalytically. So far it appears largely as a theoretical possibility, but I would like to emphasise that here is another possible way in which, after the removal of the original inducer or substrate, you may expect to get continuing enzyme induction and therefore a degree of stabilisation of the induced character.

Now, a final way in which you can get perpetuation of an acquired character like this, after the elimination of the original stimulus, is the phenomenon of sequential induction, which has been studied largely by

Stanier [18]. He has shown that you may get chain reactions as in Fig. 7.7, where the first substance added from outside in the medium will induce enzyme alpha, and that will act on A to produce B, and that in turn is an

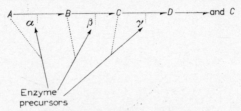

FIG. 7.7 Sequential induction.

inducer for a second enzyme beta, and so on. There are a number of cases where that has been shown to be true in micro-organisms, and even one or two possible cases in mammals. One of the best instances is that of the oxidation of mandelic acid to α-ketoglutaric acid by *Pseudomonas fluorescens* [18]. Each of the reactions involved—and altogether there are seven of them I think—are catalysed by inducible enzymes, induced by the previous substrate. In such a case therefore one might expect continuance of an effect for some time after the original inducing substance has been removed. How long depends on the rate of growth, how many substrates are intervening, and how fast they are destroyed by the enzymes they induce.

One can speculate further along these lines and postulate—the idea here is a purely theoretical one—a type of sequential induction (see Fig. 7.8)

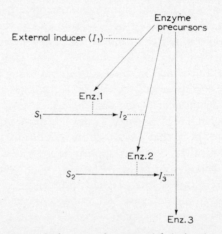

FIG. 7.8. A hypothetical case of sequential induction, with specific properties postulated in order to emphasise the possibility of evoking long-term effects following a single induction stimulus.

where you have an external inducer which controls the formation of enzyme I, and this acts not only on the inducer, but on a second endogenous internal substrate to form a second inducer, which I actually call I_2 here, and this induces a second enzyme which acts on another endogenous substrate to form I_3, the third inducer, and so on; and you get a series of enzymes formed like that. In this particular case, I have assumed that the inducers are not in fact destroyed by the enzymes they induce. This is simply in order to make the mathematics a bit simpler, for this particular hypothetical case of sequential induction. For such a hypothetical case you get the following equation for the amount of enzyme n, i.e. formed after n steps in a sequential induction chain: $y = kt^{2n-2}$. The concentration Y of an enzyme n in the series would be proportional to the nth power of the time, so you would get a piling up of the enzymes, the last one still being formed at a considerable rate after the removal of the original external inducer. You would get a very long continued effect, even of increasing magnitude, after you had removed the original stimulus.

One might go one step further in speculating on the effects of sequential induction. Figure 7.9 shows again a case which is completely hypothetical,

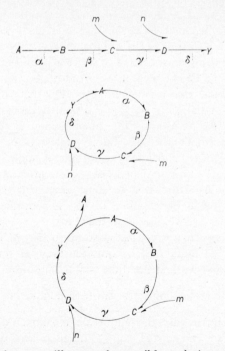

FIG. 7.9 ⎫ Schemes to illustrate the possible evolution of a "self repro-
FIG. 7.10 ⎬ ducing" biochemical cycle initiated by an external inducer
FIG. 7.11 ⎭ (A) functioning through a pathway of sequential inductions.

at least after the first stage. It is a sequential induction of a chain of enzymes, originally initiated by substance A (i.e. analogous to that shown in Fig. 7.7) going through B, C and D with additional components coming in from the cell to form Y. Now, let us suppose that in a special case Y turns into A again (Fig. 7.10). There is no reason why that should not occur if you were adding components from the rest of the cell, and in this way you can get a cycle which is obviously going to be much more stable than a chain with respect to independence from the supply of the original inducer. There are of course a number of instances of cycles known in intermediary metabolism [19], though it is not established that they are operated through inducible enzymes as we have postulated here. Now, going a little further still you could also postulate that under certain circumstances you may get more than one molecule of A formed for every turn of the cycle; in other words you would get two cycles formed where there was originally one (Fig. 7.11). You've then got an autocatalytic "self-reproducing cycle", which theoretically would go on for ever—at least as long as it is reproducing itself as rapidly as the cell.

However, I don't want to emphasise that too much, as there really isn't yet a case where this is known to occur. But looking at the picture as a whole we do see, I think, that there are quite a number of ways in which a particular cell can be canalised in one direction, and where this canalisation may persist for a time after the original stimulus has been withdrawn. This is the kind of thing one needs in order to explain such a phenomenon as differentiation on a biochemical basis. Waddington pointed out right at the beginning, I think, that it is essential to show that you get a relatively permanent canalisation when you have switched the cell into one of a number of alternative pathways. The phenomenon of enzyme induction is not normally permanently irreversible (unless some of these highly speculative arrangements do actually exist), but it might in fact appear so if the cells did not multiply to a great extent after application of the original stimulus. We know that in some cases cells can maintain the original character for 8 or possibly 12 cell generations, and there are probably some cases even longer than that [20].

I don't know how many cell generations occur in a mammal after zygote formation. It might not be quite so large as one would at first think. Somebody has worked that out, I have no doubt.

WADDINGTON: In tissue culture it can be indefinite.

POLLOCK: Well, in any case, the point really is that you don't immediately switch back to where you started from. The effect lasts quite a long time. It may depend on how fast the cells are growing.

DEAN: There is one point I would like to make. Dr. Pollock, I think, in his induced enzyme systems referred to one application of his inducing agent, and the persistence of the effect for eight to ten generations.

POLLOCK: Yes.

DEAN: In the drug adaptation experiments I was speaking about the drug has been applied for a long time and in these cases the rate of reversion can be very slow. The strains of bacteria were trained gradually to the given concentration and were given a large number of subcultures at this concentration. Each subculture is about ten generations. The strains were then subcultured in the absence of the drug and the number of subcultures before reversion began was noted. In the example where proflavine was the drug used the cells were gradually trained to a concentration of 200 mg/l. and were given 105 subcultures at this concentration. On subculture in the absence of drug about 600 generations elapsed before any reversion took place at all.

WADDINGTON: During the 600 generations it retained its full resistance?

DEAN: Yes. So if you keep on applying the inducing agent you get what seems by an ordinary test to be a fully stable resistance.

WADDINGTON: As I understand it, you imagine that during your training you change quite a lot of the bacterial metabolism, whereas Pollock has been speaking as though when he gives his bacteria an inducing substrate, he changes just one aspect of it.

POLLOCK: Well, one change seems to be the main thing. There may of course be some other effects. But it does look as though one is not changing more than a few enzymes to any large extent.

WADDINGTON: But in one of your early slides, your first, I think, you showed that after the addition of penicillin you got a big increase in penicillinase. Now the formation of that is presumably using up amino acids that might have been put to some other use, and one feels that must produce some other effects on the cell.

POLLOCK: That is a point, of course, but we don't usually investigate whether there are other effects—except in sequential induction.

WADDINGTON: Spiegelman at one time showed pictures of competition between enzymes which were being induced. I don't know if that is still valid?

POLLOCK: There seems to be some evidence that this can occur, but it is a bit shaky still, I think. The general secondary effects wouldn't be very profound, because one enzyme is not often more than about 0·2% of the whole dry weight of the cell. You wouldn't therefore expect the formation of just one to have much influence on anything else, unless the effect were specific, which is theoretically possible.

WEISS: There is one thing I should like to ask our colleagues in this subject, which somewhat disturbs me in all these discussions. That is whether what the cell lives on normally can be distinguished from what we impose on it when we introduce a so-called inducer. When you remove the inducer, all you are doing is to put the cell back into contact with another inducer, don't you? Simply owing to the fact that we normally see the cell living in that latter "inducer", we are paying less attention to it. But in embryonic development, in differentiation, you don't just bring the cell back into its original environment, but you put it into a third inducing environment, and so on; and in tissue culture you transfer it again into another kind of environment. Isn't there something hidden there, where we fool ourselves by elevating the inducer, which may be something like galactose, into a special category as compared with the normal sucrose?

POLLOCK: The trouble is, of course, that you can't really carry out a critical test to see whether any of the normal endogenous metabolites are inducing the enzymes which metabolise them. I mean it is, at the best, very difficult. There have been attempts to do it, but . . .

WEISS: It's impossible!

WADDINGTON: Isn't the sort of thing Weiss is suggesting, this: grow your bacteria first in sucrose, then give them some penicillin and get the penicillinase induction; then if you take them out of penicillin and put them back into galactose, would that make any difference to the rate of reversion?

DEAN: Yes, it would make considerable difference, because if you train cells to various substrates you can either pile up a new adaptation or knock out the old one. But there is just one point I should like to make with reference to an earlier comment of Professor Waddington. What Dr. Pollock is investigating with penicillinase is increase in one particular enzyme. What we are doing is determining the effect of a drug, or some substance, on the growth of the organism, which is the end product of the whole complement of enzymes in the cell. This is not necessarily the same thing.

POLLOCK: I think that's the trouble. You are not only studying the whole organism; you are studying populations of organisms, and you don't know how far they are mixtures of all kinds of different types. You interpret your results in terms of enzymes, but in fact you don't usually study enzymes.

DEAN: No, we study the growth.

WADDINGTON: There is another point that arises if we try to apply these ideas to differentiation. For instance, Hinshelwood and Dean work with training periods measured in tens or scores of cell generations. These lead to long-lasting changes. But differentiation usually happens much quicker than that. It may often happen in one or two cell generations. It seems to me, therefore, that their results can't be transferred at all directly to the development of higher organisms, because of this difference in the length of time involved.

LEHMANN: I would like to ask for my own benefit about the genetical side of the work. You are speaking here about biological modification. There is no direction here of particular mutations? When the cultures are moved back into another medium, you do not think of selection, but only of modifications?

POLLOCK: There is no question of selection as far as enzymic induction is concerned. It is too quick, and there are all kinds of other direct and indirect evidence showing pretty conclusively that what really happens— at least in cultures studied in conditions where maximal induction occurs —is a change in the rate of synthesis of a particular protein in all or most of the cells.

DEAN: But in other cases you have other possibilities. It is quite possible to conceive that the training is simply the selection out of already existing mutants, and detraining the selecting out of the reverse mutants. One has to weigh out all the possibilities and sort them out.

WADDINGTON: It seems likely that it is different in different cases. In some cases I think it is pretty well proved that it is selection of pre-existing mutants. In fact, I think the Lederbergs [21] have shown that you can select them before applying the drug, but in other cases it may be different. Hinshelwood and Dean I think claim that in their cases it is not actually selection but is change in the general metabolic system.

RUSCH: There is a case of some work that A. H. Conney, E. C. Miller and J. A. Miller did at the McArdle Laboratory concerning apparent enzyme induction in mammalian liver [22]. This is along rather different lines than we have just been discussing. It may involve dedifferentiation. If one feeds the carcinogenic azo dye 4-dimethylaminoazobenzene to rats, one will get carcinoma of the liver in about four months. Now during the time tumour formation is going on, the carcinogenicity of much of the dye is destroyed by enzymes in the liver microsomes which demethylate, reduce, and hydroxylate the dye. However, when enough dye is fed the amounts of these enzymes in the liver fall to low levels for reasons still unknown. It is very intriguing that the tumour does not contain detectable amounts of these enzymes, and this may represent a dedifferentiation. Now it is interesting that several years ago Richardson found that simultaneous feeding of another carcinogen of quite a different type, 3-methylcholanthrene, will greatly reduce the carcinogenicity of the azo dye. It does this apparently by increasing the synthesis of those enzymes which destroy the carcinogenicity of the dye. Incidentally, methylcholanthrene is not a liver carcinogen. These enzymes have not been isolated as such, and this is why it cannot be definitely said that this is enzyme induction. However, no evidence could be obtained for the presence of enzyme activators or inhibitors, and ethionine, an inhibitor of protein synthesis, completely inhibited the increase of enzyme due to the methylcholanthrene although it had no effect on the normal levels of these enzymes. Hence, it appears that methylcholanthrene has induced the synthesis of these enzymes. It may only appear that way, but it is rather interesting—Dr. Pollock brought this out earlier—that one can have induction of an enzyme with another type of compound that is apparently rather different from the substrate.

POLLOCK: Chemically, you wouldn't consider those two to be very closely related.

RUSCH: No, you would not consider them related chemically.

WADDINGTON: Of course, in multicellular organisms, one has the difficulty of deciding how long is the step between putting the inducer in and getting the induced enzyme. I mean, in amphibian embryos the mesoderm induces the neural tissue which very soon produces choline esterase. If you wanted to, you could say you have the induced synthesis of choline esterase, but I don't really think it would be justifiable to draw a very close parallel between that type of induced synthesis of choline esterase and the type of induction of penicillinase which Pollock has been talking about in bacteria. There are presumably many more steps in the former than in the latter between the things we recognise as the inducer and the induced end result.

POLLOCK: There is nothing intrinsically different about them, would you say? This is a guess perhaps at the moment, but the facts of enzyme induction are reasonably consistent with those of differentiation, don't you think?

WEISS: Could I make a suggestion here for consolidating the views at the present time? I feel there is some possibility of a bridge between your facts on enzyme adaptation and differentiation. Waddington suggests that the time is far too short; but consider the experiments on the vitamin A switch of some cells into a line which produces keratin as against a line which will produce mucus. Here, the time of exposure required is about 15 min, and the cells do not grow during that period [23]. They are in suspension. Now, since you say, Pollock, that the adapted enzyme is present in traces, it is presumably a question of relative proportion between two competing enzyme species; that is, of which molecular species will be produced more actively while the other is just lingering on. We could, presumably, use that picture, assuming that there is a switch between two pre-existing systems into conditions where one will become permanently fixed, and given permanently a master position, or an opportunity to perpetuate itself, and no longer be crowded out by the action of the other system; and then we would have what we have in differentiation. It may not be a matter of presence or absence but merely a question of the conditions under which they can reproduce, or be catalytically active. I suppose that on that hypothesis the two cases may come quite close.

POLLOCK: I think this situation about the time fits in quite well.

WADDINGTON: What I meant before was that it doesn't fit in with the Hinshelwood type of training.

WEISS: Yes, in Pollock's cases, the time of induction is short, but also the time of reversion is very short, whereas in the case of differentiation it is permanent. That you have to accept from the people who are empirically familiar with these things; whereas yours can adapt very quickly and go back very quickly. A cell which has differentiated in a particular line will keep on breeding true, producing the same type on and on without attenuation.

HOLTZER: I am not certain that that time of reaction in Weiss's experiments has been measured in terms of washing, etc.

WEISS: It has now, in experiments which are not yet published.

HOLTZER: One problem which has cropped up several times in this discussion is that of irreversibility. It is certainly something which as far as I am concerned is not well established. You can quote about half a dozen experiments in tissue culture in which the cell type appears to have been retained. However, I would recommend that some people reread these original papers and see whether they would still be convinced. There is the work of Eberling with the thyroid and this looks very shaky, and indeed somebody about ten years later questioned the retention of thyroidness in these cultures.

WADDINGTON: But the thing that has not been produced is definite evidence against irreversibility. What you have to do is to take some cells out of a well differentiated tissue, grow them in any way you like and then persuade them to turn back into something else of a reasonably differentiated kind.

HOLTZER: Well, we have very good approximations of that in terms of Stone's experiments, and I think in the experiments of Fell more recently, with the vitamin A story, where she claims, and I think the evidence seems rather substantial, that a given cell has both the characteristics of a keratinising and a mucus-secreting cell.

WEISS: I should like to make clear some facts here. The stem cell retains both the capacities for producing either a line of keratinising or a line of mucus secreting cells remains bipotential and can be switched into one or the other type according to the environment. But the cells that are switched into one of these directions, and do actually show the phenomena of mucus secretion or keratinisation, are not then reversible. They are single-tracked into one type or the other, and that is that. As for the tissue culture experiments, Dr. Moscona in my laboratory has recently made tests on human liver cells, which have been kept continuously in tissue culture for more than two years, and they produce the same amount of liver specific products, for instance, glycogen, as they did at first. If you take that number of generations, with the cell dividing about every other day for two years, I think one is justified in throwing the burden of evidence on those who claim that they eventually lose their specificity. I think the positive case is this one. Eberling's experiments are no longer quoted.

WADDINGTON: Well, I think we'll come back again this afternoon, when we are talking about embryonic induction, to the analogies between that and enzyme induction. I think that Pollock by his ingenious suggestion of cycles has really coped with the permanency problem, or got somewhere near it anyway. The major difference to my mind is that there is no evidence that the things that are doing the induction in the embryos are anything like metabolites; though Wilde, I dare say, is going to cast some doubt on that argument. But in spite of Wilde's evidence, one must remember that a great many inducing substances in embryos don't look at all like metabolites, and that makes one rather hesitant in pressing analogies with the enzyme-inducing effects of substrates. I think we might as well leave that point until this afternoon, but I think that Brenner has got another point to bring up.

BRENNER: I should like to make a clarification, and nothing more, of the possibilities that we should think about when considering the causal processes underlying the change in a particular enzyme. I don't want to make a special case for induction, or a special case for differentiation, but I want to frame the problem in a very simple way. Suppose you have a cell that makes one sort of protein, as opposed to related cells which don't make that protein. This, as you can see, would be like comparing the induced cell to the uninduced cell, or comparing the muscle cell which makes myosin and actin to a cell from a similar line which doesn't make these proteins. In order to put this problem in terms of the hypothesis that I presented on the first day one should enumerate the stages in the flux of information at which interference is possible. Just to remind you of the essential aspects of the theory that I did propose, we think that the way in which a specific protein is made is as follows: There is a DNA template, which transfers information to an RNA template, and this acts as an assembly template on which eventually the folded fully active protein is made. All cases of differentiation can, in principle, be reduced to changes in the activity and composition of populations of folded protein molecules. The first possible way of interfering with this system is, of course, to change the activity of the enzyme molecule, for example, by means of a competitive substrate or an inhibitor. Neither the presence nor the structure of the enzyme is affected. The second possibility is to consider intermediates which precede the fully folded molecule, in which the total information is not present. In other words, we could say that the mere sequence has still some degrees of freedom which have to be restricted. The simple postulate of the sequence hypothesis states that once the sequence of amino acids is given, everything else follows automatically, but we could, for example, postulate semi-folded enzymes, that is, an enzyme molecule with a configuration which could oscillate between the active and the inactive state. We could also postulate that there were precursors of enzymes which had to have something removed or something added on before it showed activity. For example, in mammalian liver phosphorylase is formed from a precursor which has to have a phosphate group added to it before it can act as an enzyme. This phosphate group is added by another specific enzyme, and the reaction of adding is controlled by hormones. In enzyme induction and enzyme regression, synthesis of an enzyme is controlled by a small molecule which may be converting a semi-folded state to the properly folded state. There is also the third point of interference and that is at the stage of formation of the RNA templates. Finally, there is interference directly at the gene level by changing the structure of the cistron. At which levels do the control mechanisms of differentiation act? Do these mechanisms control the amount of RNA made by the DNA?

WADDINGTON: Surely the quantity of RNA made is not part of the information problem at all?

BRENNER: Yes.

WADDINGTON: You consider *quantity* of RNA as part of your information?

BRENNER: No. What I mean is this. Suppose every cell produces one template that can produce myosin, so that every cell makes at least one molecule of myosin, and every cell produces one molecule of serum albumen and so on. But in some cells there has been a selection of templates; muscle cells have millions of the myosin templates. We could think of differentiation on this kind of quantitative basis, every cell having all the proteins but in different proportions. Every cell would have the same potentiality. On the other hand, the differentiation process may result in the cessation of formation of one class of templates.

NEW SPEAKER: Do you postulate a stability of the RNA in the life of the cell?

BRENNER: No, we don't.

SAME SPEAKER: Then you go to more complicated processes?

BRENNER: Of course; you have got to put this in a time sequence as well. You have to say that a cell not only knows what RNA to produce initially, but knows that it has to go on doing it for the rest of its developmental history.

WADDINGTON: If the RNA is involved in the metabolic activities, surely you would expect it eventually to become used up or drawn off for other purposes in some way?

BRENNER: I do not think that this is a chemical kinetic problem. I don't think that you have an unstable system with a thousand possibilities and that the switch merely emphasises one system which acts as a sink so that everything else is blocked. I think there must be an active process which delineates the path. In other words, the establishment of a new pattern does not occur by a perturbation, so to speak, but by an actual direction of the synthesis.

WADDINGTON: At the gene level or at the RNA level? Is this purely in the cytoplasm?

BRENNER: That is the crux of the problem. Until one can do genetics on somatic cells, there is no answer.

WILDE: It would seem to me that the causal mechanisms of differentiation may be expressed at any one of these stages which you assume to occur. For instance, all the usual hormonally induced things may be considered to be differentiation steps.

POLLOCK: We really don't know, of course, how and where genes and inducers act in their control of protein synthesis.

BRENNER: Quite. I just gave one opinion.

POLLOCK: You would have to produce some *ad hoc* hypotheses to substantiate the point, which at first I thought you were almost dogmatising about, that the inducer acts mainly between the extended polypeptide chain and the folded chain. Because we do know one thing about enzyme production; that is, that the quantity of precursor between free amino acid and final enzyme is so small that you can't estimate it. Therefore, you have got to introduce some *ad hoc* hypotheses in order to maintain that it is simply in the folding that the inducer acts.

BRENNER: This hypothesis would state that you will never find that semifolded precursor—unless you looked very hard.

POLLOCK: You have to add something else to it?

BRENNER: Yes; in other words, you will only find it when you turn it into enzyme. It may remain stuck to the template and block further synthesis, or it may come off as a different product, which, when folded in the incorrect way, cannot be converted into the enzyme.

WADDINGTON: I confess that remains a little obscure to me, but I think perhaps it is hypothetical enough to remain in that condition. I'm afraid it's now time we brought this meeting to a close.

REFERENCES

1. BRIGGS, R. and J. J. KING (1955) in *Biological Specificity and Growth*, Princeton University Press.
2. LEHMANN, F. E. (1948) *Arch. J. Klaus Stift.* **23**, 586.
3. GRÜNEBERG, H. (1952) *J. Genet.* **51**, 95.
4. LEHMANN, F. E. (1954) *Rev. Suisse Zool.* **61**, 428.
5. TSCHUMI, P. (1953) *Rev. Suisse Zool.* **60**, 496.
6. HINSHELWOOD, Sir C. (1953) *J. Chem. Soc.* p. 1947.
7. WEISS, P. and J. L. KAVANAU (1957) *J. Gen. Physiol.* **41**, 1.
8. ROSE, S. M. (1957) *Biol. Rev.* **32**, 351.
9. TARDENT, P. (1955) *Rev. Suisse Zool.* **62**, 289.
10. VOGEL, H. J. (1956) in *Chemical Basis of Heredity*, p. 246, Johns Hopkins Press, Baltimore.
11. POLLOCK, M. R. (1952) *Brit. J. Exp. Path.* **33**, 587.
12. MONOD, J. and M. COHN (1952) *Advanc. Enzymol.* **13**, 67.
13. POLLOCK, M. R. (1956) *J. Gen. Microbiol.* **14**, 90.

14

14. POLLOCK, M. R. (1957) *Biochem. J.* **66**, 419.
15. MONOD, J. (1956) in *Enzymes, Units of Biological Structure and Function*, p. 7. (Ed. by GAEBLER), Academic Press, New York.
16. KNOX, W. E. (1954) in *Cellular Metabolism and Infection*, p. 45 (Ed. by RACKER), Academic Press, New York.
17. POLLOCK, M. R. (1958) *Proc. Roy. Soc.* B**148**, 340.
18. STANIER, R. Y. (1955) in *Aspects of Synthesis and Order in Growth*, p. 43. (Ed. by RUDNICK), Princeton University Press.
19. KREBS, H. A. (1947) *Enzymology* **12**, 88.
20. COHN, M. (1956) in *Enzymes, Units of Biological Structure and Function*, p. 41. (Ed. by GAEBLER), Academic Press, New York.
21. LEDERBERG, J. and G. E. M. LEDERBERG (1952) *J. Bacteriol.* **63**, 399.
22. CONNEY, A. H., E. C. MILLER and J. A. MILLER (1956) *Cancer Res.* **16**, 450; (1957) *J. Biol. Chem.* **228**, 753.
23. WEISS, P. and R. JAMES (1955) *Exp. Cell Res.* Suppl. **3**, 381.

CHAPTER VIII

Tissue Interactions:
Embryonic Induction

WADDINGTON: This afternoon we want to talk about embryonic induction. I think as good a bridge as any between this subject and the enzyme induction we were discussing this morning would be provided by Wilde. I wonder if he would tell us about some of the ideas arising from his experiments?

WILDE: Professor Waddington has expressed, this forenoon, many of the concepts I wish to consider. I will try to speak in detail concerning some of them. As a person who has attempted to design experiments concerning the biochemistry of cellular differentiation, I would prefer to be a little more cautious. One of the things which must concern us, in studying the changes which occur in the development of an embryo from the time of fertilisation up until the time of recognisably cellular parts is: "What possible mechanism of differentiation exist about which one can devise experiments?" One hopes experiments will give us information about the manner in which the cells carry out the development of a series of differences. To design worthwhile experiments we must ask questions which have an element of causality in them. One must ask what *type* of events will bring about the choice between alternative pathways. This is a convenient and heuristic method of thinking about cells becoming different. Let's examine for example the fine biochemical analysis by Boell and Shen [1] on the development of the central nervous system in amphibia. These investigators were able to show, in a very beautiful way, that by the time primitive nervous function was manifest in the cells of the central nervous system, the same cells also had the ability to synthesise cholinesterase. That is, cholinesterase was available and could be detected. Boell and Shen, however, were very careful not to say that a cell developed the quality "nerveness" through the agency of its ability to synthesise cholinesterase. The two events apparently occur simultaneously. So the following important question is still unanswered:
What properties did cause the development of the cell into a neurone? This is the question for which we seek an answer. The development of

particular properties in a cell is probably due to the development of particular patterns of chemical work. By and large, we still ultimately have to think in terms of chemical work, in terms of patterns of electron flow. It is convenient, probably, to consider that there is a relatively broad range of chemical work which has to do with the maintenance of the life of the cell, which is common to most or to all cells. But the thing for which search must be made in embryogenesis is to find and to demonstrate differences in work patterns as they develop. Boell and Shen's demonstration that cholinesterase exists in appreciable concentration at the time we can begin to call these cells neurones is a case in point, but this is not yet sufficient demonstration of a casual factor in differentiation. The next step in the analysis should be to attempt to show that there are sets of pathways which become more and more fixed, and are the means by which a cell assumes a definite functional type. Such a functional type must (in a practical sense) be capable of easy identification. This forces us to use morphological criteria. There are a lot of difficulties in the process of experiment design in the field and I am aware of some of them. One needs a recognisable morphological end-point upon which to test hypotheses and the causal postulate. This means that one must select cells which are at first mutually indistinguishable. Then one must show that these cells will follow a pathway from this state to some other state; let us say, Holtzer's type of muscle cell. This, you will agree, will be a change in form and a change in function from one type to another. The causality of the change must ultimately be demonstrated through finite biochemical pathways.

The particular end-point chosen for my studies has been the development of the pigment cell and related other types from the amphibian neural crest. This again is a morphologically and biochemically specific end-product cell, and is therefore a satisfactory identification mark for the experiment. It is a spidery cell, evenly loaded with melano-protein granules. In its final state it is easily recognisable. Most of the factual data have been published (cf. [2, 3, 4]). I should like to use now a summary diagram (Fig. 8.1) which puts together much that we have done. We have been working on the basis that there may be a peculiar and specific series of metabolic steps, starting from substrate phenylalanine, causal to the differentiation of pigment cells and ectomesenchyme cells from amphibian neural crest cells. Ectomesenchyme cells will go in the normal embryo and in organotypic tissue culture, as many people have shown, ([5], a review) to form cartilages, tooth germs, and connective tissues, but in our restricted *in vitro* system we have been dealing only with the development of pigment cells and ectomesenchyme cells, that is to say, fibroblast-like cells and Schwann cells. For comparison, as a cell type unaffected by the test system, we have dealt with striated muscle, whose precursor cells, of course, do not come from the neural crest.

This diagram shows how a sort of molecular dissection has been carried out by choosing a series of unnatural structural analogues of phenylalanine and presenting these molecules to the environment of precise explants from particular early embryonic stages. At this time the cells of the embryo are still mutually undistinguishable "amoebae" (i.e. undifferentiated). The cultures are studied to discover whether the cells

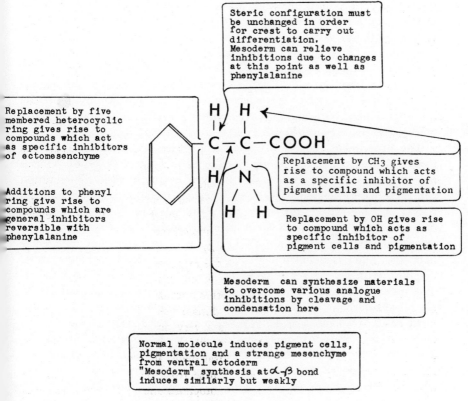

Steric configuration must be unchanged in order for crest to carry out differentiation. Mesoderm can relieve inhibitions due to changes at this point as well as phenylalanine

Replacement by five membered heterocyclic ring gives rise to compounds which act as specific inhibitors of ectomesenchyme

Additions to phenyl ring give rise to compounds which are general inhibitors reversible with phenylalanine

Replacement by CH_3 gives rise to compound which acts as a specific inhibitor of pigment cells and pigmentation

Replacement by OH gives rise to compound which acts as specific inhibitor of pigment cells and pigmentation

Mesoderm can synthesize materials to overcome various analogue inhibitions by cleavage and condensation here

Normal molecule induces pigment cells, pigmentation and a strange mesenchyme from ventral ectoderm "Mesoderm" synthesis at α-β bond induces similarly but weakly

FIG. 8.1.

undergo differentiation into pigment cells and ectomesenchyme. The system is a restricted one, but a highly repeatable one. The cells can be handled by the microsurgeon quite easily with little practice. One can be sure, on a cell-for-cell basis, that he is dealing with particular presumptive areas.

The outcome of the experiments is that the compounds chosen have shown effects on the cells which are in large part dependent on the particular structural alteration, characteristic of the individual analogue. For instance, if the α-amino group is replaced with hydroxyl, then phenyl-lactic acid is formed. When this compound is placed in the environment of undifferentiated neural crest cells, the ectomesenchyme component (fibroblasts and the Schwann cells), pays no attention to its presence and differentiates normally, whereas no pigment cells or pigmentation develop in the cultures. If the phenyl ring of the compound is altered and replaced with a heterocyclic ring, then the reverse effect is shown. The pigment cells differentiate quite normally while the ectomesenchymal component does not appear. This was the first truly differential effect obtained. By varying additions to the molecule at the phenyl ring a series of compounds can be formed which have a general inhibitory effect on all cells. This has proven to be quite a fortunate thing, because now one can use the two systems for later testing. A large series of experiments of this nature, supplemented by experiments concerning the release of the inhibition by the normal metabolite, and the development of specific inhibitory response, have led to the cartoon (Fig. 8.1).

The experiments enable us to make a series of statements about the functional significance of portions of the normal molecule [3, 4]. One is forced to consider the concept that a molecule with a steric configuration similar to phenylalanine is an essential causal metabolite in the differentiation of these cells. Further studies about whether the whole molecule or its parts are the required agent have shown that the whole molecule is essential. The next diagram (Fig. 8.2) will indicate what apparently happens. The tissue which is making the response, the upper layer in the diagram, requires the presence of the whole molecule of phenylalanine. The making of phenylalanine or something similar to it is carried out by the next underlying cells. These then donate the material to the environment of the responding cells. This is a very tantalising scheme for the embryologist. These are the very cells, which are responsible in classical embryology for the induction of a neural plate, and the neural tube, and all of the necessary structures which arise from them [6, 7]. They are also the cells which differentiate into notochord and into striated muscle. You will recall that our criterion of specificity has been that these cells will develop into striated muscle even in the presence of analogues which act specifically on the neural crest cells.

It does appear that the major thing which is happening in these cells, as far as synthesis of this particular metabolite is concerned, is a condensation of fragments across the α–β carbon to carbon bond. This system makes one think of oxidation of fatty acids. It also reminds the embryologist of embryonic induction. However, it is premature by far to consider this as the substantive mechanism of embryonic induction. The data, perhaps, give us just the beginning of an insight into the mechanism whereby one cellular component, which is the actual inducing component, presents to the environment of nearby cells material which, in the proper substrate concentrations, acts as a key to canalise their future development. Under these circumstances their pool of metabolites begins to have a restricted range, and their development begins to show discrete direction. Once this begins, there is no other response possible and the cells go on into neural crest type of differentiation (i.e. a decreased probability of divergent responses).

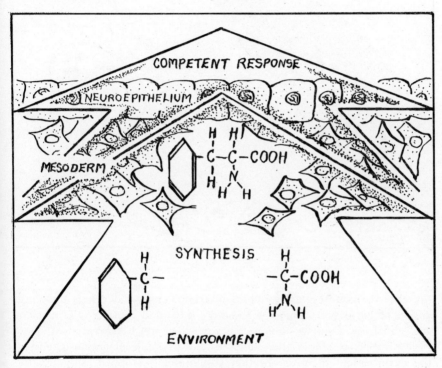

FIG. 8.2.

We have been able to approach this system from the other end. That is, to force cells to become something they normally would not. This has been carried out by using cells which have no normal potentiality or history of becoming pigment cells and which come from an entirely different part of the body. If such cells are presented with a small concentration of phenylalanine in their environment they may respond by forming pigment cells almost indistinguishable from those of the neural crest. In normal embryogenesis they have no history of this activity. The external metabolite concentration has forced a new differentiative pathway upon them.

We are now beginning to extend a similar test system to striated muscle differentiation, another good morphological and functional end-point. The preliminary data are interesting. The next diagram (Fig. 8.3a) illustrates the fine degree of differentiation which we obtain in striated

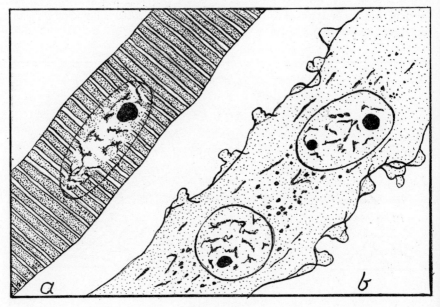

FIG. 8.3a, b

muscle. In tissue culture amphibian striated muscle develops to a high degree of perfection. Figure 8.3b shows a band of muscle, of equivalent age, and from a similar donor embryo, which has been reared in a low concentration of amino-guanidine. In the presence of amino-guanidine the development of cross striation is completely stopped, although the formation of multi-nuclear aggregates showing exactly the same outgrowth characteristics as normal striated muscle takes place. There is also a peculiarity in that amoeboid movement is retained all over the surface, instead of just at the growing tip. What we hope to do here is to discover a series of biochemical steps perhaps related to actomyosin biosynthesis causally leading to the differentiation of striated muscle.

BRACHET: Is anything known about the incorporation of phenylalanine into pigment and other cells?

WILDE: No, it is not, but this work is very preliminary. What we do, Dr. Brachet, is to search the literature of biochemistry and of experimental teratology. There was good evidence that amino guanidine in rats was very antagonistic to liver development [8]. We looked at the published photographs and it seemed to us that the connective tissue component was much affected. We were at that time in search of a possible connective tissue inhibitor. While this reasoning may appear devious we must search for such possible clues in order to find compounds that may later give us a logical and causal rationale for explanation. We have also used Ebert's compound, antimycin A [9, 10]: those results are too preliminary to talk about. But it is on this sort of basis that one searches for substances. In the phenylalanine pigment cell story it is obvious to everyone why we tested it.

WADDINGTON: I was interested in that last slide of yours which seemed to show multi-nucleate cells, in many ways similar to early muscle cells, but not showing any striation which would indicate the presence of myosin. This, if true, gives a negative answer to one of the questions I asked; whether there are histogenetic key substances, and whether myosin is possibly a key substance around which the whole of muscle development is organised? If that were so, you couldn't get a muscle cell without any myosin in it.

WILDE: I don't think this is evidence that there is no myosin. The evidence is that there is no cross-striated pattern, and I would like to be a little cautious about equating absence of cross striation with the absence of myosin. After all, there are smooth muscle cells, which are optically homogeneous *in vivo*, yet which are contractile.

WADDINGTON: Did I understand you correctly that the neural crest cells cannot condense the two halves of the molecule?

WILDE: No, but they may themselves have a mechanism for the formation of phenylalanine for which we presently have no test. We are now attempting to get at the absolute presence of or absence of compounds by electrophoresis and chromatography.

BRACHET: You don't know whether there is any incorporation of phenylalanine?

WILDE: No, we do not yet.

POLLOCK: This would seem to be another case where a small molecule has induced a different type of cell.

WILDE: Excellent work which precedes mine is that published by Miss Fell and the late Sir Edward Mellanby [11], which was almost immediately followed up by Dr. Weiss [12]. In this work vitamin A, which is a reasonably small compound, gives a specific effect in causing metaplasia of keratinising epithelium into mucous secreting, ciliated epithelium.

POLLOCK: But that's not in the same tissue. I was wondering whether in the same tissue you might have two different compounds acting differently; but at the moment is it not simply a trigger reaction, producing only one end-result?

WADDINGTON: But you have two different compounds acting as different inhibitors or suppressors in your tissue, don't you?

WILDE: Oh, yes. There is a variety of compounds which act as suppressors.

BERENBLUM: Can anyone tell me of another case where the production of a specific effect in a tissue culture results from a direct effect of a substance like this and not an indirect one through, let us say, increased growth or anything else. There are many ways in which a cell cannot differentiate completely. Can one always tell whether the action is direct or indirect?

WILDE: We can only say that in our case the specific effect is connected with the particular way in which the molecule has been altered, but I agree your argument is valid. We do not have a clear way of distinguishing primary and secondary effects.

BRENNER: I take it tryosine does not work.

WILDE: Tyrosine is a good metabolite. In fact we started off with tyrosine but went on to phenylalanine in view of the well known concept that phenylalanine is a precursor of tyrosine.

WADDINGTON: A peculiar point in this is that when you take a lot of neural crest cells and treat them with phenylalanine only some of them develop into normal pigment cells. Of course, in normal differentiation some of them turn into cartilage, some into pigment cells, some into ganglion cells, and so on. It is obscure to me why some of them react and others do not. Do you find that they are in some way different before you start, or is this some sort of stochastic process or something of that kind, some of them getting over a threshold and others not?

WILDE: I don't know that I have any ideas about that, and our evidence goes no further than I have presented it. We were surprised at the degree of specificity which turned up in the experiments. There are four or five compounds in each class, which, dependent on their molecular configuration, give very different types of result. We have recently added to the phenyllactic acid class the compound alpha methyl phenylalanine. This has very fine inhibitory action which acts specifically against pigment cell differentiation. In this line, it is interesting that earlier biochemical work by the Lerner group [13] suggested that through the formylation or the acetylation of the alpha amino group compounds like acetyl phenylalanine or acetyl tryosine are formed which act as very specific inhibitors of tyrosinase in the Harding–Passey mouse melanoma. This is one of the clues with which we started.

WADDINGTON: I should like to ask another question, going back to the thing you mentioned before about a cell looking like a muscle fibre but having no evidence of myosin in it: Do you get any pigment cells with no pigment in them?

WILDE: No.

WADDINGTON: Well, a final question then. Many people have regarded the induction of neural crest as a weak grade of an action which in other grades involves the induction of actual neural tissue. Can you by increasing the concentrations of any of your substances, change from inducing pigment cells to inducing nerve cells?

WILDE: Not within the limits of the tests we have made, which is from something below one to eight millimoles per litre. At eight millimoles the cells begin to show degenerative changes, and so it is not within that range.

NIEUWKOOP: May I make a small remark about this point. The analysis of neural crest formation has made much progress. The idea that neural crest production is simply due to a weak induction does not fit in with the facts any more. There is a good number of data [14, 15, 16] indicating that the neural crest develops from cell material which has first been neuralised, so that it is a second step in the induction process which leads to neural crest formation. Just the reverse as through neural crest to neural.

WADDINGTON: But I think you would agree that it can be brought into a series of inductions which also involves neural tissue, either as a primary induction or as a secondary transformation.

WILDE: I should just like to add that this is a system which matures at the time of gastrulation. Prior to gastrulation, the system is only permissive. That is, at an optimal concentration of phenylalanine, as gastrulation is approached there are more and more cases in which cellular differentiation occurs. It never reaches a level of beyond 20%; but it is high at stage 10 just before gastrulation, and low at stage 8, which is the earliest at which we have been able to work. Earlier than that the cells are so large that there's not much sense in trying to work with them.

BRENNER: Could one return to the point which Professor Waddington made. I am not clear now whether you would agree that one could consider that there is some event before the application of phenylalanine; in other words, that if the phenylalanine is analogous to enzyme induction, and that what went before is analogous to something which created the conditions for enzyme induction.

WILDE: This is a way of interpreting the data, but I am a little loth to restrict myself to any single scheme. There may be a large group of phenomena involved of which this is only one, all of which are classed under the head of embryonic induction and all of which are taking place at this time. There may be a great many different machines which are being made ready, and the little bit of control with phenylalanine which we have achieved may come in as a second stage, or as the thing which fires off the whole system.

BRENNER: The only point—it is a suspicion more than anything else— is that this is a substrate for something which is going to make pigment and that is why one thinks about the rest of the system.

WILDE: Surely. The evidence now is that it is a substrate for many more things in morphogenesis than just the making of pigment, because melanoprotein is very inert in the chemical sense. There are many pieces of evidence that the content of melanoprotein in a cell has very little morphogenetic effect. It can for instance end up in a fibroblast, where there is surely no real reason for its being there.

WADDINGTON: Of course, even if the pigment is chemically inert it may yet affect the cell. It would be quite a factor in one's kinetic speculation if one could suppose that cells have a certain number of "sinks" in them. It may be that the melanin pigment is a very convenient sink for removing some things from the metabolic system.

I think we must pass on now to the ancient and hoary subject of the normal embryonic induction in the amphibia, which has been worked on now for so long that we know more about it than about any other case of tissue interaction, but which still remains so obscure. Possibly Drs. Nieuwkoop and Toivonen can clear it up for us. I think Nieuwkoop is going to make some remarks first, then Toivonen, and then we shall go back to Nieuwkoop.

NIEUWKOOP: When we move to the neural induction we are going to make quite a jump from the subcellular and cellular levels to the supra-cellular level. We first have to realise that the process of induction and organisation in development is a fairly long-lasting process. It is necessary to divide it up into certain phases, as I think Professor Waddington has always suggested in his terminology of evocation and individuation. There is one point which I would like to make first. We can really divide the

whole process into a period of primary induction and a period of organisation. This is not because the induction processes are essentially different
during the various periods; we know that the archenteron roof exerts an
inductive action for a very long period [17]. It is because the reaction
system, in this case the ectoderm, has a very restricted "reactability". It
can primarily only react to stimuli during a very restricted period. There
is a beginning of the period of neural competence, but there is also a very
sharp end to it [17–20]. So we can say that the period of primary induction
is restricted by the reactability of the reaction system. Therefore it is
quite reasonable to distinguish it from the further phase of organisation.
But once the process of induction has started, the processes of further
organisation are, I think, direct consequences of it. We cannot prevent
them any more; they just go on, up to the very end [21].

A second point deals with the term induction. We must be very careful
with the term induction, because it has been used for a great variety of
processes which are not at all uniform. We have discussed very extensively
the question of enzyme induction. I am quite sure that a number of processes in embryonic induction cannot be put under that heading. We must
therefore be very careful with generalisations. We even have indications
that in the classical induction experiments on the amphibian organiser we
probably have to do with a number of quite different processes; and very
probably they are different really from the very beginning.

A third point I should like to make is that there is a lot of evidence that
very different inducing agents may evoke the same effect. This does however not necessarily imply that they have an identical action, or even that
they have, let us say, converging actions. It might simply be due to the
fact that the reacting system, here the ectoderm, has only very restricted
possibilities of response; in other words, the number of pathways which
the tissue can choose is very restricted. A large number of agents might
only be able to push the reaction system into one of these pathways, but
these actions may also not be identical with the factors which are
responsible for doing this in normal development.

These are just a few general points I should like to make.

WADDINGTON: After those general points I think it might be best to go
on to some of the more factual data. I think Dr. Toivonen might tell us
about some of his recent work on some, at any rate, of these inducing
substances.

TOIVONEN: These results I shall now deal with belong to the experiments
done together with Dr. Saxen, using some malignant tissues as inductors
in young *Triturus* gastrulae, and comparing their action to the action of
corresponding normal tissue. Our experiments have, however, nothing to
do with the cancer problem itself.

In 1933, Holtfreter [22] found that inductive activity is not confined to embryonic tissue alone, but that differentiated adult tissues are also able to induce different kinds of formations when implanted into the blastocoele of a young amphibian gastrula or into an epidermis sandwich. The next step was the observation by Chuang [23] and myself [24] in 1938 that the inductive action of adult tissues is not of a random nature; these heterogeneous inductors can have a specific inductive action on the young embryonic tissues, which corresponds to the actions of the different regions of the archenteron roof.

On the other hand, Andres [25] has found that embryonic tissues implanted into late amphibian larvae can cause there teratoid tumours containing different kinds of differentiation.

These discoveries naturally raise the question, do the same or similar agents regulate both embryonic differentiation, and subsequent growth and regeneration of the tissues, as Levander and his collaborators [26] have assumed ?

Three years ago we hit on the idea that when we assume that tissue growth and differentiation are always regulated by specific agents, it seems logical to assume also that the situation regarding these factors will differ from the normal in malignant, markedly abnormal growth, and that the difference will be detectable by tests with competent embryonic tissue.

When trying to investigate the difference which may possibly exist between the inducing actions of normal and malignant tissue, one has to choose a tissue as homogeneous and pure as possible. In addition, the inductive action of the normal control tissue should be strong enough and readily analysable. Therefore, we first chose the bone marrow of normal and leukaemic rats for these experiments.

In my earlier investigations I had established that the bone marrow of the guinea-pig is a strong and nearly purely mesodermalising inductor [27, Text—fig. 1]. Unfortunately, no leukaemic strain of the guinea-pig was available; therefore we decided to use normal and leukaemic rats in our experiments.

In preliminary experiments made in 1955, we used for implantation bone marrow of one normal and one leukaemic rat. The results of these experiments are published in a preliminary note [28], which I hope, all participating in this symposium have received. In these experiments the inductive action of the bone marrow of the guinea-pig was very strong, but to our astonishment, the bone marrow of the leukaemic rat was completely inactive. This inactivity of the leukaemic bone marrow was very surprising, because normal bone marrow is a very strong inductor, and because no adult tissue has hitherto been found to be entirely inactive, as everyone knows who has made experiments with heterogeneous inductors.

In the operation season of 1956 we made additional experiments with bone marrow from normal and four leukaemic rats.   Thus the results which I shall now deal with will concern experiments with five normal and five leukaemic rats.

Both the normal and the leukaemic rats were all of the genetically pure Wistar strain, and they were 8–12 weeks old when used. Immediately after sacrifice, the entire bone marrow was taken from both femurs. The tissue was treated in 70% alcohol for 8–48 hr. Before implantation, minced tissue was washed for 3–4 hr in sterile Holtfreter solution. The pieces of tissue were implanted into the blastocoele of young gastrulae of the common newt, *Triturus vulgaris*. After operation, the experimental animals were reared for 10–14 days in Holtfreter saline.

The total number of useful cases in the control series with normal bone marrow was 100. In two cases only was no induction observable, so that 98% of the cases were positive. Just as in previous experiments with guinea-pig bone marrow, the reaction of the host was mainly mesodermal. No cephalic structures or sensory organs were encountered, but in about one-third of the cases a short spinal cord primordium was seen at the tip of the induced tail, which had also appeared in experiments with guinea-pig bone marrow, but less frequently. Also the action of the bone marrow taken from different individual rats was very similar, as you can see from the diagram, where the action of the bone marrow of the four different rats are indicated separately [29, Text—fig. 1]. There are practically no

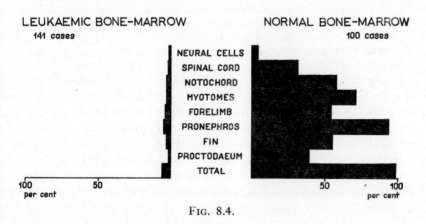

LEUKAEMIC BONE-MARROW
141 cases

NORMAL BONE-MARROW
100 cases

NEURAL CELLS
SPINAL CORD
NOTOCHORD
MYOTOMES
FORELIMB
PRONEPHROS
FIN
PROCTODAEUM
TOTAL

100   50
per cent

50   100
per cent

FIG. 8.4.

individual differences in the qualitative action of the bone marrow. Also the action of the bone marrow of the different individuals was equally strong.

The transplantable myeloid rat leukaemia used in our experiments, was developed by Dr. Shay at the Fels Research Institute, Temple University, Philadelphia. This leukaemia had been induced by gastric instillation of methylcholanthrene. The leukaemia of our rats was transplanted by subcutaneous injections into 7 day old rats with 0·1 cm³ of a homogenate prepared from leukaemic tumour tissue diluted with the same volume of physiological saline. Following transplantation, the peripheral blood picture of the animals was continuously observed. After the manifestation of leukaemia the rats were killed, and their bone marrow used for implantation into the blastocoele of the newt gastrulae by exactly the same procedures as with normal bone marrow.

At the time of sacrifice, the peripheral blood pictures of the rats were as indicated in the table (Table 8.1).

TABLE 8.1.   THE PERIPERRAL BLOOD PICTURES OF LEUKAEMIC INDIVIDUALS AT THE TIME OF SACRIFICE

	1955	1956				Normal values*
		1	2	3	4	
Leucocytes	52.000	97.000	44.400	89.300	48.300	6.000–25.600
Granulocytes	49	15	25	42	12	19–40
Myelocytes	10	9	8	17	38	−†
Lymphocytes	41	57	58	36	44	62–75
Monocytes	—	19	9	5	6	1–6
Normoblasts/ 100 Leucocytes	35	11	2	2	4	0–3‡

* The nomal blood values are indicated as suggested by Scherner, 1954.
† In investigations carried out over several years in our laboratory, myelocytes have not been observed in the peripheral blood of normal rats.
‡ In our laboratory, normoblasts to the number of 0–3 per leucocyte have been observed in young rats.

In the diagram (Fig. 8.4) you see the analysis of the induced formations as revealed by microscopic examination of the slides: On the right side the action of normal bone marrow and on the left the action of leukaemic bone marrow. The leukaemic bone marrow, as you can see has been practically inactive. The difference is striking.

In the table (Table 8.2) you see the same analysis. There the action of the bone marrows of the different rat individuals is indicated separately. You see that the bone marrow of the leukaemic rat from 1955 and the first rat from 1956 were completely inactive. Also the bone marrow of rats numbers 3 and 4 have been practically inactive: There is only one host in the series with the rat No. 3 in which a weak archencephalic induction is observed, and two positive cases with the rat No. 4, of which one has a weak archencephalic reaction and the other a very weak mesodermal reaction with pronephros tubules and fin. By contrast, the bone marrow of leukaemic rat No. 2 from 1956 gave a typical mesodermal bone marrow reaction in half of the cases, whilst in the other half it was completely

TABLE 8.2. THE ANALYSIS OF DIFFERENTIATIONS INDUCED BY NORMAL AND LEUKAEMIC RAT BONE MARROW SEPARATELY AND SIMULTANEOUSLY OBSERVED ON HISTOLOGICAL EXAMINATION

Implantation tissue	Number of cases	Number of positive cases	Induction percentage	Neural inductions					Mesodermal inductions					
				Archencephalon	Eye	Nasal pit	Neural cells	Spinal cord	Notochord	Myotomes	Pronephros	Limb rudiment	Fin	Proctodeum
Leukaemic bone marrow														
1955	33	0	0	—	—	—	—	—	—	—	—	—	—	—
1956: 1	12	0	0	—	—	—	—	—	—	—	—	—	—	—
2	12	6	50	—	—	—	—	3	4	4	5	5	4	—
3	50	1	2	1	—	1	—	—	—	—	—	—	—	—
4	34	2	6	—	1	—	1	—	—	—	1	—	1	—
Total	141	9	6	1	1	1	1	3	4	4	6	5	5	—
Normal bone marrow														
1955	34	34	100	—	—	—	3	8	19	28	31	15	26	22
1956: 1	18	18	100	—	—	—	—	8	10	12	17	11	8	4
2	18	18	100	—	—	—	—	8	12	13	18	14	11	7
3	20	19	95	—	—	—	1	5	12	13	18	10	9	6
4	10	9	90	—	—	—	—	2	4	5	9	5	1	—
Total	100	98	98	—	—	—	4	31	57	71	93	55	55	39
Simultaneous implantation: Normal 1956: 4 + Leukaemic 1956: 4	22	22	100	—	—	—	—	8	14	19	19	8	11	10

inactive. The explanation of this seems to be that the leukaemia of this rat individual was in an earlier stage than of the other animals used in the experiments, and that therefore the bone marrow employed was not yet completely infiltrated by leukaemic tissue. Thus, some implants must also have contained intact tissue, which caused the bone marrow reaction. You remember that the peripheral blood picture of this animal was also more benign, and the leucocyte count and number of juventile forms were lower than in the others.

In the table and in the corresponding diagram we have included those

15

cases only, in which the implant was observable on histological examination of the slides and in which the implant was in contact with the ectoderm of the host. Numerous cases were discarded because the implant had either sunk into the entoderm mass or was absent.

In the table you also see a third series, in which normal and leukaemic bone marrow have been implanted into the same embryo simultaneously, in order to learn if leukaemic bone marrow contains any agents absent in normal bone marrow that would inhibit the action of the mesodermalising inductive agents. As you can see, the resulting induction corresponds both qualitatively and quantitatively to the results obtained with normal bone marrow alone. In this series results were accepted only if both implants were histologically observable in the host.

According to these results it seems obvious that in leukaemic bone marrow one or more agents are lacking or inactivated, which are always present in normal bone marrow and which after implantation into a young embryo, induce the formation of additional mesodermal structures.

For many reasons, the present observations cannot as yet be coupled, even in part, with the problem of carcinogenesis. Firstly, the finding in question cannot be generalised so as to refer to other malignant tissues, or even to other leukaemias, and owing to the time-consuming nature of the technique employed, the exploration of other tissues is a distant goal. Secondly, information regarding both the process of embryonic induction and carcinogenesis is so scanty that correlation of the relevant data is impossible. Purely as a working hypothesis this correlation is tempting. However, as mentioned, it seems very probable that embryonic differentiation is regulated by certain active factors and numerous investigations have, in addition, yielded evidence to suggest that this chemical regulation is not confined to early gastrulation alone, later organogenesis being also, at least in part, subject to the regulation of such substances.

Last spring we continued our experiments with malignant tissues. Although this material has not yet been examined microscopically, there are some interesting facts detectable in the whole larvae. We have, for instance, made different kinds of series, in which malignant HeLa-cells have been used as implants. When these cancer cells are cultured in human sera, they have a very strong inducing action after alcohol treatment. There are always complete tails and hindbrains with ear vesicles, but no archencephalic formations are induced. When these cells are reared in synthetic Parker-saline without sera, and the saline is changed different times, the tail-inducing action becomes stepwise weaker, and gradually disappears almost completely. In contrast, a weak cephalic reaction is now observed, in which archencephalic sense organs are obtainable, too. Also rearing of HeLa-cells in a sera heated for half an hour at 65°C in a water bath has the same effect.

On the basis of these results, and taking into account the results with leukaemic bone marrow, our working hypothesis is at the moment this: The active mesodermalising agents in malignant HeLa-cells are taken from the sera. They are not from among the structural proteins of the cells, but in the normal environment they are always present in the cell or between the cells. In leukaemic animals, maybe, the serum also lacks these agents, because leukaemic bone marrow is not able to induce mesodermal structures.

In the recent operation season we were unable to get leukaemic human sera to investigate whether the HeLa-cells would lose their mesodermalising inducing action when reared in it.

I should like to make some further remarks about the mesodermalising inductive action. I shall tell you something about the key system which we use in Finland. I have here a key. This key fits the door of my flat and this key will also open the outer door A in that part of the building where I am living. In this part of the house there are ten different flats, and everyone has his own special key. All these keys have a very specific action in the sense that every key opens the door of one flat only, but they also have a less specific action, since they all also open the outside door A. In the same house there is another part with the outer door B. That part also contains ten flats with special keys, which all open the door B, but not the door A. Thus, all the twenty keys have a specific action and a somewhat less specific action. I do not call the latter action unspecific, because there must be thousands of keys which do not fit either of those two outer doors. I think the situation in the normal archenteron roof will be something of this kind, too. We may be able to think of, e.g., twenty different mesodermalising inductive agents which all induce mesodermal formations, and we may assume that of these agents, e.g., numbers 1 to 10 will open only one "door" A, while the other ten will open another "door" B for further development. We do not think that all those twenty agents are normally present in the archenteron roof in the final form—perhaps only two sorts may be present—but during the differentiation of tissues a chemical differentiation will also occur and, later, all the different active substances will have a specific form and action.

We may assume that all the substances which open the "door" A, will be used for the induction of axial mesoderm, whereas those agents from 11 to 20, which open the "door" B, will form, for instance, mesenchyme and so on. All these key substances will have specific actions: e.g. this substance 1 may be able to induce muscle cells and this substance 11 induces pronephros tubules. When we now use adult tissues as inductors in induction experiments, we may use a tissue in which only some of those agents are present. When I have pieces of a tissue implanted into a young gastrula, we may get only the part A of the mesoderm induced—only the axial mesoderm. In that manner acts, e.g., the kidney tissue of the guinea-pig. But if I use for experiments bone marrow tissue, I will get the whole mesoderm, the parts A and B, induced. I think that the HeLa-cells induce in that manner too.

But, though the kidney tissue opens the door A, it is not necessary that it contains all the substances from 1 to 10. It is enough, if it contains one key substance only. Likewise, for bone marrow it is enough to open both the doors if it at least contains one substance from those two groups. With these contents bone marrow is able to induce the whole mesodermal system.

With this idea we can also explain why, e.g., Dr. Holtzer has not been able to induce cartilages from the somites by bone marrow as inductor, as he has told me, though I have got cartilages, when I have used bone marrow as inductor in a young gastrula. Maybe, bone marrow contains, e.g., the agents from 1 to 5, but not the substance 6, which would be a specific agent for inducing the cartilages.

In my opinion, the reaction material is always able to react in a manner characteristic of its stage. The mesoderm rudiment of a young gastrula is able to produce all of these agents, if both the "doors" are opened using an inductor containing some of the agents belonging to the two groups. But later the reaction material requires the very specific action of a key substance for a definite effect, for instance the somites require the action of a specific agent for forming the cartilages.

Another question is, why the adult tissues contain those key substances? What is the importance they have there? For the present, we have to be satisfied with the assumption, expressed many times, that there are, in every tissue, tissue specific agents present, which control the normal growth and regeneration. These agents will also be able to cause the primary induction, if these tissues are used as heterogeneous inductors.

LEHMANN: I should like to bring one interesting biochemical fact into the discussion. I think several people here will have heard the interesting paper which has been given by Yamada [30] at several places in Europe. I think that he has shown that it is possible to extract from bone marrow of the guinea-pig a complex substance—probably a protein. It can be purified by electrophoresis and shows a rather uniform band. This material is able to induce in the gastrula the formation of mesoderm. If Yamada spreads this same substance on glass and heats it for a short period—only about several seconds—it is converted rapidly into a substance which only induces archencephalic differentiations. Biochemists have had the idea that this is maybe an unstable complex which has in one type one action, but if it's treated by steam the same material may be converted into a second type with a different action; and I was thinking of the model which was discussed this morning by Dr. Brenner of the coiled type of protein, where the thread was first coiled up in a definite pattern and then you get your particular type. I only wanted to ask this question: Are there really known in biochemistry now situations where you have a large complex molecule with definite properties and places for two prosthetic groups so that when you change these groups it changes into another biochemical type?

BRENNER: Trypsinogen?

LEHMANN: Yes.

POLLOCK: Well, a better case than that is the different types of chymo-trypsinogen and trypsin which can be converted one into another [31]. But they all have a very similar type of enzymatic action. There are also the muscle phosphorylases a and b [32] which can be converted one into another, but they, again, have very similar action. I should say that up to now there isn't any evidence at all that you can convert one type of protein directly into a completely different type of protein. It is only very closely related proteins which are inter-convertable.

WADDINGTON: How far are we dealing with native proteins in this situation? Because tissues which have been treated with 70% alcohol often induce quite well and I should have thought the proteins must have been denatured.

LEHMANN: Yamada has extracted these various proteins, as far as I remember, with salt. I do not think he used them after alcohol treatment.

WADDINGTON: I don't think he did, but other people have done and they get the same sort of result. You can certainly get induction of brains and archencephalic structures with materials which do not contain proteins in an undenatured state. So if you take a native protein as Yamada did and subjected it to steam, which would presumably denature it quite considerably, I should not be surprised to find it still active in this remarkably sensitive system.

BRENNER: I think there are two comments to make. What one would like to know is, in a general sense, what is the size and what is the general chemical nature of the substance which goes from the implant to what is being induced? There doesn't seem to be any agreement on that. We have heard of cases of very small molecules, and I understand there are cases of large molecules. But, I should like to make a general point which I think people working in this field should keep in mind. That is to mention the work of Puck [33] in which he has shown that a certain number of the large molecular weight components of serum, which are necessary for tissue culture, acts as carriers of small molecules; that is, he is able to replace a lot of the albumen requirement, which some cells seem to have, with a tryptic hydrolysate of albumen; and in one case he has actually pinned down the type of compound carried as cholesterol.

WADDINGTON: I don't want to interrupt the discussion here but before we get down to what we do know, or perhaps what we don't know, about the chemical nature of inducing agents, I think it may be better to get Nieuwkoop to give his slightly different picture of the system we are dealing with. He will talk about a more multi-phasic system, which you cannot avoid when you consider not only that you are inducing something, but exactly what it is that you induce. I think we should have that in front of us before going any further.

NIEUWKOOP: I think I shall have to make a very sharp restriction in the various aspects of neural induction to be dealt with here. There are far too many data available for a comprehensive discussion, and we shall just have to pick out some of the main perspectives. Before I do so I should like to make a remark about techniques because the question of techniques has probably something to do with the controversies in the literature.

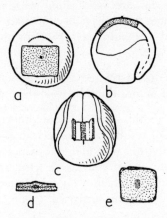

FIG. 8.5.

There have been a large number of older techniques, for instance, those of extirpation, transplantation from one place to another, translocation, and so on. All these techniques have one thing in common, viz. that they operate upon a very complex system in which there are a large number of variables which cannot be kept under control. When one tries to draw conclusions from such experiments it has to be kept in mind that the effect of the actual experimental interference might be camouflaged by variables which one has not had under control. So we have been looking for some other techniques, which may be a bit more simple, although since we are working on the supracellular level, they must still be considered as quite complicated. I just want to show you on two slides two techniques which are of some importance here. The first is the explantation technique [34]. In this technique one explants the reacting system, *in casu* the ectoderm, and tests its properties by making so-called sandwiches, with which one can easily test the capacities of certain inductive materials as well as the properties of the reaction system. Moreover, one can test the temporal aspects of the induction process by keeping the inductive material in the sandwich only for a certain length of time. This technique has the advantage that one replaces the normal, very complex system by a simpler one (see Fig. 8.5). But, there is also a second technique which can be used in the intact embryo; that is the so-called fold implantation technique [35]. In this technique, instead of introducing the reacting system as a flat piece into another embryo, one attaches it at a certain point. This has the great advantage that we can examine the inductive actions at a certain point in the system. In this way we can analyse the spatial relationships in the normal induction process (see Fig. 8.6).

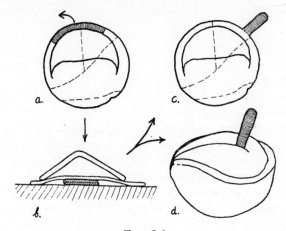

FIG. 8.6.

Now there are a few general points I would like to make. There is a growing amount of data which indicate that the process of induction takes place in several phases. At the moment we can distinguish at least two different phases. I have given these phases names in order to characterise them. The first phase I called "activation" and the second "transformation". In normal development these two processes apparently act one after the other. One can nicely illustrate this with the following slide (see Fig. 8.7). Here we have three successive stages of gastrulation, in which three areas of the future neurectoderm as well as the invaginating archenteron roof are indicated. In normal development region 1 will form the most caudal part of the nervous system, region 2 the middle part and region 3 the anterior part. If one however isolates region 1 just at the beginning of the induction process, then it does not form the caudal part as it would have done in normal development but forms the anterior part of the nervous system, namely, an archencephalon. The regions 2 and 3 only form epidermis. At the next stage, when the archenteron roof has moved forward, region 2 will form the archencephalic structures after isolation, while 3 still forms epidermis and part 1 is now forming deuterencephalic structures. At a still later stage the process has gone again

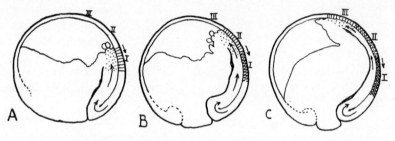

FIG. 8.7.

a step further and region 3 forms archencephalic, region 2 deuterencephalic and region 1 spinal cord structures. This means, that in normal development region 1 starts off in the direction of archencephalon, and only after the invagination process has proceeded for some time does it acquire the tendency to become deuterencephalon and still later spinal cord. Only a short period of action is needed, however, to allow development to continue in the direction which it has acquired at the moment the action is interrupted experimentally [36].

When one uses the sandwich technique, and one takes for instance notochordal material as inductor, but leaves it in only for a short time, one finds that it induces in the overlying reaction system only the anterior structures of the brain. It has to be left in for a much longer time before the same inductor is able to cause the reacting system to develop into rhombencephalic or spinal cord structures. Miss Johnen from Cologne has recently analysed the time requirements for such a process. In *Amblystoma mexicanum* it is found that the minimal time requirement for the first process of activation is about 5–15 min. It requires about ten hours of contact before the second process becomes effective and results in the formation of more posterior structures. When using *Triturus alpestris* the picture is different. It requires about four hours of contact before the first process starts in the reaction system, and it needs about

ten hours before the second becomes effective. This shows that there are
quite pronounced differences between the species used, so that results
obtained with one species cannot be generalised for other species [37].
It has still other implications. As I mentioned before, the reaction system
is only able to react during a certain period of time. Now, it turns out
that there is a close relationship between the time necessary for activation
and the duration of the period of competence. In *Amblystoma* a very
obvious decrease in competence begins shortly after stage 11, after which
it drops very rapidly and has almost disappeared by stage $12\frac{1}{2}$ (see Fig 8.8).

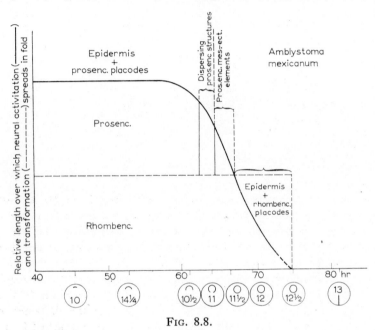

FIG. 8.8.

But, we know from the literature and from Gallera's work that in *Triturus*
the period of competence lasts longer. It can be stated that in species in
which the reaction system is very susceptible to inducing influences the
period of competence is rather short. Within a very short period after
the archenteron roof has reached its final extension the neural competence
has already disappeared in *Amblystoma*, whereas in *Triturus*, where the
reactivity of the ectoderm is much lower, the period over which it can
respond to inducing influences is considerably longer [18, 20].

Figure 8.9 shows a very preliminary experiment I did last spring in
order to see what forms the first visible effect of the inductive action.
I used fully competent ectoderm of a young gastrula, folded it double and
cut it up into two equal strips. One was kept in Holtfreter solution and

the other was attached to the neural plate of a neurula. Then the behaviour of these two, originally identical masses of tissue was recorded. After a short time, about three hours, a different behaviour can already be seen. The isolated piece begins to show a folding process. This continues and a strongly folded epithelium, typical for isolated ectoderm, is formed.

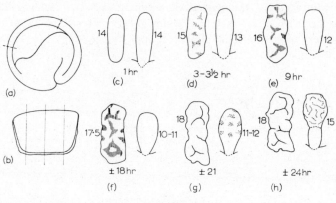

FIG. 8.9.

The implanted piece, however, behaves differently. As far as can be detected by this method, the whole area of the implant is from the very beginning under the control of the induction. It is not so that the basal part of the fold behaves differently from the rest, but some action spreads rapidly through the whole implant. Finally only a small part of the implant will become neuralised, indicating that it has passed the threshold value necessary for activation. But in spite of this, the whole fold must be under some form of control, which seems to have the character of an inhibition of the intrinsic epidermal tendencies. In the attached fold epidermal tendencies do not become expressed before a much later stage, but eventually show the same type of folding as was found in the isolated ectoderm at a much earlier stage. It therefore seems possible that in neural induction a certain action spreads very rapidly from the inductor. Although this primary action reaches the critical value for neural development only over a certain area, it probably also has some sort of effect in the regions where it is subliminal. The formation of secondary inductions, placode formation, etc., may be influenced by this subliminal inductive action [38].

After this primary activating action a second action takes place, which I called "transformation". This either starts much later, or expresses itself much later. We cannot yet distinguish between both possibilities. It is responsible for the regional differentiation within the nervous system.

I don't think we should go into detail about the spatial relationships in neural induction [15, 35]. I will for the moment restrict my remarks to the question of specificity, which seems to have more to do with our meeting here. One gets the impression that the process of activation can be brought about by quite a variety of agents, which seem to be fairly divergent in character. On the contrary, the process of transformation seems to have a more specific character. We cannot say very much more. In *in vivo* experiments it looks as if one needs a living system for the transforming action, but Toivonen has shown that one can also get the same effects with heterogeneous inductors [39, 40]. Anyhow, there seems to be a different specificity in both actions. However, the highest specificity is probably not to be found in the inducing agents but in the reaction system. This can only respond in one particular way or in a very restricted number of ways. It might be useful for discussion to make a small scheme about the pathways which are, as far as we know, possible in the differentiating ectoderm.

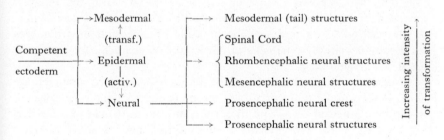

There are three primary pathways: the epidermal; the neural, dependent on the process of activation; and very probably also the direct pathway to mesodermal structures. As soon as the ectoderm has been activated and switched into the neural pathway, some further pathways are opened. After activation and without any subsequent action the ectoderm develops into typical prosencephalic structures. But, depending on the intensity of the second, transforming action one gets a series of successive secondary pathways, viz. to mes- and rhomb-encephalic, spinal cord and very probably also to mesodermal (tail) structures. Thus, mesoderm may also secondarily be obtained through the pathways opening up after neural activation. Besides these we have the pathway to neural crest formation. The secondary pathways lead therefore to neural, neural crest and also mesodermal development.

WADDINGTON: I think we need to discuss Dr. Nieuwkoop's two phases of induction before we start into the chemical nature of the inducing agents. My own reaction is this. When one says that so-and-so induces prosencephalic structures, or archencephalic structures, or mentions some other anatomical part of the animal, it seems to me difficult to make a definite picture of how that can happen. It is one thing to consider cells being transformed from one histological type to the other at the cellular level, but it is more difficult to conceive how a chemical substance can produce a complicated structure like a fore-brain with the eyes in the right place and all the rest of the pattern properly arranged. That form of organisation would seem to me what I should call a self-organisation, or self-individuation, which the tissue must produce from within itself.

Of course I agree with Nieuwkoop that if you take a piece of the living blastopore lip of a newt embryo and maltreat it in some way, chemically for instance, it will still go on inducing something, for instance, pieces of neural tissue. Those pieces of neural tissue, if left to themselves for several days, will quite often transform themselves into a quite well-organised fore-brain. That seems to be the hard core of the process of induction, which persists more or less however you treat the inducer. The capacity for later self-individuation into a definite organ may or may not be realised. In some morphogenetically unfavourable environments the tissue may simply retain the original induced character for perhaps a dozen cell generations.

A capacity to induce mid-brain, hind-brain, or spinal cord is much more labile, but I wonder whether we are forced to consider these two phases, first inducing neural tissue and then transforming it. Could one say that one induces, with some relatively quick-acting and resistant inducer, simple neural cells which if left to themselves will transform themselves into a fore-brain-like structure, while a further action by a more labile inducer may induce mesoderm; and then according to the proportion of mesoderm and neural material the complex moulds itself into other parts of the embryonic axis. If there is a lot of mesoderm it may tend to form an elongated structure with a neural tube and a row of somites on each side of it: if there is an intermediate amount of mesoderm, it may form a larger neural structure, which may eventually attain the appearance of a mid-brain or hind-brain. I should find the situation easier to understand if we could interpret it in that way, and in my opinion some of Toivonen's work, in which he seems to induce purely mesodermal structures, with no accompanying neural material, seems to me easier to accommodate in a scheme in which you have a neural inductor and a mesodermal inductor, rather than a scheme in which everything is first induced as neural material and then maybe transformed further into complete anatomical entities.

Another point I should like to make is that I think it is important to consider, not only the final organs which can be recognised in the induction many days after the inducing action has taken place, but also to consider the character of the reacting material during this intervening period. I believe that the specificity gradually becomes more well defined; shortly after the inducing action a piece of neural tissue may have a rather indefinite regional character, even though later it may develop into a perfectly well-defined mid-brain, for instance.

NIEUWKOOP: I should like to reply to some of the remarks. I completely agree that it is much easier to speak of neural and mesodermal inductors than of prosencephalic, rhombencephalic and spinal cord inductors. The process of development is however so complicated and we know so little about the various steps that we can only characterise the processes by their end-products. We have to use words which characterise the phenomena as accurately as possible.

As I hope to show in the next session the formation of a prosencephalon out of "activated" cell material is for the greater part due to self-organisation or self-individuation. The induction phenomena only concern the first steps in the chain reaction.

The distinction between a "neural" and a "mesodermal" inductor is however too simplistic. This distinction would only hold for the first step in the induction process (primary pathways) where a direct neural and a direct mesodermal pathway seem to exist. However, the same "mesodermal" inductor is, as far as we know, also responsible for the formation of mes- and rhomb-encephalic and spinal cord structures which are purely neural and not at all mesodermal in character. Only the secondary tail mesoderm formation out of neural material is again mesodermal in character. A characterisation of the second inductive action as mesodermal therefore does not seem adequate.

TOIVONEN: I agree with Nieuwkoop in many points. For instance, in this, that normally there is first an archencephalic action and afterwards there will occur a "transformation", as Nieuwkoop call its, to the formations of more caudal regions. But I don't like the expressions activation and transformation, because these expressions imply that the first action would be unspecific. In my opinion, they are both specific inductive actions. I have called them neuralising and mesodermalising actions; and they are both specific, caused by different inductive principles.

I have done some experiments using bone marrow tissue as an inductor. I have removed the inductor after different lapses of time. If I removed the inductor after two hours from an epidermis sandwich, the explant will form only mesodermal structures. The first action is now purely mesodermalising.—According to Nieuwkoop there would always firstly be an unspecific archencephalic "activation".—These results of mine are possible because the bone marrow, contrary to living notochord which Nieuwkoop has used, is a mesodermalising inductor, since it contains mesodermalising agents.

In my opinion in the normogenesis there are also two kinds of principles, the neuralising one and the mesodermalising one. The former forms a dorsal field with lateral decrements, and the latter forms a caudocranial gradient. When the neuralising agent acts alone, the result will be archencephalic formations; but when the neuralising principle acts together with a moderate mesodermalising principle, the result will be the deuterencephalic formations; and when a strong mesodermalising action is combined with a moderate neuralising action, there will be formed trunk formations, such as spinal cord, somites, notochord, etc. We have been able to test this scheme [41] by putting simultaneously two inductors, liver tissue and bone marrow tissue, into the same epidermis explant or into the same gastrula. The liver tissue is an almost purely neuralising inductor, though there is a weak mesodermalising tendency, which would make it possible that deuterencephalic formations may also be formed; whereas the bone marrow is an almost pure mesodermalising inductor, though a very weak neuralising action may also be present. When both inductors are present in the same gastrula or in the same sandwich, I have got the whole dorsal system induced with normal sequence of the different regions. There are the archencephalic region, deuterencephalic region and also the spino-caudal region with the spinal cord and the complete tail. The spinal cord is never induced by liver tissue alone, the liver induces cephalic formation only—and it is only exceptionally induced by bone marrow.

I have also made some experiments like this. I have first put into an epidermis explant a piece of bone marrow and removed it after three hours and replaced it into the same explant with a piece of liver. Now I have got a very similar result as in the simultaneous series. This material is very scanty, and it is not yet examined microscopically, but it appears that though the first action is the mesodermalising one and the second the neuralising, the result is the same as in the simultaneous series. That would mean that you can also get experimentally a mesodermalising "activation" and a neuralising "transformation", in Nieuwkoop's words.

NIEUWKOOP: There seems to be some misunderstanding. I fully agree with Dr. Toivonen that there are from the beginning two or three separate pathways. Either the tissue goes in the epidermal, or in the neural, or, probably directly, in the mesodermal, direction. But this concerns only the first phase of primary pathways. Afterwards we have to do with secondary pathways. If one tests the inducing capacity of a certain part of the mesoderm of a neurula, for instance the notochordal tissue, this never directly induces mesodermal structures in competent ectoderm. When one leaves it in only for a very *short* time a neural formation is formed, which finally develops into prosencephalon. From this notochord also a secondary action emanates, which is effective only after a *longer* period of contact. Removal of the notochord after a sufficiently long period of contact leads to the formation of rhombencephalon or spinal cord, which neural structures are however *not* associated with mesodermal elements. Caudal neural structures can therefore be formed without any additional induction of mesodermal structures.

WADDINGTON: I don't think we had better try to pursue the full details of this controversy, because I think even its proponents would probably agree that it cannot be fully resolved at the present time. The point has been sufficiently made that the normal inducing system in the amphibian gastrula is a complex system, in which there are several phases, and probably several different types of active substance are involved. Exactly how those phases are related to one another is still unclear, and leaving the controversy unresolved except for agreement that we are dealing with complex reactions, I feel that the next question we should discuss is what is the general nature of those reactions?

We are dealing with a phenomenon in which the type of chemical change going on in the cell will be specified by influences coming in from outside. What type of influences are they? One possibility is that they are purely surface reactions, as Weiss has suggested in connection with certain types of induction. Another possibility, of course, is the actual diffusion of chemical substances. In order to introduce the question of whether, or in how far, diffusable substances can be supposed to be involved, I should like myself to show a few slides, illustrating some work we have been doing here, in an attempt to discover whether any diffusion really occurs.

We have tried to investigate this by radioactive labelling. If the organiser region from an amphibian gastrula is cultivated for some time in a radioactive amino acid or other suitable metabolite, you get labelled tissue which can then be used as the graft. One can then investigate by autoradiography whether in the next few hours—we have usually left the grafts for 24 hr before fixing—anything diffuses out of the graft into the surrounding tissues. It very quickly becomes apparent that there is some diffusion of label from the graft into the host tissues. When the labelling is done with amino acids (e.g. methionine, glycine) or purine bases such as adenine, it is found that this label which has diffused is largely located in the nuclei of the host ectoderm cells. Now, we know that free labelled amino acids or purines applied to those cells will also tend to be accumulated in the nuclei. It is therefore possible to argue that what has moved from the graft into the ectoderm is simply the free labelled molecules, which have been liberated by degradation processes in the organiser tissue.

These experiments make it difficult to argue that there has been any movement from the graft of massive quantities of cytoplasmic labelled material. I am not quite sure how far Brachet, when he suggested that induction might depend on the movement of ribonucleo-protein granules, thought of this as a massive movement. In our experience one cannot detect any large scale movement of cytoplasmic material. Typical situations are illustrated in [42]. In the grafted organiser material there is a strong concentration of label over the nuclei. In the reacting ectoderm it is, perhaps, possible to argue that the concentration on the nuclei is not quite so well marked. We have not yet been able to put this impression on a quantitative basis, and I think the furthest one could go is to say that the slides give a slight impression that the diffused label is rather more concentrated in the cytoplasm than would be expected from a free amino acid; but the difference is at best only a slight one in this amphibian material. Certainly, in the cells of the host ectoderm you can still see the concentration of grains over the nucleoli which you find when cells are provided with free amino acids.

In Fig. 8.10, the graft was one of the inducing adult tissues—the so-called heterologous inducers such as those Toivonen has worked with. The graft was mouse kidney, taken from a mouse which has been injected with labelled adenine. The kidney was treated with 70% alcohol, in the way that has been done in many of Toivonen's experiments. In this case you can see that the label which has passed out of the graft is predominantly in the cytoplasm, and the nuclei of the reacting tissues are relatively clear of label. This is a completely different disposition of label from what one finds if the cells are given free labelled adenine, and also quite different from what one finds, if they have picked up their label from the organiser of the gastrula, as we have just seen. This suggests that from adult tissues the transferred tracer does not go into the cytological locations at which free amino acid or free purine is absorbed. It would seem likely that the tracer is not diffusing in the form the free small-molecular compounds. We cannot yet go further than that as to the nature of the vehicle in which the tracer passes, nor, of course, can we yet say that it is definitely concerned with the induction; but at least here we have the possibility that one is observing the transfer of the actually effective inducing agent.

Perhaps I should mention one other case, since we want to be able to consider all the different sorts of induction. We have one example of induction where you get a really massive transfer of label from the inducer into the reacting material. When optic vesicles of *Xenopus* are labelled with methionine or phenylalanine, and allowed to induce lenses from competent ectoderm, we find that after a short time the induced lens comes to contain more tracer than the graft from which it has picked up

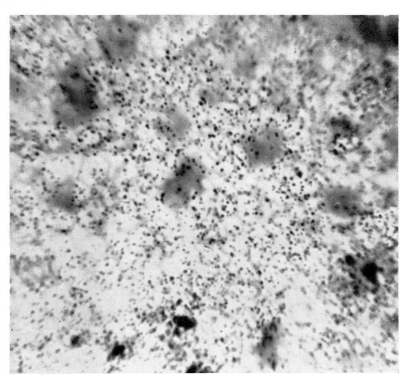

FIG. 8.10.

the radioactive atoms [43]. Possibly that is connected with rapid protein synthesis in the lens, but it is a very different situation from what one finds with the normal induction by the blastopore lip region.

It therefore seems that in some cases, at least, induction may very well involve the diffusion of substances from one tissue to another, but different types of induction show rather different behaviour in this respect.

POLLOCK: What you've got there in the reacting tissue is a concentration of the tracer?

WADDINGTON: Yes.

BRENNER: May I ask you if you've done these experiments in the presence of a pool of cold amino acids?

WADDINGTON: We have not yet done that with amphibia, but we have done it in the chick [44]. In these experiments the inducing material was labelled with methionine, and the presence of a pool of unlabelled methionine *did* reduce the uptake into the reacting ectoderm. Actually, in the chick there were rather divergent types of evidence as to whether the diffusion was in the form of free amino acid or not. The fact that cold amino acid reduces the uptake from the graft suggests that it is free amino acid which is diffusing. On the other hand, the tracer moves rather slowly into its surroundings, suggesting a slow process of diffusion such as might be expected for a large molecular compound. Again, Dr. Brahma [43a] did some experiments involving gradocol membranes—porous membranes of known pore size—and found no evidence of tracer going right through the membrane; also, we got no induction through the membrane. However, in the autoradiographs, when the membrane had been dissolved away, there was clearly tracer in the place where the membrane had been. That tracer must have been in an insoluble form, suggesting that it was attached to large molecules, such as proteins, which were in process of diffusing slowly through the membranes and were left behind by the histological treatment. That seems to provide some evidence on the other side, arguing against the diffusion being only in the form of small molecules.

POLLOCK: But you did not abolish the effects by the pool of cool amino acids, did you? Was it only a 10% reduction or something like that?

WADDINGTON: A larger reduction. It didn't abolish the effect, but it was more like a 60% reduction.

POLLOCK: You're almost certainly going to get *some* protein breakdown products, so the cool amino acids are certain to reduce the transfer. I don't myself think that it's very significant.

BRENNER: Yes.

16

POLLOCK: You've got some residual transfer which happened even in the presence of free amino acid. That, I should say, is the important thing.

WADDINGTON: Yes, I agree.

BRENNER: I was just going to remark that these sort of experiments seem to be in the peculiar stage that phage transfer experiments were a few years ago. What I want to know is, is it technically possible to distinguish between say a ^{14}C amino acid and a ^{35}N one? Can you distinguish the autoradiographs?

WADDINGTON: We have thought of trying to do double labelling.

BRENNER: I mean can you put, for instance, a filter between the section and the stripping film, which will block out the ^{14}C but not the ^{35}N?

PLAUT: The energies are much too close; but you might be able to distinguish by the half lives.

BRENNER: If so, the thing to do would be to do double labelling experiments and show that the ratios of the specific activities remain constant even on transfer.

WADDINGTON: I think you could distinguish a tritium label from a ^{14}C label.

CALLAN: As regards the membranes, has there been much work done recently with membranes of different pore size placed between the inducer and the induced material?

WADDINGTON: Quite a lot of work has been done in certain other inductive systems, but not much in connection with the primary amphibian organiser. In particular, Grobstein has made such studies on the induction of tubule formation in mouse kidney epithelia. But the difficulty here is that probably all these different inductive systems operate quite differently from one another. The fact that something passes through a filter in one kind does not mean that you are likely to find a similar phenomenon in another inductive process.

WEISS: I should like to say, in connection with lens induction in the chick, for instance, that I think it is pretty well established now that there is one phase which does not require contact with the eye vesicle. In this the lens area is roughly blocked out so as to produce one of the lens specific proteins. Langman has shown that. The next phase picks out one part of that area and carries through another step of induction on top of the first. This does require contact. The definitive lens area is coextensive with the area of contact, and can be experimentally varied by changing the area of contact; for instance, by putting a membrane in.

It is probably connected with the induction of a second lens protein. So, it is as you said; one part of the induction may require contact and the other one may not require contact.

BRACHET: In some experiments made some years ago, when the ectoderm was separated from the organiser by a Cellophane membrane, I got a complete interruption of induction [45, 46]. That might be due to the fact that there is no contact, owing to the Cellophane; but it might also be that the diffusion of large molecules is required for the induction. I do not know of any other explanations, but we cannot decide between those two. The experiment only shows, I think, that one cannot get induction in this system by small molecules that can penetrate the Cellophane. This Cellophane had fairly large pores; though the size is not absolutely known. I know, for instance, that the nucleotides and even commercial RNA could quickly go though these membranes. Other experiments have been made in our Institute using a series of millipore membranes which had been given us by Dr. Grabar of Paris, and had been used for trying to measure the diameter of virus particles. The results have never been published in full for the following reason: when using the membranes with the largest pores, we got rather weak inductive reactions on the other side—not proper neural tissue, but a sort of palisade. This might, however, be due to purely mechanical reasons; the membrane might modify the polarity of the cells which are in contact with it. But the catch to these experiments was that when we started to make controls—that is, placing a piece of membrane between two pieces of ectoderm—a high proportion of them showed the same sort of effect. Therefore, we cannot conclude anything except to say that the membranes exerted some sort of an inductive effect by a non-specific mechanism. Still I think, however, that there may be a diffusion of large molecules during induction and I also think that autoradiography has done nothing to disprove this; neither the work of Waddington [47], nor the work of Madame Ficq did [48]. But these experiments also show that there is almost certainly a transfer also of free amino acids or free purine bases, which is to be expected.

I have made other experiments of almost the same kind as those I have just mentioned; but, in these, instead of using tracers—because it was before their day—I used a vital stain applied either to the organiser or the ectoderm [49]. One point which came out is that, if you homogenise the tissue after the vital staining, you cannot find any stain which is free in solution: it all goes with the sedimentable material and the supernatant is absolutely colourless. So there is reason to believe that there is probably no free dye in the living cells. Now if you do this sort of experiment even for a very short time—the action goes very quickly as Dr. Nieuwkoop said—even if you remove the organiser after only 15 min—you find that unstained ectoderm is coloured. But, in the reverse experiment (i.e. contact between stained ectoderm and unstained organiser) one also gets staining of the organiser. This is, therefore, no specific, unidirectional transfer of the stained material from the organiser to the ectoderm.

WADDINGTON: I think we might now go to a rather more biochemical level, and perhaps Jean Brachet would give us a few words about the biochemistry of induction as he sees it at the present time.

BRACHET: All I can do is to give you a very short account of this problem, because I think it is so complex that if we were to go into details, it could involve a whole symposium. Now there are two possible approaches to the biochemical mechanisms of induction. One is to try to isolate an inducing substance, or to extract from adult tissues an active substance. The other is to stick closer to the embryological material and try to find out what is going on in the living organiser and in the ectoderm in normal development. Of course, as you know, attempts have been made to go along both these lines.

Now the efforts which have been made to try to isolate an active substance have, on the whole, been rather frustrating for a very long time. When one came to the realisation that many different substances would induce and that substances which do not exist in normal tissues also induce, one became rather worried. The possibility is, of course—as was pointed out by Waddington [50] a long time ago when I was in Cambridge with him—that one is dealing with a sort of relay mechanism; that is, that there may be a potential inducing substance in the ectoderm; in some unspecific way, you can set it free and it then becomes active. There is really no good way to get around that difficulty. In experiments where one has grafted a chemical substance and where one wants to get an explanation on a biochemical level, there is always a possibility that the host may not be inactive. There is no doubt that, in many cases, the graft undergoes a certain degree of degeneration, in which usually RNA is broken down pretty quickly and disappears from the cytoplasm, as indicated by a decrease in basophilia. So one has to deal with a rather complex situation. If one adds some substance, it is not necessarily this substance which is still active at the time of the induction. On the other hand, I think that the new results, about which we heard today from Toivonen and what Lehmann told us about Yamada's last work, indicates that one should not be too pessimistic. We may be reaching a stage at which this type of work may become very useful again and lead to conclusive results. Thanks to Toivonen and Yamada, we know now which are the tissues and organs which are most active in induction, particularly in relation to the specific types of induction. This is, of course, a considerable improvement as compared with the situation as it was before the war.

Now, the little reliable work which has been done on the chemical composition of the various fractions which are present in adult tissues indicates that, as a general rule, ribonucleoproteins are very active. That is the result which I found many years ago [51], and which Yamada [52] has confirmed using better methods for the isolation of the ribonucleoproteins. There is thus a certain tendency—it might not be an absolute rule—to find inducing activity associated with the ribonucleoprotein fraction. Regarding the active part of the ribonucleoprotein, I think it is pretty clear now that you can eliminate the ribonucleic acid, or at any rate most of it, by extensive digestion with ribonuclease, without any loss of activity. Thus the proteins —to which of course there is always attached a little bit of nucleic acid— are active by themselves. I will just mention in passing that in my first experiments in 1943 [53], carried out under war-time conditions, I got opposite results; I got a loss of activity when the ribonucleoproteins were treated with ribonuclease. But there is absolutely no doubt now that that was due to contamination of the ribonuclease which was available with proteolytic enzymes [54]. On the other hand, one has found that RNA isolated from various sources is not active, or shows only very slight activity [55], but to me that does not carry much weight since RNA might be very specific; one would have to find the right RNA, and obtain it in a form which was not degraded. Since we know that that presents a very difficult problem I think we must leave this question for the future.

Another thing is that it is not certain that the same agent or chemical substance, or even the same mechanism, which operates in the case of induction by killed tissue is active in the induction by the living organiser. That is another reason why I think one will have to make parallel experiments on the living organiser and on killed tissues.

Regarding what is happening in the living embryo, we have a little information, but it does not go very far. What is certainly the most striking thing is the existence of gradient systems. In amphibian eggs, and also in all vertebrate eggs, there are gradients of the distribution of a number of substances. These gradients are particularly easy to show for RNA, because we have nice cytological methods to detect RNA [56]; but that does not mean, of course, that the gradients do not exist for quite a number of other substances which are more difficult to demonstrate cyto-chemically. Also there may be specific proteins attached to the RNA, but we have no sort of way to demonstrate that the proteins are distributed in the same gradient as is the RNA. One could also say that these gradients are metabolic gradients, in the sense that the oxygen consumption of the egg varies in different regions [57], and the reducing activity also follows the same type of gradients [58, 59]. We have also found in our laboratory that the incorporation of $^{14}CO_2$ into proteins and RNA follows the same type of gradients [60].

The situation regarding these gradients is fairly simple. What one essentially finds is that, if you start with an unfertilised or newly fertilised egg, there is an animal–vegetative gradient; this is essentially due to the higher concentration of the cytoplasm, which contains RNA granules and so on near the animal pole. Nothing changes very much during the whole period of cleavage. If you study the incorporation of $^{14}CO_2$ with the auto-radiographic method, you can also hardly find this animal–vegetative gradient; during the morula and blastula stages, there is practically only one thing labelled, and that is the nuclei. These become very strongly labelled, and it looks as though the only thing happening during cleavage is the synthesis of DNA and the proteins associated with it. There seems to be no appreciable RNA or protein synthesis in the cytoplasm at that time. It is only at the time of gastrulation that things start moving; by that time, you find that the RNA content of the organiser, and the $^{14}CO_2$ incorporation in that region, progressively increase. Thus one has the impression that one starts with a primary animal–vegetative gradient, and that one has the superposition of a secondary dorsal–ventral gradient on top of this. The co-existence of these two gradients, and the progressive increase in the intensity of the dorsal–ventral gradient, will lead to a situation of some complexity. I will not try to describe this in detail, but it will finally lead to the following situation in the neurula: There is an anterior–posterior gradient existing everywhere in any organ—in the neural system, as well as in the chorda and in the somites. Then there is a second type of gradient which is visible particularly in the chorda-mesoderm; this is a dorsal–ventral gradient so that there is more RNA in the chorda than in the somites, and more of it there than in the pronephros; there is still less RNA in the ventral mesoblast.

There are, of course, many changes in the biochemical activities of the egg during development, and perhaps all that one is observing is a change of the yolk reserve into cytoplasm. It looks as if the conversion of the yolk into pure cytoplasm—and in that I include the mitochondria, ergasto-plasm and so on—occurs faster on the dorsal side than on the ventral side, and in fact proceeds according to these gradients. There is one further remark I want to make in regard to these gradients and CO_2 incorporation. In the young gastrula, you get a picture which is absolutely identical with what you see with the RNA detection method; but, as I told you before, one has a strong incorporation in the various nuclei. In the young gastrula —in our experiments, the situation is rather different from the photo-graph Dr. Waddington showed the other day—we did not observe any great difference in the activity of the nuclei of the various regions, although they are placed in a cytoplasm which is obviously different; but, in the late gastrula at the yolk plug stage, which is about the period at which according to the transplantation experiments of Briggs and King [61] the nuclei begin to differentiate, we could find great differences. On the whole, these differences now follow the incorporation in the cytoplasm; that is, at this stage, the nuclei which are in the cytoplasm which incorporates most will also themselves incorporate most rapidly [60].

The only other thing I would like to mention to close this short discussion is that I have little doubt that the maintenance of these gradients is in some way really essential for morphogenesis. There have been a lot of experiments done—there are still not enough—of many different types, in which one has tried to interfere with the synthesis of RNA, or with the distribution of RNA; and one always finds that there are parallel changes in morphogenesis. For instance, if you add chemical analogues of purines, you will inhibit RNA synthesis, and you will also inhibit morphogenesis without any very marked abnormality, at least with the analogues I have been using [46].

Another way, which is entirely different, is the study of lethal hybridisation [62]. If one fertilises the egg of one species with the sperm of another species, it often stops at the early gastrula. That is the time when RNA and protein synthesis should normally begin, but they do not begin in the lethal hybrid. If, however, one transplants a piece of this lethal hybrid into a normal host, then one observes a resumption of RNA synthesis and DNA synthesis, with mitoses, cytoplasmic RNA synthesis and presumably protein synthesis coming back. Another way you can do almost the same thing is to submit the young gastrula to a heat shock [63]. If you heat the embryo for about one hour at around 37°C, you completely block its development, and you also completely block RNA, DNA and protein synthesis. Again, if you take a piece of the heated gastrula and transplant it into a normal gastrula, you can find the resumption of all activities, including morphogenesis. Still another way is to centrifuge the eggs: what you do then is really to destroy the gradients. I cannot go into the details of these experiments, but, if you centrifuge the young fertilised egg, you will get considerable reduction of the formation of the head; the embryo is microcephalic and you may, in some cases, have practically no nervous system whatever. This can be explained by the gradients being disturbed. Instead of having a RNA gradient, you have now a RNA layer with a yolk layer beneath it so that what invaginates has much less RNA than it should. On the other hand, if you centrifuge a young gastrula, you can obtain double embryos or triple embryos. In this case, you find that there are strong local accumulations of RNA which precede the formation of the individual embryonic axes [64].

So I think that what we should do for the future is, on the one hand, to be interested in the work being done by Toivonen and Yamada and others—that is certainly to be followed—but, on the other hand, there are a lot more experiments—purely embryological experiments I would say—

which should be analysed with cytochemical methods. For instance, we should check the RNA distribution and the incorporation of isotopes in ectoderm which is neuralised by chemical means, and by a living organiser. I am sure that experiments like those of Nieuwkoop would be extremely interesting to analyse from such a viewpoint. It is only by combining these two types of method and thinking that we shall make any progress.

LEHMANN: I should like also to recommend the combination of electron microscope studies with just the point of view Brachet has emphasised. As regards the neural plate and the roof of the archenteron, Richard Eakin [65] has made some electron microscope studies in our laboratory, and he has been shown that there is a rather complicated pattern of structures. If you take just one neural cell and just one notochord cell, then he has found that there are some pseudopodia-like processes coming out from the neural cell and these meet very closely some parts coming out from the notochord cell. Looking with the electron microscope Eakin has not been able to find very strong boundaries between these cells, it rather looks as though they were in some places anastosmoses; and between them there are always a great many cavities which have a well defined limiting membrane, so it appears that we have in this special case a double system. Then in the neural system there are many mitochondria, as there are in the ventral epidermis also. In the later stages, as soon as the epidermis begins to produce glandlike structures you get a dense layer of mitochondria which seem to be very active. So one gets from these observations also some information about the presumed activity of the cell components. The same seems to be true of the nuclei. They rather look empty in the gastrula, whereas the nuclei in the early neurula are full of substance—what it is we don't know yet, I only want to indicate that the low power electron micrography is very useful for all kinds of studies and reveals physiological phenomena of interest.

BRACHET: I would only like to add that some structure of the membrane definitely contains RNA. I saw that a long time ago with ordinary microscopy. People have suggested that these RNA containing elements of the membrane might be an artifact; but these thin membranes can be seen very well and they stain strongly with pyronin [51].

LEHMANN: They are very dense.

NIEUWKOOP: As regards these observations with the electron microscope made by Eakin in Lehmann's laboratory, I can confirm this with the chick. Some years ago at the Institute of Professor Weiss in Chicago, we could see in the region where the induction takes place, particularly on the mid-line, that not only is there an intimate contact, but also some indication of interdigitation, and it is questionable whether there is any membrane formation in that area in contrast to the areas more lateral.

WEISS: Just to supplement what Dr. Nieuwkoop has said: During the critical stage of induction you can make a microdissection experiment with the electron microscope by burning the plastic film with a heavy dose of electrons. Then you find that there will be breaks right through the cells rather than between cells engaged in inductive interaction. McKeehan found the same firm bonding between the eye-cup and the lens during the actual period of induction, which is only about two hours. During that time this connection cannot be readily broken. For that reason I suggested at St. Andrews that perhaps a molecular bridge is formed at that time between the two cells which open pathways for substance transfer. I think such a due consideration of structure plus physiological analyses is absolutely essential.

Let me point out that if you have in your laboratory two bottles on your shelves, containing different solutions, unless you break them both you won't get a reaction. This illustrates the relation of structure to chemistry. In the cell, likewise, it is primarily the structural conditions under which the reactions take place, and not simply the presence of the ingredients, that we have to consider. Now, recently Balinsky has published a paper [66] suggesting that the appearance of the basement membrane between the epidermis and the underlying mesoderm, which I showed you the other day, seems to preclude inductive interactions between them. He has evidence that at the time the basement membrane is interposed it insulates the two tissues against each other's inductive interactions. He worked with limb induction, but the same thing may be true in other cases. Now if that is true, then we have a natural experiment concerning the types of molecules which would be active in those conditions. Because we know that the epidermis receives its entire supply of nutrients, nuclear and otherwise, across the basement membrane. It is not vascularised; it gets all its needs and its regular supplies across the basement membrane. So if the basement membrane precludes inductive interactions, but still passes everything that is being required later on, then whatever is involved in the inductive interaction must be of larger molecular size than what goes through in the form of nutrients.

WADDINGTON: I presume that in this case the inductive molecules must be large ones, but membranes do not always pass molecules strictly according to size. It may be that there is something pretty specific about the molecules which perform the induction.

WEISS: It is true, of course, that the polysaccharide which forms the matrix of the basement is probably not too permeable for the hydrophilic molecules which may be involved. The point I wanted to make is that it is really a system which is worth further exploration, and is perhaps more favourable than the artificial membranes that have been used so far.

NIEUWKOOP: In the experiments in which the notochord has been introduced into ectodermal sandwiches and then removed again one finds that the notochord very quickly becomes attached to the ectoderm. The time requirements I have shown are extremely short, and they are about the same as the time requirements for the attachment of the two layers. This is perhaps some evidence in the same direction.

BRENNER: May I ask whether anyone has just dissociated the two pieces into individual cells, and seen whether these cells mate? If the dissociated cells of the two layers are morphologically different, or if they could be marked with tracers, would one find that in mixtures one got mating of opposite cell types?

WADDINGTON: I think one of the points that ought to be taken up by somebody next—I hope not by myself, as it's rather tricky—should be the study of induction with disaggregated cells. One would like to know what happens if one changes the relative numbers; one, two or more ectoderm cells to one, two or more archenteron roof cells and so on; and also what would happen if you let them reaggregate for a certain length of time and then took them apart again. It seems to me that the aggregation and disaggregation technique ought to provide one with a very beautiful quantitative method of tackling the problem of induction.

BRENNER: Exactly as Jacob and Wollman [67] have tackled the problem of conjugation. If there is a sort of conjugation, if we can call it that, and if material is passing, you have got the copy-book for investigating such situations; you can work out the dependence on the length of conjugation, the amount of the injection, if we can use that word.

WADDINGTON: Unfortunately, I don't think you can stop and start re-aggregation quite so quickly as you can with phages sitting on bacteria, but even so I think the technique ought to be explored.

PONTECORVO: Would trypsin digestion do the trick?

WEISS: I think Holtfreter has made experiments along those lines, but this particular research cannot be carried out in that way for technical reasons.

WILDE: I would just like to make a plea, that we should remember that not only may large molecules be transferred from cell to cell but that it may be possible to transfer particulate mixtures of macro- or supra-molecular structure. I mean that an actual piece of cytoplasm may be transferred in this way. Indeed Spratt [68] has raised this question in chick embryogenesis; not only does a cell have a machine which will transfer large molecules, but it may have one which will pass organised or oriented pieces of cytoplasm. I do not think this should be forgotten.

WADDINGTON: A mechanism something like *in vivo* pinocytosis?

WILDE? Yes, that's right.

WEISS: Well, as a matter of fact, I have maintained for years that it is illogical that a cell can pick up large chunks, as we can see in phagocytosis, and small molecules, but that the region of the size spectrum in between is left out. Schechtman has recently made the same point. You probably have cells picking up things of all sizes down to individual molecules, depending on the conditions.

WILDE: A point I should like to make is to remind the group of the obvious relevance of the whole question of active transport. That is to say, whether the cells pick up only particular molecules, and whether energy is used to pass them selectively across the membrane. This may be a point of view from which part of the experimental analysis of this problem should be done. I think cellular physiologists would be rather upset if we neglected this particular aspect of bio-energetics.

WADDINGTON: I think we shall have to continue with induction to some extent tomorrow, when we are discussing tissue organisation. For instance, we shall want to talk about Zwilling's interactions between ecto-derm and mesenchyme in the limb bud and I think Holtzer would prob-ably like to say something further about his induction of cartilage, which seems to be a rather different type of process in which perhaps cell-to-cell contact is not essential. In the last part of this discussion we've been emphasising the important part that may be played by cellular contact and anastomosis and so on, but in other types of induction they may not be so important.

DAN: I should like to know what sort of picture you get when you use a labelled non-inducing piece for autoradiography.

WADDINGTON: When you make an autoradiograph with a labelled non-inducing piece of the gastrula you get very much the same picture as with the inducing region; that is to say, the passage of a substance which might very well be the free tracer. I think in these cases there is always so much free amino acid passing that it obscures anything else. With adult tissues, where you do get passage into the cytoplasm—that is to say, not where the free tracer would be expected to go—I think all the tissues we have used would be expected to be inducing, so I can't give you a very definite answer for adult tissues.

BRENNER: I wanted to ask whether anyone has examined the range of species difference permissible in such systems of induction. I don't mean with dead tissues; but would you get this contact between cells if you used living cells of different species?

WADDINGTON: I'm not sure about the phenomenon of cell-contact, but certainly within the amphibia the range within which you can get induction is extremely wide. Almost any amphibian species will induce in almost any other, and the two different tissues remain perfectly healthy. Even if you go outside the amphibia, you can again get induction; but if the inducing tissue is taken from a fish or a chick or something of that kind, it probably does not remain alive very long. Of course, with these very wide differences you may be getting the induction by a secondary reaction, through a relay mechanism.

WEISS: As far as contact is concerned, Moscona in my laboratory has now shown very extensively that mouse cells and chick cells live happily together and form chimaeric organs, but only if they are of the same tissue; that is to say, tissue specificity overrides species specificity in contact relations. That answers your question but at the same time it proves that you cannot carry out the experiment as you were thinking.

WADDINGTON: There is one remark I would like to make, but I'm not absolutely sure of the whole story; perhaps Lehmann knows it all. It seems to me that in some of Baltzer's work, where they combine tissues from two quite different classes of amphibia, they could get a piece of anuran tissue to become induced to form a part of a chondrocranium of a newt which the anuran does not have [69]. Thus anuran tissue can be induced early to form elements which that species (*Bombinator*) does not possess at the larval stage. That seems to me a very surprising situation.

WEISS: You are talking about Wagner, and Andres, and so on!

LEHMANN: As far as I recall there are chimaeric teeth formed from *Bombinator* neural crest grafted on to newt [70].

WADDINGTON: Yes, and also ears and the associated structure around the ear. The point is that one had always considered it as rather a dogma that cells would only form organs for which they had the genes, but I think there are some cases in this field in which the cells at least take part in the formation of quite foreign organs.

WEISS: It takes part in the formation, but according to its own innate repertory; the cell forms a corresponding piece but it has the species characteristics of the donor.

WADDINGTON: Yes, that is the dogma; but I thought that these cases were an exception to it.

WEISS: I just went over that material recently. These beasts have chimaeric labyrinths, but I don't know whether there are any intermediate structures. Lehmann has seen the experiments.

LEHMANN: I have not seen them, but I gather that at least the teeth are formed by *Bombinator* papilla as early as in the newt, and the *Bombinator* part in those teeth was able to develop as early as the newt enamel organ.

WADDINGTON: So the *Bombinator* cells were taking part in the formation of the structure which *Bombinator* does not possess so early?

ZWILLING: I think before we leave this discussion it may be well to emphasise again that there are cases in which it seems as though contact induction is not taking place. I think the sort of thing that Grobstein [71] has done with his millipore membranes must be borne in mind, as applicable to some induction systems. In this sort of induction system it seems as though a large molecule is involved, presumably not of a nucleic acid nature. There is some evidence that this is more likely a mucopolysaccharide.

WEISS: I think we are pretty well agreed by now that the term induction is merely a property of the observer, who lumps all kind of phenomena, which are intrinsically different and have different mechanisms, under a common label; it would be quite illogical to expect that they all have the same mechanisms. Therefore, I think we should quit talking about contact versus diffusable inductions and simply study each case in its own right.

ZWILLING: And I think we should also stop talking about *the inductive process*.

WEISS: Quite. I hope you don't accuse me of having coined that phrase.

REFERENCES

1. BOELL, E. J. and S. C. SHEN (1950) *J. Exp. Zool.* **113**, 583.
2. WILDE, C. E. Jr. (1955a) *J. Exp. Zool.* **130**, 573.
3. WILDE, C. E. Jr. (1955b) *J. Morphol.* **97**, 313.
4. WILDE, C. E. Jr. (1956) *J. Exp. Zool.* **133**, 409.
5. HÖRSTADIUS, S. (1950) Oxford University Press (review).
6. SPEMANN, H. (1938) Yale University Press.
7. SPEMANN, H. and H. MANGOLD (1924) *Arch. Entw. Mech.* **100**, 599.
8. NEUMAN, R. E. and T. A. McCOY (1955) *Proc. Soc. Exp. Biol. Med.* **90**, 339.
9. EBERT, J. D. and L. M. DUFFEY (1956) *Anat. Rec.* **124**, 283.
10. DUFFEY, L. M. and J. D. EBERT (1957) *J. Embryol. Exp. Morphol.* **5**, 324.
11. FELL, H. B. and E. MELLANBY (1953) *J. Physiol.* **119**, 470.
12. WEISS, P. and R. JONES (1954) *Science* **119**, 587.
13. LERNER, A. B. *et al.* (1949) *Fed. Proc.* **8**, 218.

14. HORI, R. and P. D. NIEUWKOOP (1955) *Proc. Kon. Ned. Akad. Wetensch.* C **58**, 266–272.
15. SALA, M. (1955) *Proc. Kon. Ned. Akad. Wetensch.* C **58**, 635–647.
16. NIEUWKOOP, P. D., I. OIKAWA and J. BODDINGIUS (1958) *Arch. Neerl. Zool.* **12** Suppl. 18 p.
17. HOLTFRETER, J. (1938) *Roux Archiv.* **138**, 163–196.
18. GALLERA, J. (1952) *Roux Archiv.* **146**, 21–67.
19. CHUANG, H. H. (1955) *Chin. J. Exp. Biol.* **4**, 151–186.
20. NIEUWKOOP, P. D. (1958). *Acta. Embryol. Morphol. Exp.* **2**, 13–53.
21. BOTERENBROOD, E. C. (1958) *Kon. Ned. Akad. Wet. Amsterdam* C **61**, 470–81.
22. HOLTFRETER, J. (1933) *Naturwissenschaften* **21**, 766.
23. CHUANG, H. H. (1938) *Biol. Zbl.* **58**, 472.
24. TOIVONEN, S. (1938) *Ann. Zool. Soc. 'Vanamo'* **5**, Nr. 8, 1.
25. ANDRES, G. (1950) *Rev. Suisse Zool.* **57**, 1.
26. LEVANDER, G. (1945) *Nature, Lond.* **155**, 148.
27. TOIVONEN, S. (1953) *J. Embryol. Exp. Morphol.* **1**, 97.
28. SAXEN, L. and S. TOIVONEN (1956) *Ann. Med. Exptl. Fenn.* **34**, 235.
29. TOIVONEN, S. and L. SAXEN (1957) *J. Nat. Cancer Inst.* **19**.
30. YAMADA, T. (1958) *Experientia* **14**, 81.
31. JACOBSEN, C. F. (1947) *C. R. Lab. Carlsberg, Ser Chim.* **25**, No. 14.
32. KELLER, P. J. and G. T. CORI (1958) *Biochim. Biophys. Acta* **12**, 235.
33. PUCK, T. T. (unpublished).
34. NIEUWKOOP, P. D. and G. v. NIGTEVECHT (1954) *J. Embryol. Exp. Morphol.* **2**, 175–193.
35. NIEUWKOOP, P. D. *et al.* (1952) *J. Exp. Zool.* **120**, 1–108.
36. EYAL–GILADI, H. (1954) *Arch. Biol.* **65**, 179–259.
37. JOHNEN, A. G. (1956) *Proc. Kon. Ned. Akad. Wetensch.* C **59**, 554–561, 652–660.
38. NIEUWKOOP, P. D. Unpublished results.
39. TOIVONEN, S. (1950) *Rev. Suisse Zool.* **57**, Suppl. 1, 41–56.
40. TOIVONEN, S. (1953) *J. Embryol. Exp. Morphol.* **1**, 97–104.
41. TOIVONEN, S. and L. SAXEN (1955) *Ann. Acad. Sci. Fenn. A, Biol.* **30**, 1.
42. WADDINGTON, C. H. and J. L. SIRLIN (1955) *Proc. Roy. Phys. Soc., Edinb.* **24**, 28. SIRLIN, J. L., S. K. BRAHMA and C. H. WADDINGTON (1956) *J. Embryol. Exp. Morphol.* **4**, 248.
43. SIRLIN, J. L. and S. K. BRAHMA (1959) *Devel. Biol.* **2** (in press).
43a.BRAHMA, S. K. (1958) *J. Embryol. Exp. Morphol.* **6**, 418.
44. PANTELOURIS, E. M. and L. MULHERKAR (1957) *J. Embryol. Exp. Morphol.* **5**, 51.
45. BRACHET, J. and F. HUGON DE SCOEUX (1949) *Journées cytoembryolog. belgonéerland.* p. 56. Gand.
46. BRACHET, J. (1950) *Experientia* **6**, 56.
47. WADDINGTON, C. H. and J. L. SIRLIN (1955) *Proc. Roy. Phys. Soc.,* **24**, 28.
48. FICQ, A. (1954) *J. Embryol. Exptl. Morphol.* **2**, 194.
49. BRACHET, J. (1950) *Experientia* **6**, 56.
50. WADDINGTON, C. H., J. NEEDHAM and J. BRACHET (1936) *Proc. Roy. Soc.* B**120**, 173.
51. BRACHET, J. (1945) *Embryologie chimique,* Desoer, Liège.
52. YAMADA, T. and K. TAKATA (1955) *J. Exp. Zool.* **128**, 291.
53. BRACHET, J. (1944) *Bull. Acad. Roy. Belg.* **29**, 707.
54. BRACHET, J., S. GOTHIE and T. KUUSI (1952) *Arch. Biol. (Liége)* **63**, 429.
55. YAMADA, T., K. TAKATA and S. OSAWA (1954) *Embryologia* **2**, 123.

56. BRACHET, J. (1942) *Arch. Biol. (Liége)* **53**, 207.
57. BRACHET, J. (1939) *Arch. Biol. (Liége)* **50**, 233.
58. FISCHER, F. G. and H. HARTWIG (1936) *Z. vergl. Physiol.* **24**, 1.
59. PIEPHO, H. (1938) *Biol. Zbl.* **58**, 90.
60. TENCER, R. (1957) *Arch. Int. Physiol. Biochim.* **65**, 166.
61. KING, T. J. and R. BRIGGS (1955) *Proc. Nat. Acad. Sci., Wash.* **41**, 321.
62. BRACHET, J. (1944) *Ann. Soc. Roy. Zool. Belg.* **75**, 49.
63. BRACHET, J. (1949) *Pubbl. Staz. zool. Napoli* **21**, 77.
64. BRACHET, J. (1957) *Biochemical Cytology*, Academic Press, New York.
65. EAKIN, R. M. and F. E. LEHMANN (1957) *Roux Archiv.* **150**, 177.
66. BALINSKY, B. I. (1956) *Proc. Nat. Acad. Sci., Wash.* **42**, 781.
67. JACOB, F. and E. L. WOLLMAN (1958) *Symp. Soc. Exp. Biol.* **12**, 75.
68. SPRATT, N. T. JR. (1957) *J. Exp. Zool.* **134**, 577.
69. BALTZER, F. (1952) *Experientia* **8**, 285.
70. WAGNER, G. (1955) *J. Embryol. Exptl. Morphol.* **3**, 160.
71. GROBSTEIN, C. and A. J. DALTON (1947) *J. Exp. Zool.* **135**, 57.

CHAPTER IX

The Organisation of Tissues into Organs

WADDINGTON: I think we'll start this morning with Ed Zwilling telling us about the different type of induction in the limb bud and that will lead on to a more general consideration of tissue organisation.

ZWILLING: Up till now we have been discussing a rather complicated organisational setup, namely the establishment of the primary axis of the embryo. Now we will focus on a somewhat more simple system and see what are some of the factors involved. The system I have dealt with is the developing limb of the chick embryo [1–5]. The study of limb development has a venerable history, much of it concerned with amphibian limbs; but I should like, today, to concentrate my discussion on chick embryo limbs.

The limb rudiment at the time it can first be seen is a rather simple two-component structure. If one looks at a cross-section of a limb bud one sees a mesodermal core and an ectodermal covering which is distinguished by a little apical cap or ridge. Experiments done by Saunders [6] in the States indicate that this ectodermal cap is of considerable importance for the further development of the limb. On its removal outgrowth ceases completely. A number of experiments indicate that the apical ectodermal ridge is responsible for the induction of the outgrowth of the limb. If the ridge is removed and another one placed in contact with the mesoderm at any level of the limb bud an outgrowth will occur at this level [3]. In this way one may get multiple limbs. An interesting thing about this system is that when outgrowth of an early bud is inhibited by removal of the apical ridge only the most proximal part of the limb forms, while if the ridge is removed from older limb buds more distal regions develop. The most distal structures of the limb develop only when the ridge is in contact with the developing mesoderm until the digital condensations are formed. The portion of the limb which does develop after removal of the ridge is normal in size. If only a humeral stump develops it is as large as an equivalent piece from a normal humerus. From observations of this sort Saunders developed the concept that the limb is laid down in proximo-distal sequence.

The wing and leg of the chicken are quite different and have readily identifiable specific characteristics. Interchange experiments indicate that these specificities are retained under a variety of conditions. If one places the ectoderm from a wing bud on the mesoderm of a leg bud a leg develops. If one transplants small pieces of leg bud mesoderm under the ridge of a wing bud [7] recognisable leg structures develop on the end of the wing. Saunders has also shown [8] that when a proximal part of one type of limb bud is grafted to the distal region of a limb bud of the other type there is no fixity in proximo-distal structuring. A piece of presumptive thigh may become a foot digit—at the end of a wing. The lack of proximo–distal fixity can be demonstrated by placing an entire ectodermal ridge from one limb bud across the base of an intact limb bud. Under these circumstances one may get two outgrowths which develop into two little limbs—180° to each other. These few remarks make it evident that the limb bud is far from the mosaic that it was held to be some twenty years ago and that it is quite labile after it is disrupted in the proper way.

Some of the experiments which I've done, and which are described in the literature which was sent to you [4, 5], have involved two mutations, a polydactylous mutation and a wingless mutation. These experiments indicate that the relationship between the mesoderm and the ectoderm is such that outgrowth is due to the action of the ectodermal ridge on the mesoderm, and that the maintenance of the ridge in an active condition which continues to promote outgrowth is dependent on some contribution from the mesoderm. What this mesodermal contribution is we don't know, but whatever its nature it is distributed in an asymmetrical fashion which is reflected in an asymmetrical development of the ectodermal thickening and consequent asymmetries of the developing limb. Wherever there is a greater concentration of, for want of a better name, the maintenance factor, there is a thicker and more active ectodermal ridge which is associated with a more pronounced outgrowth. A number of experiments have shown that the ectodermal ridge conforms to the pattern inherent in the mesoderm. This is illustrated by the combination of polydactylous mesoderm with genetically normal ectoderm. In this situation a more extensive than normal apical ridge develops and a much more extensive outgrowth, associated with the excess digits, is formed. A similar conformity of the ectoderm can be shown by interchanges between wings and legs, as I mentioned before. The wing and the leg bud each have a different asymmetry and the ectoderm, in cases of heterologous combinations, conforms to the asymmetry of the mesoderm. This is also true of the axis orientation of the limb system, except when the amount of the original system involved in the outgrowth is limited very seriously. If one reorients the ectoderm so that it is 180° to its original orientation with respect to the mesoderm, the axial relations which develop are those of the mesoderm [2]. However, if one turns the ectoderm so that it is 90° to its original orientation there is an outgrowth which is 90° to the original long axis of the limb mesoderm, and all the axial relationships which develop are those which were originally present in the ectoderm. Here we again see lability which, I think, depends upon the fact that only a part of the limb system—the part in the central area—can respond to the outgrowth induction and that the new outgrowth conforms to the ectodermal component, which has been left intact.

I would like to illustrate some of the experiments we have done recently in an attempt to learn more about the limb system. One of the things we have done is to take the mesoderm from a limb bud and cut it into small pieces about 0.1 mm in diameter. We then stuff a number of these pieces into an intact ectodermal jacket, and graft the "reconstituted" limb bud to another embryo. We find that something like 10 or 12 of these pieces, which represent about one-third of the mesoderm of the intact bud, may regulate and form a recognisable limb. There are several interesting things about the limbs which develop following this type of operation. The limbs are considerably smaller than normal; the constancy in the size of the structure which forms after the stripping off of the apical ridge is here eradicated and there is a size regulation. However, the mesoderm retains many of the limb specificities following such treatment. When fragments of wing bud mesoderm were placed in ectoderm from a leg bud a well formed little wing developed; limb type specificity of the mesoderm was retained. When bits of duck leg bud mesoderm were stuffed into the ectoderm from a chick leg bud recognisable duck characteristics were found in the graft. That duckness is retained is illustrated by the presence of webbing.

The next thing was to reduce the mesoderm to a lower level of organisation. This was done by converting the mesoderm to a cell suspension. In this system we can keep an ectodermal component intact and assess what has been done to the mesoderm by the manner in which it will react to the intact component. A complete cell suspension may be made, the cells packed back together again (or allowed to re-aggregate spontaneously) and such mesoderm may then be placed into an ectodermal jacket and grafted in the usual way. The best development that we have had to date is a little spike-like mound which contains a core of cartilage and muscle. When one observes such a graft immediately following the operation and for a couple of days thereafter, one sees that the ectodermal ridge regresses. It actually degenerates at either end of the limb bud first, and then in the middle, and development is attenuated. The same sort of thing happens when the ectodermal ridge is confronted with non-limb mesoderm of various sorts, or with the genetically deficient mesoderm from our wingless mutation.

The point of interest here is that following this disaggregation procedure the re-aggregated tissue retains a number of its developmental capacities, as in the experiments which Moscona [9] did. It can form cartilage and it can form muscle. Both the cartilage and muscle are quite typical. However, the mesoderm cannot maintain the apical ridge and it hasn't, in the conditions of our experiments, become involved in the development of formed long bones. I have the impression that the formation of an ordered limb, in which bones of the right sort are cut out at the right level, seems to be dependent on the integrity of the system, or on the re-establishment of the proper interactions of the mesodermal with the apical ridge. After complete dissociation of the whole system this seems to be lost.

These latter experiments are suggestive of a number of different approaches to the problems still to be solved.

WADDINGTON: There we have an example, it seems to me, of a process of organisation which only takes place at all completely when you get interaction between the parts—an interaction between the apical ridge and the mesoderm, which is certainly mutual and goes in both directions. I don't know how much the amphibian limb people feel that their system is a similar one.

ZWILLING: I believe that information has come from one of Dr. Lehmann's students. Tschumi [10] indicates that the system is quite similar in *Xenopus*. Once the limb bud is formed essentially the same sort of things happen, but there are differences which make some of the last described experiments a bit difficult to duplicate with the amphibian material. Unlike that of the chick the ectodermal ridge of *Xenopus* can regenerate, or can be formed anew when the ectoderm is shifted somewhat [11]. I think there is some advantage in having an ectodermal ridge which doesn't regenerate, and which isn't labile, while the mesoderm is regulable.

PONTECORVO: This polydactylous condition is recessive or dominant?

ZWILLING: It's dominant. It seems from our work that the polydactylous mutation operates via our postulated maintenance factor, and this also seems to be true of the wingless mutation, which is a recessive one.

NIEUWKOOP: Isn't it possible that the absence of the normal limb organisation after the disaggregation and re-aggregation of the mesoderm is due to the fact that after the re-aggregation the mesodermal elements have to establish a certain unity again, which might take so much time that the ectoderm has regressed too far, and is no longer able to react to the newly established maintenance factor?

ZWILLING: Yes, I think this could be put in terms of unity, or possibly

in terms of something being leached which is required for the establishment of the unity. The mesoderm does reacquire the capacity to induce
feathers in the ectoderm later on. There may be a time sequence involved
here.

WADDINGTON: According to the idea that Nieuwkoop was saying, it may
acquire the complete organisation capacity, but acquire it too late.

ZWILLING: Yes.

WADDINGTON: One point I should like to ask about is what is the
evidence relating to reduction of pattern. When you get a limb formed
with one too few toes; is this a step-wise process, in which you knock out
a whole unit from the pattern, or is there a general quantitative distortion
of the pattern?

ZWILLING: We haven't done this in the chick, but again some of
Lehmann's people have done this very nicely in *Xenopus*. It seems as
though there is a reduction in the number of digital elements when the
size of the limb paddle is reduced. This happens in a very precise way.
The elements which are knocked out first are the most lateral; they go
from the two ends first, and the central one remains. With the smallest
amount of material which will still allow a digit to be formed it is the
middle one which develops. Tschumi's [10] work is concerned with reduction of the amount of digital material; a similar though opposite
relationship may be shown in a situation where there is an excess of
digital material, as in polydactyly.

WADDINGTON: But in the initial stages of reduction, is there any stage
in which you get a whole hand, but smaller; and only when it has got to
a minimum size you start knocking out digits?

LEHMANN: That is so. You see first the traces of the natural digits and
then they disappear rapidly. The cells are attracted by the central region,
so that these digits are not any longer formed [10].

WADDINGTON: So by the time the lateral ones are going, the central ones
are still a fully normal size?

LEHMANN: They even become greater than normal.

ZWILLING: Apparently there is a drawing in of material which isn't
used for a lateral condensation, and this produces a longer central digit.
There seem to be indications in a few preliminary experiments I have
done that the ectodermal ridge is involved in the formation of digits even
after the condensation has begun. If the ridge is removed distal to one
digital condensation, this digit will regress; the condensation will disappear

and no digit will form. I have not analysed this to see whether the other digits then become larger.

WADDINGTON: I think this is one of the fundamental questions about animal form: whether, when the pattern first appears, its size is a fixed quantity, or whether you can get the same pattern appearing both large and small? In this case it sounds as though initially size is one of its characteristics, and if the paddle isn't big enough to have five normal digits fitted inside it, then it fits in only four reasonably normal sized digits and not five small ones. Later you may get secondary absorptions of any small digits by the large ones, but what you do not seem to get is, in a small paddle, a small but still normal pattern. How far can this be generalised to other organs? I know that in their time Nieuwkoop and Lehmann have both written about the stages in reduction of the head structures which you can induce in amphibians. Would either of them like to discuss this question in relation to the reduction of the pattern of the head in the amphibian? I think, Lehmann, you found that you could knock out the fore-brain, leaving the mid- and hind-brain more or less normal?

LEHMANN: There may be a step-wise reduction of the pattern; at least I thought so, but I admit that in this case the statistical evidence is by far not so good as it is now for the amphibian limb. But one point which turns out in both cases is that there are steps of reduction, and there is never a gradual reduction (Lehmann [11]). We would have to postulate a kind of threshold, and if this threshold is not surpassed this part of the pattern does not appear at all. That seems to me a very important question, and I always wonder whether this cannot also be true for many types of enzymatic systems, which may also require some sort of threshold otherwise the system cannot act. I do not know whether that is true for enzymatic systems, but it is certainly true for many morphogenetic systems.

ZWILLING: I think if we look at other organisms we have examples of both the types of situation. Within the hydroids, we have some forms in which both blastomeres, if separated, at the two-blastomere stage, will form a small embryo with the typical number of smaller tentacles, while in other forms the tentacles are constant in size and the number of tentacles produced is directly related to the initial mass of the developing system.

WILDE: In the amphibian it seems there is also a time element in the maturation of the form. I remember some experiments of mine some time ago in which, say, the early limb had received the signal to form humerus and the tissues immediately lateral and adjacent to it, but the signal to form the distal joints and the radius and ulna had not been given. Then what happens is that a little rod of cartilage continues to grow in a unitary fashion. This is a pattern involving time. It is later on that the limb receives the signal to form radius and ulna, so I think there are two elements involved here [12].

WADDINGTON: Yes, I suppose the evidence is that for the limb the signals are given in proximo–distal sequence.

NIEUWKOOP: I have the impression that in the development of the nervous system each organ system can actually develop in a great variety of sizes. It can appear as a very small but quite complete unit, or as an overlarge but also complete unit [13]. In more normal conditions each organ system does not develop in such a wide range of sizes because there is competition with other systems, and this fixes a certain maximal and minimal size between which it will develop.

WADDINGTON: Yes, and I wonder if that is not really the case also in the limb. Certainly in tissue cultures of the chick femur for instance—of course these were explanted at rather a late stage; I'm referring to the old work of Dr. Fell and Canti and so on—you get a relatively normal shaped femur, with the joint surfaces indicated, but a great deal smaller than it normally should be.

ZWILLING: Yes, but I think you have to distinguish between several things. One of these is a growth phase, dependent completely on nutritional conditions, and setting in after the initial organisation has taken place.

WADDINGTON: Of course I admit that later on one is in a growth phase but I think they originally explanted a piece of mesodermal condensation, before the rudiment of the femur was separated off from the rest of the limb skeleton.

ZWILLING: But there you have regulation depending on the size of the explant. If one takes more tissue than is normally involved in femur formation, a somewhat larger bone, which incorporates extra femoral tissue, will develop. The size of this will depend on the amount of tissue explanted. There is still a certain amount of plasticity at these stages.

WADDINGTON: That is coming very close to what Nieuwkoop was saying, that an organ system may in isolation develop with its complete pattern in a very small piece, but if that small piece were attached to a large mass the competition between it and the neighbouring pieces might cause that organ system to get eliminated.

CALLAN: Aren't there some results of P. D. F. Murray showing that if you break up a limb bud into larger or smaller pieces you will get a larger or smaller femur, if that is the region you have taken?

ZWILLING: Murray did not do this in culture, he did it with chorio-allantoic grafts [14]. It is essentially the same sort of thing that Fell did but with a different growth situation.

LEHMANN: I wonder about this competition you mentioned. There seem to be two possibilities; either one piece exerts an inhibiting influence on the neighbouring material or the various regions are producing some attractive influences. It seems to me this cannot be decided yet. I was wondering if you know cases where we can differentiate these two factors; I mean these limiting factors or attractive factors both belong to such a system of competition.

HOLTZER: The cartilaginous vertebra of the spinal column looks like a unitary structure, consisting of neural arches and a centrum. Normally in the salamander, the first indications of a vertebra are the paired neural arches; only after metamorphosis does the centrum develop. However, if you remove the notochord in the embryo, the centrum forms precociously in the embryo, and only later will the neural arches appear [15, 16]. This is a complete reversal of the normal sequences, so that here you have an organ which, when you look at it, looks like a single structure, and yet you can dissociate it both in space and in time.

ZWILLING: I think the point Dr. Lehmann mentioned about competition can be demonstrated in the developing limb system too. Very frequently when there is an excess of digitation, as in extreme polydactyly, the region immediately proximal to the digits may be defective. You may get a tibia without any distal part because its material has been drawn up to satisfy the requirements of the digits. This sort of competition, I think, has actually been demonstrated.

WILDE: We have had in some experiments some results which bear on this question of inhibition or attraction. We were able to demonstrate that the gill region of the amphibian embryo does in effect act as one of the mediators of limb growth rate. We came to feel that this was fully an inhibition when, in explants, if the gill existed as an intact unit and was separated by non-living tissue culture fluid from the limb anlagen, the limb still reacted as though the gill were attached to it, and was inhibited. It was from experiments of this nature that we felt that there was a rather specific factor inter-regulating between the two. Later it was demonstrated that this did occur in the intact embryo, by transplanting limb disks anteriorly and demonstrating the same thing. I think one must think in terms of a real specificity rather than a general stimulus to growth or non-growth [17].

WADDINGTON: There is one further aspect of this I should like to ask people about before we pass on to something else. That is the supposed specificity of fore limb and hind limb, which always astonishes me. You take a piece of mesoderm out of a hind limb bud and put it into a fore limb; the position it is put into in the fore limb bud will change its developmental fate from that of a proximal piece to that of a distal piece; but if it turns into a distal piece it will still be into a distal *leg* piece, maintaining its leg specificity though changing its position within the proximo–distal system. There you have the specification of a character which I think you wouldn't expect to be specified. What would the information theory people say about this? Is there a special DNA sequence for the hind limb and another for the fore limb; and are there other cases of the same thing? I mean, for instance, can you in the nervous system of the amphibia take a piece which retains its prosencephalic character but changes from the central nervous correlate of the nose to that of the eye, and thus changes around within the region?

LEHMANN: I remember an experiment by Balinsky [18] in which he induced limbs all along the trunk, and he found that there was a very large region which responded with fore limbs, and there was a rather sharp boundary, and then you got into the field of the hind limb.

ZWILLING: If you look at the presumptive areas of the limb material in the chick embryo you will find that they are at first virtually contiguous, in the sinus rhondoidalis area, Rudnick [19] has mapped out these areas, and they are practically touching at this early stage.

WADDINGTON: I'm not surprised that you can induce a fore limb, or induce a hind limb, any more than that you can induce an ear or induce an eye. The odd thing to my mind is that the distinction between the fore and hind limb should be settled before the distinction whether it should be a toe or a femur. One isn't used to thinking of a complex structure like a fore limb as having any chemical unity, but this presumably must mean that there is some chemical identity belonging to the fore limb as a whole.

PONTECORVO: Could it be a kind of polarity, something like the difference between right handed and left handed?

WADDINGTON: We know from Harrison's work that if you determine handedness you do determine polarities, but that happens later on in the sequence.

LEHMANN: There is a large region which also in regeneration determines the character as fore limb or hind limb [20]; this means there must be a general quality spread throughout a wide region. This may be present before any actual differentiation takes place; these are phylogenetically very ancient characters, you find them away back in the history of the vertebrates.

WADDINGTON: If you have determined a limb bud so that it will later develop into a fore limb, or in another case into a hind limb, that observation does not say that each small part must have its fore-limbness fixed in it. If you induce a series of limbs along the flank of an amphibian, and look at the final result, you could see that you've got fore limbs in one part and hind limbs in another part; but this would not imply that from the very beginning the small parts have their fore or hind limb character fixed although they have not got the proximo-distal character fixed.

ZWILLING: It may be that we can discover what is going on in some of these cases if we do the sort of experiments that Moscona has done recently. We may find that the gelatinous materials, which come out of a cell or from between cells when the tissue is disaggregated, are important. These may have the specificities that he has demonstrated, and they may also have the specificity involved in wingness versus legness and it may be possible to transfer such material from a leg bud to the cells of a wing bud.

WADDINGTON: You get the same sort or regional specificities coming into operation in some of the feather regeneration and feather transplantation work, don't you? There I think it is the ectoderm which carries the specificity although it is the mesoderm which does the induction. Here again the tissue is labile as to whether it turns into feather or not, but if it does turn into a feather, this feather belongs to its own region of the body.

WILDE: We attempted with the hind limb to demonstrate the inhibition by gill which we had seen with the fore limb, but with the hind limb there was no sign of this [21]. These specificities, I think, force us to take a much more extreme position than we have ever considered before. There is some recent work from Cal. Tech. which indicates that the composition of the keratin of the feather varies with the species from which the feather comes and the anatomical part of the feather concerned [22]; that is, the barbs have a particular type of keratin, the rachis another type, and these differences are distinct for the different parts of the feathers. All feathers in a turkey are alike, but they are different from all feathers in a goose; down to the level of a few amino acids residue specificity is now established. I think this is of fundamental morphogenetic importance.

PONTECORVO: Could I ask a question on genetics? If you use mesoderm from a heterozygous polydactylous donor, do you get quantitatively different effects?

ZWILLING: In heterozygotes the range of expression is the same as in homozygotes. Any differences in expression in either case seem to be due to modifiers or residual genetic factors.

PONTECORVO: This is so in the whole animal, but in the individual tissues?

ZWILLING: One of the things which Hansborough and I found [24] was that the pattern of polydactyly, in a graft in which genetically normal ectoderm was placed on polydactylous mesoderm, was almost identical with that in the control, which was the unoperated wing on the other side of the polydactylous donor.

NIEUWKOOP: Could I perhaps add something about limb regeneration which seems to be of interest here. In the regeneration of the *Axolotl* fore limb Faber [unpubl.] finds a very clear interaction between intrinsic differentiation tendencies and polarising influences from the stump. The diagram (Fig. 9.1) gives a brief survey of the stages which can be distin-

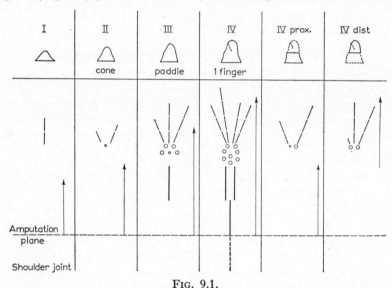

FIG. 9.1.

guished in the regenarating limb (stage I–IV). If one follows the prospective significance of the mesenchymal component of the blastema at the successive stages with the aid of carbon marking (*cf.* the arrows), one sees that the blastema of stage I represents only the most proximal region of the regenerated limb. The tip of the somewhat older blastema (stages II and III respectively) forms the distal forearm and wrist, while the blastema of stage IV finally represents almost the entire limb. The diagram further indicates the skeletal differentiation tendencies of the various stages when transplanted into a "neutral" environment. If one transplants the young blastema (stage I), it paradoxically develops only into the most distal structures. Transplanting the somewhat older blastema of stage II, also a part of the wrist is formed. In the transplanted blastema of stage III the first indications of the forearm appear. The grafted blastema of stage IV finally forms the complete limb. If, however, in stage IV the blastema is cut into a proximal and a distal half, then after transplantation both halves form only distal structures. This points to a great plasticity in the system. The intrinsic differentiation tendency of the blastemal mesenchyme is that for distal elements. For the formation of proximal elements later influences from the stump are essential. The picture one gets shows a great similarity with that found in the regional development of the nervous system. One can compare it with the induction in an ectodermal fold. When the induction proceeds, a certain area becomes neuralised, and will after isolation form the most anterior structures of the brain. As soon as secondary actions start the most proximal portions are transformed into more caudal segments of the nervous system. So a cranio–caudal polarity is formed in the neural material of the fold. In the limb regenerate we find essentially the same. The first differentiation tendencies are those for distal elements, but later influences from the stump lead to the formation of more and more proximal elements. In both systems we have to do with an interaction between the intrinsic differentiation tendencies of the cell material itself and a polarising factor coming from outside, in the case of limb regeneration from the stump, and in the case of neural induction from the underlying archenteron roof.

WADDINGTON: Zwilling, have you any comment on that or do you accept that as a parallel sort of behaviour?

ZWILLING: Perhaps it's parallel but in a somewhat different direction. The differentiation here seems to occur first at the distal end, but this is complicated by the existence of a well organised stump which may contribute another factor.

WADDINGTON: Well, do you want to tell us some more about disaggregation and re-aggregation in relation to pieces of blastoderms.

ZWILLING: I can, very briefly. I think we have already heard a considerable amount about the kind of organisation one can get following tissue dissociation. I think by now that none of us is surprised by the fact that there is a tendency towards self organisation following the disruption of a previously formed tissue. The sort of thing which I have done has been to perpetrate this procedure on early embryos which have not formed definitive tissues or adult type of structures. I have used the definitive streak (DPS) stage chick embryo. At this stage there is a blastoderm which has already become fairly highly organised, and has formed a streak. Experiments which have involved the transplantation of small pieces of such embryos have indicated that the nodal area has a tremendous tendency to form all sorts of tissues. I was attempting to set the stage for a series of experiments which may tell us something about what factors determine that a cell develops in one direction or another. Much of the discussion yesterday dealt with cells which have already taken a decided direction and are going along a particular track. One of the important things is to learn something about the factors which are involved in their starting on a divergent track. Wilde's experiments have been provocative in this regard.

We find that when the entire DPS is disaggregated it re-aggregates very nicely, and that the re-aggregate has a very characteristic behaviour. Under a variety of tissue culture conditions it forms a very compact little mass which then grows out and spreads. Cell division may be involved, but I suspect that the spreading is due mainly to the migratory behaviour of the cells. Such cultures do not give a picture that is typical of cultures of fibroblasts, instead there is a plasmoidal sort of growth and the centre gradually migrates out and one ends with just a thin sheet which grows for a long time. Sometimes small sinus-like channels develop in the sheet. These contain pigmented erythrocytes. A sort of primitive skin may develop and sometimes some gut-like tissue forms.

When the nodal area alone is treated the same, it behaves the same during disaggregation and re-aggregation. Re-aggregated masses from the nodal area occasionally form tongue-like outgrowths, but the characteristic thing is that the tissues remain very massive and fairly quickly form organoids which develop into neural tissue, cartilage and so on. Both types of cultures were grown under the same conditions and for the same length of time. I believe that we have here a behavioural distinction between two cell types. The sort of thing which happens in the cultures from the whole blastoderm is what you would expect from the extra embryonic area. Apparently the main characteristic of the cells of the nodal area is the tendency to clump and remain massed, whereas those from the rest of the blastoderm tend to spread.

There are several interesting things to me in these observations. One is that in the disaggregate of the entire blastoderm apparently the nodal cells are infected by the spreading tendency of the rest and the tissues which one usually expects from that area do not develop. In fact if one makes separate cell suspensions of the nodal area and of the rest of the embryo, and combines them in different proportions, one finds that even when half of the cells in the re-aggregate come from the nodal area they are not expressed. The spreading behaviour is very predominant in such combinations. Apparently we have a behavioural characteristic in these cultures which is related to the capacity of the cells to differentiate. I think this system now gives us the possibility of doing a variety of things. Many of the hypotheses which have been discussed, for instance those which involve the possibility that induced enzyme synthesis is a mechanism for switching the cells in one direction or another, may be attacked here. People have tried to detect such enzyme systems in intact embryos. I think this has been a tactical error, because the intact embryo has built into it a number of regulative capacities. When one disaggregates the embryos the cells may be exposed to conditioning by various adaptive substrates and may possibly be altered. This is especially promising because there has been a demonstration of differential substrate requirement in the nodal area as compared with other areas of the embryo.

PONTECORVO: What sort of differences are these?

ZWILLING: Very simple ones; they have been demonstrated by Spratt [23]. For instance, the nodal area will utilise fructose but the rest of the blastoderm will not. A series of relatively simple carbohydrates will be utilised by one area and not by the other.

WADDINGTON: And of course there are also differences in the rate of amino acid incorporation, and so on [24]. This tendency to re-aggregate or stick together is rather similar to what you see in the normal embryo, when the lateral tissues move in towards the primitive streak and invaginate through it. This area of clumping together in the streak is the region of highest uptake of methionine or glycine, so I think there certainly are metabolic differences.

LEHMANN: About pattern formation we didn't learn too much this morning. That is a question which is puzzling me very much. We have seen these complicated patterns arising also in the limb but I feel we are still waiting for appropriate methods to see the very first stages of pattern formation. Imagine for instance that such a dissociated mass would later form a pattern again. This is possible but we have no cytochemical or histochemical method of observing the stages by which the different regions become different. And there is another point that I feel is not at all clear. We have this small ectodermal ridge of the limb and there is certainly a pattern formation going on there. There must be mutual influences between the cells keeping them in a definite order, but we have no methods at all for stating what kinds of influences are passing from one cell to another. I think that in this connection we are just now in a rather unsatisfactory situation.

WADDINGTON: I think it is not merely that we have no methods for detecting the early arising of pattern, but we don't even know in what terms we should look for it. If we have a mass of mesoderm which starts to condense, and will eventually turn into a pattern giving rise to a five-fingered hand, what type of chemical differences are we to suppose will distinguish the initial condensations? In what chemical terms is the pattern first expressed? It seems to me that we have no clue to that. Is it first expressed in terms of protein metabolism, or what sort of metabolism? I suppose eventually someone will discover histochemical methods which will reveal this pattern earlier than anyone had seen it before, and that may perhaps give us a clue as to what kind of material it is being expressed in. But at present I have no views at all either as to what kind of chemical substances are involved, or what kind of interactions give rise to the pattern.

POLLOCK: I can't answer that question at all, but listening to the discussion this morning one thing did occur to me. It appears that the differences involved in embryonic induction might perhaps be largely quantitative; there is a sort of spontaneous element leading to differentiation which is either complemented or hastened under certain particular conditions. I wonder if I could just give you an example which is illustrative of the kind of thing that happens in enzyme induction and other biochemical processes, involving largely quantitative changes in the first place, which give rise to quite profound end differences in the chain of reactions. I'm thinking particularly of the example discovered by Tatum and Gross [25] in *Neurospora*. In this you have a substance, dehydroshikimic acid, which normally metabolises to shikimic acid on a pathway involving the synthesis of various amino acids. But there is an alternative pathway for metabolism of dehydroshikimic acid, which under certain conditions, may be broken down to β-ketoadipic acid instead of being reduced to shikimic acid. In fact, the condition these workers studied was mutation involving a block in ther eaction: dehydroshikimic $\rightarrow$ shikimic. The point of this is that as soon as this reaction is inhibited the precursor compound (dehydroshikimic acid) of course accumulates; and it accumulates in sufficient quantities to induce an enzyme which metabolises it to

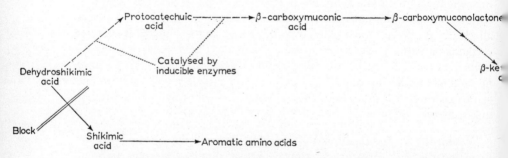

FIG. 9.2. Scheme to show how an alternative pathway of metabolism of dehydroshikimic acid to β-ketoadipic acid is opened up by sequential induction following a block to the normal pathway of reduction to shikimic acid.

a substance (protocatechuic acid) which itself induces another enzyme
—protocatechuic acid oxidase. Thus a whole new chain of reactions is
opened up. I think there were about four or five, leading in the end of the
formation of β-ketoadipic acid (see Fig. 9.2). If you didn't know the biochemical basis you might, of course, have considered the primary change
to have been the gain of the enzyme forming protocatechuic acid from
the dehydroshikimic, rather than a loss of the enzyme forming shikimic
acid. A similar metabolic switch might result from anything which caused
inhibition of this reaction and thus opened up this new reaction chain
dehydroshikimic → shikimic. It seems to me just the kind of thing that
might possibly be occurring in embryonic induction. You might normally
be having just a trickle along one particular chain of reactions, which would
not normally manifest itself in the embryo until you got a slight change
of conditions which might switch the whole thing in another direction.
This is a principle often discussed by Waddington. The effect would be
greatly magnified if sequential induction were superimposed.

ZWILLING: I would like to add one thing to this. We have heard a good
deal about the importance of architecture in development and tissue
differentiation and so on. Architecture in its very simplest form may be
important at just this point. For instance, it is conceivable that in the
experiment I have just described the spreading of the cells has prevented
the presumptive neural cells from achieving enough mass to accumulate
some necessary substance, or that they have been losing whatever they
should have accumulated. In this way, a relatively simple architectural
factor can have very important consequences along the lines which Pollock
has just mentioned.

WADDINGTON: I think there are very many different types of kinetic
system in which a small change at some stage shunts the whole system
into a different reaction chain. I have often discussed this myself in
relation to embryonic induction but I do not think this point enlightens
us much about the question Lehmann raised, about the initiation of
patterns.

HOLTZER: The problems of pattern, or morphogenesis proper are, of
course, most intriguing and, again, I would like to mention some simple
experiments on the developing cartilaginous vertebra that bears on this
point. In normal development in all vertebrates some factor diffuses out
of the ventral half of the embryonic spinal cord which induces some
somite cells to transform into cartilage cells [16, 26]. These cartilage
cells, in a manner quite unknown to us, gradually encase the spinal cord,
forming the cartilaginous vertebra. Now what interests us here, is the
following: If you plot the activity of the cartilage transforming factor

secreted by the embryonic spinal cord, you find it rapidly reaches a peak and then, in a matter of two days or so, drops to zero. The early fetal or adult spinal cord does not have this cartilage promoting activity. However, at the stage when the cartilage promoting activity declines, at this stage another type of activity appears, in the spinal cord, namely that of causing the regression of cartilage. This second factor released from the spinal cord appears to attack the polysaccharide matrix of *formed* cartilage, resulting in the disappearance of the cartilage structure. Now, in normal development, the diameter of the spinal cord increases many times and so does the diameter of the vertebral canal. In short, as the spinal cord enlarges, the lumen of the cartilaginous cage surrounding the spinal cord must also enlarge. Thus, first the spinal cord releases a factor which induces mesenchyme cells to transform into cartilage. Then later it releases another factor which, by dissolving the cartilage on the medial aspects of the vertebra, results in a widening of the spinal canal to keep up with the growing spinal cord. It is this type of sequential tissue interaction that I suspect may ultimately be responsible for pattern formation.

WADDINGTON: Once you have got an elongated neural axis and segmented somites beside it, it's not too difficult to see how, by such diffusing substances, you could get cartilage induced, and the cartilage might then become segmented along the longitudinal axis, by some factor related to the somites. The problem which I think is the difficult and interesting one is, how do you get the pattern of the somites in the first place? That is an exceedingly simple example of pattern formation. You start with an apparently relatively homogeneous sheet of axial mesoderm, which then divides itself into somites. Now what forces, are we to suppose, cause the breaking-up of the uniform sheet into a series of segments? I can give you a largely speculative scheme, which indicates one sort of process which might occur, and which would not be at all mysterious if it did occur.

Let us start with the uniform sheet of mesoderm. It is not completely structureless, but has a polarity; an anterior end which was invaginated first, and a posterior end which was invaginated later on. What we have to explain is how it breaks up into a structure with a central column which is the notochord, and two lateral thickened columns which become segmented into a series of somites, and still more laterally the undivided lateral mesoderm. One conceivable way in which this pattern might develop could be based on a tendency of cells which were originally more or less equidimensional to increase their surfaces of contact with one another. They would then tend to become less equidimensional; for instance, they might acquire a columnar shape which allows each cell to have a large area of contact with its neighbouring cells. In the notochord in the amphibia you can see that the cells do change their shape in much this sort of way [27].

Now, suppose this tendency becomes manifest first in the central anterior region, and spreads rapidly posteriorly down the mid-line. The first stage then would be that the cells near the mid-line would pull themselves together into a column by assuming flattened shapes with large areas of contact. If the intensity of this tendency to increase cell-to-cell contact falls off sufficiently rapidly as one goes from the mid-line towards the sides, then the cells in the central area might pull together so strongly that they split apart from the cells which lie more laterally. That would give you the first element of the pattern, a central strand which might be the notochord (Fig. 9.3).

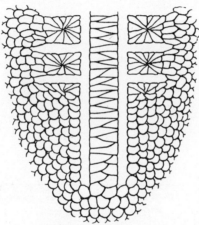

FIG. 9.3.

Now one might imagine that this tendency for the cells to pull together not only decreases away from the mid-line towards the sides but also falls off in a gradient from the anterior to the posterior. Then the first of these gradients would cause the cells to pull together into a thickened column on each side of the notochord; and then, because of the anterior–posterior gradient, an anterior group of cells might pull themselves away from the more posterior cells to form the first pair of somites and the intersomitic groove; and then a second group behind these would behave similarly and so on. Thus you would get the series of blocks of somites down each side of the notochord.

One could therefore explain the appearance of this quite complex spatial pattern on the basis of a series of gradients of tendencies for cells to pull together and increase their surfaces of mutual contact. That is a pretty speculative hypothesis, although one can see that the cells actually do change their shape roughly in the way required. I am offering it,

18

however, chiefly as an example of the *kind* of theory we have to consider
if we try to explain architecture rather than merely chemical composition.

WILDE: I think I could document at least the first phases of that. These
facts concern the differentiation of muscle in the early embryo. One of
the first things that occurs is the change from cells that are more or less
amoeboid to the development of a polarised system. This may take place
not only in explants of tissue but in free cells. Figure 9.4a shows a group

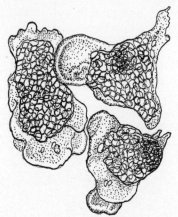

FIG. 9.4a.

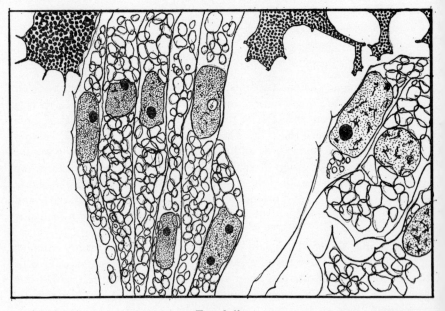

FIG. 9.4b.

of freshly isolated amoeboid cells which are free and have small surfaces of contact with one another. The first change that we can notice in the formation of striated muscle is seen in Fig. 9.4b, in which the cells begin to come together in groups of two or three. It looks to us very much as though we were seeing here something like the formation of somites in the intact embryo.

HOLTZER: I would remind you of the experiments of Townes and Holtfreter [31] where disaggregated mesodermal sheets form into a structure but they were in blocks. Of course, before you get the stretching out of myoblasts you already have the somites blocked out very well.

CALLAN: A difficulty with your scheme, Waddington, is that the cells are likely to pull out from the sides rather than pull away from one another in an anterior–posterior direction. I mean they will be tending to pull more cells in from the sides and line them up with their long axis along the long axis of the embryo and not separate from one another somite by somite.

WADDINGTON: To get my scheme you would of course have to have just the right rates of decline of the various gradients. I think that if the tendency to stick together is extremely high in one region, but falls off very rapidly, it might actually suffice to pull the cells apart and make a gap. I admit that is one of the speculative aspects of the hypothesis, but it seems to me that it is a conceivable process. What I am trying to say is that some hypothesis of that general order is necessary to explain the formation of the pattern. You can't explain the formation of a pattern by any hypothesis involving only induced enzymes or things of that kind. The chemical kinetics can only provide the raw materials, but you have to bring into the theory something which will cause translocations of material in space. Essentially, you have to have a physical theory.

LEHMANN: I remember the experiments of Hörstadius [28] with reduction gradients. They can be found before you can see any morphological changes. There must be a pattern of gradients before the morphological changes occur, and even at this time there must be a sort of steady-state developing. In a very early gastrula or blastula stage you can see a difference in these reduction patterns and if you take an animal half and treat it by lithium you find you have induced a pattern which is different, and which comes before the morphogenesis. I think that is the question: How a general pattern of gradients, occurring over a large number of cells, must be propagated from one cell to another? There must be some feedback to get an orderly scheme.

WADDINGTON: But surely in the amphibian case you would admit that there are gradients in the mesoderm even before it invaginates?

BRACHET: And many other people have demonstrated gradients of chemical constitution in the mesoderm long before it blocks itself out into somites.

WADDINGTON: I think there are many cases similar to that of Hörstadius in which you can show chemical gradients in the system before it shows morphological changes. I am not, of course, denying that these processes follow chemical gradients, but what I'm saying is that you have to have something more than a mere chemical gradient.

LEHMANN: But that is just in accordance with the morphogenetic facts; several other observed gradients have no relation to what is happening morphogenetically. I think that case of Hörstadius is the only one that shows very close correlation between morphogenetic and biochemical territories.

NIEUWKOOP: I think we have to keep in mind that before cellular movements occur, either to form a column, or to form blocks of somites, these cells have been determined to form this particular type of cell.

WADDINGTON: Well, not very much before; that is to say, you can switch the somite into chorda at a stage fairly shortly before they become morphologically distinct. You can still do it at the late gastrula stage.

NIEUWKOOP: But not at the stage at which the first morphogenesis takes place.

WADDINGTON: No. The chemical differentiation proceeds the morphogenesis, but that fact still leaves us ignorant of how the morphogenesis occurs.

POLLOCK: Would you consider that oscillating systems—I mean chemically oscillating systems—might give rise to patterns?

WADDINGTON: Yes, I once suggested in print [29] that if you had a chemical system which was periodic, this might have physical consequences which produced a periodic pattern. Actually, I tried to do some experimental work on this in relation to somite formation [30]. If the periodicity was chemical, its wavelength should not depend on the physical size of the mass of tissue; that is to say, if you increase the dorso-ventral thickness of the layer of mesoderm you shouldn't have any effect on the anterior-posterior dimensions of the somites. The sort of picture I was having was that you were dealing with an infinite sheet in which there was a process starting at one side, which went according to a periodic function and gradually diffused from that side over the sheet; the thickness of the sheet then should not make any difference, so far as I can see. However, the experimental fact is that if you thicken the mesoderm by grafting other mesoderm on top of it, the somites do get longer. This seems to me to argue against the periodicity being based on chemical kinetics.

BRENNER: Well, you have a model of this, of course, in the well-known Liesegang rings. In fact, by allowing a chelate compound and an iron compound to diffuse against each other one can show that even where you can't see Liesegang rings as a precipitation, they are there and can be revealed by growing bacteria on the system. They grow in the pattern of the rings, and so you get . . .

WADDINGTON: Can you get a central strand up the middle?

BRENNER: Well, this is solved in polar co-ordinates, so to speak, whereas you have it solved in Cartesian co-ordinates; but the fact that you get the distribution in general can be explained on the same sort of theory as explains the Liesegang phenomenon, whether it is cell adhesion or diffusion of a chemical.

The second point I wanted to raise was this. In all these experiments in tissue culture I take it you grow the cells on glass, don't you?

WILDE: The ones I was referring to are grown on glass.

ZWILLING: Mine are not grown on glass, but if they are, the behaviour is essentially the same. In most of my experiments the cells re-aggregate on glass and are then transferred to a lens paper platform or to a solid clot.

BRENNER: The point is I'm just wondering what would happen if in any of these systems we tried to force the cells not to grow in a sheet—I don't know whether this is possible, but suppose you put them, say, on the tip of a needle and siliconed the rest of it so they wouldn't adhere to it, and thus tried to force them to grow off the needle into space. I think you might get a lot of different results, because you merely restrain the cells to grow in a certain fashion.

WADDINGTON: It's been well known for years that the type of substrate that the cells are growing on has an important influence. If you want to get cells in tissue culture to differentiate, you always have to try to prevent them from out-wandering.

NIEUWKOOP: May I finally show some preliminary results about the capacity of presumptive prosencephalic neural material to organise itself into a more or less typical prosencephalon. The prosencephalic area has been chosen in Miss Boterenbrood's experiments since several very characteristic differentiations develop in the prosencephalic region of the brain. The experiments, as shown in the next slides, have been performed on *Triturus alpestris* [13].

The presumptive prosencephalon, together with the neural folds and adjacent ectoderm, has been excised at a young neurula stage (Fig. 9.5). In the control experiments this material was allowed to develop as explant and formed a characteristic prosencephalon with a tel- and di-encephalic part, two partially fused or a single symmetrical olfactory placode and one big eye, usually with two lenses. At this stage only very weak tendencies for bilateral development of the prosencephalon can be demonstrated. (See the sagittal projection in Fig. 9.6a.) In the experimental series the same material was disaggregated in a calcium-free Holtfreter solution and the cell suspension, after being stirred with a hair loop, was transferred to a normal culture medium in which the cells were allowed to re-aggregate (Fig. 9.5).

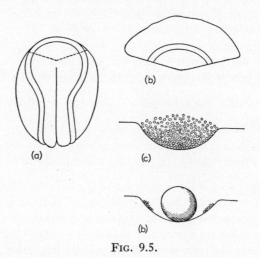

FIG. 9.5.

They primarily formed a spherical mass of cells in which, as Townes and Holtfreter demonstrated, within 24 hr a segregation takes place between epidermal, neural crest and neural elements [31].

The originally compact neural material which was completely disorganised, since any previously existing organisation pattern had been disturbed, reorganised itself into typical prosencephalic structures.

A very complex structure may be formed, like Fig. 9.6b, consisting of a central ventricle with all around it a large number of telencephalic formations with olfactory placodes, and a large number of eye structures, which elements are connected with membranous diencephalic material, which, for the sake of clearness, is however not indicated in the reconstruction. In a number of cases a much more simple structure is however formed, like in Fig. 9.6c in which the same aggregate is seen from two different sides, consisting of a very big eye formation with a few, and in some cases only a single, telencephalic brain part(s), accompanied by an olfactory placode. It must be emphasised that the structures formed represent well organised units, like small telencephalic hemispheres or typical eye formations with tapetum and retina.

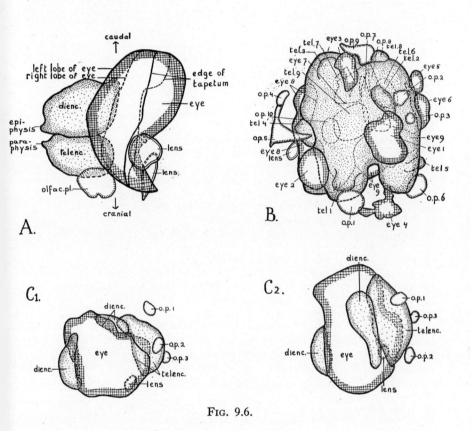

FIG. 9.6.

In the latter cases a prosencephalic structure is formed which shows much similarity with that of the controls. There is however one difference: the quantitative proportions of the various parts differ rather much from those in the controls. In many cases the eye structures dominate markedly and diencephalic nuclear structures are hardly formed.

Although the quantitative analysis is still in progress, so that accurate data are not yet available, it seems that differentiation tendencies for eye formation and for telencephalic nuclear formations are dominant in the prosencephalic neural material. Depending upon the number of centres formed a highly complex or a much more simple prosencephalic formation develops, in which the quantitative proportions of the various structures formed seem to depend upon a competition of the various centres for the cell material available.

These experiments only form a very first experimental attempt at an analysis of the still completely obscure processes of self-organisation of embryonic material.

REFERENCES

1. ZWILLING, E. (1955) *J. Exp. Zool.* **128**, 423.
2. ZWILLING, E. (1956) *J. Exp. Zool.* **132**, 157.
3. ZWILLING, E. (1956) *J. Exp. Zool.* **132**, 173.
4. ZWILLING, E. and L. A. HANSBOROUGH (1956) *J. Exp. Zool.* **132**, 219.
5. ZWILLING, E. (1956) *J. Exp. Zool.* **132**, 241.
6. SAUNDERS, J. W. JR. (1948) *J. Exp. Zool.* **108**, 363.
7. SAUNDERS, J. W., M. T. GASSELING and J. M. CAIRNS (1955) *Nature, Lond.* **175**, 673.
8. SAUNDERS, J. W., J. M. CAIRNS and M. T. GASSELING (1957) *J. Morphol.* **101**, 57.
9. MOSCONA, A. and H. MOSCONA (1952) *J. Anat.* **86**, 287.
10. TSCHUMI, P. (1954) *Rev. Suisse Zool.* **61**, 177.
11. LEHMANN. F. E. (1948) *Arch. J. Klaus Stift.* **23**, 568; (1953) *Rev. Suisse Zool.* **60**, 490.
12. WILDE, C. E. (1950) *J. Morphol.* **86**, 73.
13. BOTERENBROOD, E. C. (1958) *Proc. Kon. Ned. Akad. Wetensch.*
14. MURRAY, P. D. F. and D. SELBY (1930) *Arch. Entw. mech.* **122**, 629.
15. WEISS, P. (1925) *Arch. Entw. mech.* **104**, 359.
16. HOLTZER, H. (1952) *J. Exp. Zool.* **121**, 573.
17. WILDE, C. E. (1952a) *J. Morphol.* **90**, 119; (1952b) *J. Exp. Zool.* **119**, 65.
18. BALINSKY, B. (1933) *Roux Archiv.* **130**, 700.
19. RUDNICK, D. (1945) *Trans. Conn. Acad. Arts Sci.* **36**, 353.
20. GUYENOT, E., J. DINICHERT and M. GALLAND (1948) *Rev. Suisse Zool.* **55**, Suppl. 2.
21. WILDE, C. E. (1952) *J. Exp. Zool.* **119**, 65.
22. SCHROEDER, W. A. and L. M. KAY (1955) *J. Amer. Chem. Soc.* **77**, 3901.
23. SPRATT, N. T. (1954) *Aspects of Synthesis and Order in Growth* (Ed. RUDWICK) p. 209. Princeton Univ. Press.
24. FELDMAN, M. and C. H. WADDINGTON (1955) *J. Embryol. Exp. Morph.* **3**, 44.
25. TATUM, E. L. and S. R. GROSS (1956) *Ann. Rev. Physiol.* **18**, 53.
26. LASH, J., S. HOLTZER and H. HOLTZER (1957) *Exp. Cell Res.* **13**, 292.
27. HOLTZER, H. and S. R. DETWILER (1953) *J. Exp. Zool.* **123**, 335. MOOKERJEE, S., E. M. DEUCHAR and C. H. WADDINGTON (1953) *J. Embryol. Exp. Morphol.* **1**, 399.
28. HÖRSTADIUS, S. (1952) *J. Exp. Zool.* **120**, 421.
29. WADDINGTON, C. H. (1940) *Organisers and Genes*, Cambridge University Press, p. 101.
30. WADDINGTON, C. H. and E. M. DEUCHAR (1953) *J. Embryol. Exp. Morphol.* **1**, 349.
31. TOWNES, P. L. and J. HOLTFRETER, (1955) *J. Exp. Zool.* **128**, 53.

CHAPTER X

The Organisation of Growth Processes

WADDINGTON: We are now going on to rather a different type of organism. Dr. Rusch is first going to talk about some of his work in slime moulds and its bearing on the problems of organisation and differentiation that we have been discussing and also on the problem of cancer.

RUSCH: The problems that face the cancer researcher and the embryologist are very similar. Both are interested in the process of cell differentiation, both will have to be able to understand this chemically at some time in the future, and both are faced with very great complexities in studying this problem. The chief point of difference is that the experimental embryologist is chiefly concerned with problems of differentiation, whereas the cancer research worker's emphasis is on dedifferentiation. The biochemical approach to both problems is greatly complicated by the heterogeneous composition of both embryonic and neoplastic tissues. Both consist of cells of various types and ages, and the chemical analysis for any constituent or process at any moment simply reflects the summation of the conditions in all the cells at that time.

In order to overcome some of these problems concerning cancer, it was decided to investigate the biochemical pathways in some simpler form of life in which the processes of proliferation and differentiation could be more clearly separated into two distinct phases. The application of conclusions from such investigation to the more complicated problem of neoplasms is justified within limits because of the great similarity of life's processes in all cells. The chief problem which faced us, therefore, was the selection of an organism that would satisfy our criteria for a cell in which the various stages of its life cycle were clearly delineated and which at the same time was sufficiently large to permit chemical determination during these stages. After a painstaking search which began ten years ago, the myxomycete *Physarum polycephalum* was found suitable for our studies.

This organism has many characteristics which make it very satisfactory for investigations concerning proliferation and differentiation. It is sufficiently large to permit chemical analysis of a single "cell"; during its

263

vegetative, plasmodial stage it attains an area of several square centimetres during which nuclear divisions are essentially synchronous. Increase in its size continues until the growth medium becomes limiting or is altered in other ways. A simple form of differentiation (sporulation), which is entirely separate from the stage of proliferation, can be regularly induced by the investigator. We have succeeded in growing *Physarum* successfully in a partially defined soluble medium free of contaminating organisms and have learned how to initiate sporulation. Although a considerable part of our initial studies on this organism has dealt with requirements for growth and with its morphological and cytological characteristics under such conditions of growth, my present report will be limited to that aspect of the project concerned with the factors involved in the sporulation of the cell, since our subject at the symposium is limited to an investigation of differentiation. It is our opinion that the studies to be reported on sporulation in this model system may furnish clues for the study of this problem in more complex tissues. Gray [1] has previously studied some factors affecting the sporulation of *Physarum* grown on oats and not under conditions of pure culture.

Sporulation is entirely separate and sharply delineated from the proliferative stage of the organism. It is characterised in its early stages by a separation of the plasmodium into numerous separated globular masses, which gives rise to stalked sporangia. The multinucleate mass in the sporangial head undergoes fragmentation so that, after meiosis, numerous black-pigmented, mono- or bi-nucleate spores are formed. In the proper environment, these germinate to form gametes, pairs of which fuse into a zygote which, in turn, may develop with or without syngamy into a vegetative plasmodium, thus completing the cycle.

Physarum can be induced to sporulate by the following procedure: *Physarum* grown in pure shaken culture on a natural medium is harvested by centrifugation near or at the end of its growth phase. The plasmodia are dispersed in a sterile buffered salt solution, and the suspension (containing 1·1–1·3 g wet weight of plasmodia) is transferred to filter paper supported on glass beads contained in flasks. After spontaneous fusion of the small plasmodia into a single large one, a medium containing only salts, $CaCO_3$, and nicotinic acid at pH 5 is added, and the flasks are incubated in the dark for 4 days. Sterile technique is used in all steps. After the dark period, the flasks are illuminated at 22°C for 2 hr at a distance of approximately 0·5 in. above two 40 W fluorescent lamps and then replaced in the dark. Sporulation usually occurs within 12 hr.

This procedure induced sporulation in at least 90% of the cultures tested and was the basic test system for the subsequent studies. All tests were performed in triplicate. The use of plasmodia from shaken flask culture rather than from surface cultures insures material reproducible in quality, quantity and stage of growth, and allows considerably more flexibility in quantitative manipulation than is obtainable with large, preformed plasmodia.

In establishing the above conditions as necessary for sporulation, nicotinic acid was the only organic compound found to be required. Although either tryptophan or nicotinic acid is necessary, these alone cannot replace light for induction of sporulation (Table 10.1). Nicotinic

TABLE 10.1

NICOTINIC ACID REQUIREMENT

Addition	Concentration	Sporulation*
None	—	0/3
DL-Tryptophan	0·1%	3/3
Nicotinic acid or nicotinamide	0·01%	3/3
Nicotinic acid or tryptophan	No illumination	0/3

* Number of cultures sporulating per triplicate determination

acid or nicotinamide is active at concentrations as low as 14 μg/ml, and DL-tryptophan at levels as low as 100 μg/ml. Under assay conditions, although lack of either nicotinic acid or illumination results in failure to sporulate, the plasmodium appears in good condition and degenerates only after prolonged survival in this medium. Illumination in the absence of nicotinic acid (likewise producing no sporulation) leaves the plasmodium in equally good condition.

Since both tryptophan and nicotinic acid were active, the sporulation system appeared to be a convenient method for determining the pathway

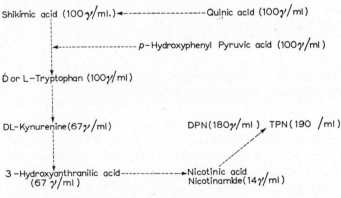

FIG. 10.1.

of nicotinic acid biosynthesis in *Physarum*. Figure 10.1 depicts diagram-matically the intermediates found to replace nicotinic acid and the mini-mum concentrations tested. This general scheme from tryptophan to nicotinic acid has been found in a number of other organisms. It is of some interest that the prearomatic compounds, quinic and shikimic acid, are also active. Whether or not DPN and TPN are taken up and used without alteration is not yet known. The levels used are equivalent to 34 μg/ml of nicotinic acid. Intermediates found to be inactive are listed in Table 10.2. Those marked with asterisks gave a weak response. The

TABLE 10.2

COMPOUNDS NOT REPLACING NICOTINIC ACID

Phenylalanine*	Anthranilic acid
Tyrosine*	Quinolinic acid*
Kynurenic acid	Indole-3-acetic acid*
Xanthurenic acid	Acetyl-tryptophan
Indole ± serine	Trigonelline

weak quinolinic acid activity may be due to contamination with nicotinic acid. Additional evidence of the prominent role of nicotinic acid is shown in Table 10.3. The inhibitors, added in a 10 to 1 ratio to nicotinic acid

TABLE 10.3

Inhibitor	Concentration per ml	Results* Inhibitor added at	
		"0" day	4 days
Pyridine-3-sulphonic acid	670 γ	0/3	3/3
3-Acetyl pyridine	670 γ	0/3	3/3
α-Picolinic acid	670 γ	0/3	2/3
Pyruvic acid	5·0 mg	0/3	—
Glucose	2·5 mg	3/3	—
	7·0 mg	0/3	—

Nicotinic acid, 67 γ/ml in all cultures
* Number of cultures sporulating per triplicate determination

(present in large excess of minimum requirements), completely blocked sporulation without obvious injury to the surviving unsporulated plas-modia when added at the onset of the dark period. However, at the end of the dark period, one day before illumination, pyridine-3-sulphonic acid and 3-acetyl pyridine showed no effect, and α-picolinic acid showed only a weak effect. These compounds at the indicated concentrations also inhibited shaken culture growth as follows: pyridine-3-sulphonic acid, 14%; 3-acetyl pyridine, 25%; α-picolinic acid, 31%. The concentrations of nicotinic acid and its immediate precursors in this natural medium are unknown, but since quinic and shikimic acids are apparently precursors, nicotinic acid may be supplied *de novo* from the same pathway or one similar to the one described by Davis and co-workers [2].

The probable relation between the inhibition by compounds containing methyl or potential methyl groups and the inactivity of trigonelline (*N*-methyl nicotinic acid) is shown in Table 10.4. Although serine,

TABLE 10.4

Compound tested	Concentration per ml	Results* Compound added at	
		"0" day	4 days
Trigonelline (no nicotinic added)	145 γ	0/3	—
Trigonelline ⎫	670 γ		
+ ⎬		2/2	—
Nicotinic acid ⎭	67 γ		
DL-Serine	5 mg	0/3	3/3
DL-Methionine	7·5 mg	0/3	3/3
Sodium formate	3 mg	0/3	3/3

Nicotinic acid, 67 γ/ml, in all tests except as indicated
* Number of cultures sporulating per number tested

methionine and formate inhibit when added early, late addition (presumably after nicotinic acid uptake is concluded), is without effect; the added nicotinic acid is probably methylated to trigonelline. Trigonelline is active neither as a replacement of nicotinic acid nor as an antagonist. Trigonelline has not been tested in the presence of added C_1 acceptor compounds.

A number of compounds found to be inactive either as replacements or inhibitors of nicotinic acid are listed in Table 10.5. Tryptone and cysteine

TABLE 10.5

COMPOUNDS INACTIVE FOR SPORULATION

Purines	Pyridoxal
Pyrimidines	Pyridoxine
Thymidine	Riboflavin
Glycine	Thiamin
Histidine	Serine
Tryptone	Cysteine
Threonine	

inhibit sporulation in the presence of tryptophan but not of nicotinic acid, and, therefore, probably interfere with the conversion of tryptophan to nicotinic acid. The growth medium with tryptone omitted (glucose, 1·0%; yeast extract, 0·15%) inhibits sporulation even in the presence of 0·01% nicotinic acid.

Originally it was thought that the requirement for nicotinic acid during sporulation arose from the use of a plasmodium grown on a medium deficient in nicotinic acid. However, the addition of 0·1% DL-tryptophan or of 0·01% nicotinic acid or nicotinamide neither stimulated nor inhibited growth on a natural growth medium of tryptone–glucose–yeast extract. Furthermore, plasmodia from such cultures, supplemented with tryptophan or nicotinic acid either at the time of inoculation or 12 hr before harvest, when tested for sporulation without further nicotinic acid addition, failed to sporulate or did so only after prolonged dark incubation following illumination. The latter result may be owing to small amounts of nicotinic acid carried over from the growth medium. Since *Physarum* can utilise prearomatic tryptophan precursors and since nicotinic acid antagonists, which inhibit sporulation, are relatively weak growth inhibitors, the nicotinic acid requirement appears to reflect not a genetic block, but rather a metabolic rebalance. In such a case nicotinic acid synthesis, although sufficient for plasmodial survival, would be insufficient to maintain the level or to increase the concentration of nicotinic acid metabolites (supposedly the pyridine nucleotides) required for sporulation.

Nicotinic acid must not only be present in a suitable concentration, it must also be present in the medium for a minimum of 4 days prior to illumination. This may be shown in two ways as tabulated in Table 10.6.

TABLE 10.6

DARK INCUBATION REQUIREMENT

Trytophan or nicotinic acid added at:	Results*	Illumination age	Results*
(days)		(days)	
0	3/3	2	0/3
1	3/3	3	1/3 (2/3 late)
2	1/3 (2/3 late)	4	3/3
3	0/3	5–7	3/3
Illumination at 5 days		Tryptophan or nicotinic acid added at "0" days	

DL-Tryptophan, 0·1%; nicotinic acid, 0·01%
* Number of cultures sporulating per number tested

When either tryptophan or nicotinic acid was added to sporulation cultures at zero time and light was applied after various intervals of dark incubation, the results obtained are shown in the right-hand column. When either tryptophan or nicotinic acid was added on successive days after preparation (the dark period) and light was applied to all cultures after 5 days of dark incubation, the results are shown in the left-hand column. In both cases, a minimum period of 3–4 days of incubation in the dark was required, presumably for the conversion of nicotinic acid to the pyridine nucleotides, which in turn reorient metabolism towards sporulation by directly or indirectly sensitising the plasmodium to light. The effect of light can apparently be retained to some extent by the plasmodium, since when light is applied prematurely (before the end of the 4-day dark period), sporulation will occur occasionally but erratically as late as a week after the 4-day period; although it usually does not occur at all.

It was next of interest to determine whether and at what stage during preparation for sporulation the organism was metabolically reoriented towards sporulation to such an extent as to interfere with or preclude growth. Such an experiment should indicate at what point a pathway essential for proliferation had been blocked or irreversibly shunted. At various stages during sporulation, with sterile technique, the salts–nicotinic acid sporulation medium was removed, replaced by the complete growth medium, the remainder of the procedure conducive to sporulation completed, and the cultures observed for growth and sporulation. The results are shown in Table 10.7. Growth medium added prior to the completion

TABLE 10.7

EFFECT OF GROWTH MEDIUM ADDED TO CULTURES
PREPARED FOR SPORULATION

Growth medium added*	Results	
	Sporulation†	Growth†
2 hr before illumination	0/5	5/5
After 1 hr illumination	1/3	2/3
After 2 hr illumination (complete)	5/5	0/5
6 hr after end of illumination	2/2	0/2

* Cultures 4 days old
† Number of cultures sporulating or growing per number tested

of illumination caused the plasmodium to expand from its typically vein-like presporulation morphology into a sheet-like plasmodium which, even after illumination, failed to sporulate but continued to grow. However, once illumination was completed, but before the characteristic series of morphological changes had begun, the growth medium was no longer capable of counteracting sporulation. The whole plasmodium then sporulated normally in the presence of growth medium, with no external evidence of abnormality. Since the minimum period of illumination required for sporulation varies from approximately 45 to 90 min for different cultures, the intermediate result obtained with one hour of illumination was to be expected.

The nicotinic acid-catalysed reactions in some manner contribute components needed for the light-sensitive reaction; these components in turn react with light, simultaneously blocking a pathway which furnishes substrates essential for growth and initiating the sequence of reactions resulting in sporulation. A normal growth substrate which specifically reversed the action of light (i.e. caused growth by furnishing the missing growth intermediate) would then serve to identify both the light-sensitive and nicotinic acid-induced reactions. The data presented in Table 10.7 indicate either that such substrates are present at ineffectively low concentrations or that the time interval after the completion of illumination is insufficient for intracellular synthesis of metabolites capable of blocking sporulation.

Various chemical and spectral properties of the particulate-localised yellow pigments, including their photolability, suggested a similarity to pteridines and their possible role in the sporulation-inducing function of light. Folic acid and its derivatives are known to be light sensitive. The effect of folic acid and "folic" antimetabolites on sporulation is shown in Table 10.8. When folic acid is added at 4 days (to avoid involvement in

TABLE 10.8

EFFECTS OF INHIBITORS ON SPORULATION

Inhibitor	Concentration	Results*
	(γ per ml)	
Folic acid	12	1/5
A-methopterin	13	3/3
Aminopterin	13	2/2
2, 4-Diamino (3'-chlorophenyl)-6-ethyl pyrimidine	2	3/3
	10	0/3
(3', 4'-Dichlorophenyl) derivative	2	0/3
Xanthopterin	64	2/3

Inhibitor added at 4 days; illumination at 5 days
* Number of cultures sporulating per number tested

the dark period) and the cultures are illuminated at 5 days, sporulation begins, is interrupted at an intermediate point, and the plasmodium disintegrates. Similar results may be obtained when folic acid is added after illumination, but the effect is not obtained with all cultures. The relatively high concentration of folic acid needed to give inhibition may reflect either a high pteridine metabolism or a relatively unspecific inhibition in which a metabolite of folic acid is the effective compound. Whether this inhibition effect is a delayed expression representing a reversal of the light-sensitive reaction or the inhibition of a later step in sporulation is not yet known. Studies on the effect of replacing the sporulation medium by growth medium, with and without added folic acid, are now in progress. Also of interest is the lack of inhibition of sporulation by aminopterin and A-methopterin, whereas growth on a natural medium is completely inhibited by the same concentration of aminopterin and 61% inhibited by A-methopterin. Added folic acid (12 μg/ml) does not stimulate growth on a natural medium.

All three experiments—the inhibition of sporulation by folic acid, the inhibition of growth by the inhibitors, and the lack of inhibition of sporulation by these same inhibitors—point to the requirement of metabolites whose synthesis is mediated by folic acid or its derivatives for growth but not for sporulation.

In this brief presentation I have described to you how *Physarum*, in the absence of growth substances, reorients its metabolism in such a way that, upon exposure to light, intracellular substrates are directed into the formation of a number of specialised products not elaborated during growth. Among these products are sporangial stalks, spore wall material, and black pigment, the production of which is associated with meiotic rather than mitotic nuclear division. Through the mediation of a differentiative process, the vegetative stage is transformed to the spore stage; the latter is characterised by lack of net cellular synthesis. Although the biochemical reactions which initiate and induce a series of reactions which culminate in sporulation are not yet understood, a model system is available which should prove of great value in assisting us to answer some of our questions about the mechanism of differentiation.

WADDINGTON: One of the interesting things here is the antagonism between growth and differentiation. One is used to having an antagonism between differentiation and growth, so that differentiated cells do not grow very fast, but here you find that cells which are growing very fast won't differentiate. In order to make the switch into the sporulation type of cellular physiology, it seems that you not only have to provide the system with nicotinic acid, allow it a certain length of time, and then illuminate it, but you seem to have also to inhibit some competing processes by cutting down the growth part of the metabolism. I don't know how far that applies in other organisms. One is used to finding that embryonic cells have alternative paths of differentiation open to them, with something that

19

switches them into one path or another, but here there are not two alternative paths of differentiation, but only one path of differentiation which seems to compete with a path leading to growth.

BERENBLUM: I think this is fairly common in adult systems. In conditions where you encourage growth, for instance, by mild injury resulting in hyperplasia, or, if you have reversible hormone action, there are indications that growth and differentiation are mutually antagonistic—that is, antagonistic both ways.

LEHMANN: Isn't this also the case in tissue culture? Don't you, according to the amount of embryonic extract, get either growth or differentiation? A few years ago a paper was published by Gaillard [3] where I thought it was fairly clearly shown. If you take the serum from older animals then you get differentiation but very little growth, but if you take it from younger ones you get a good deal of growth and very little differentiation.

WADDINGTON: Yes, I think that is an accepted observation. Dr. Fell and her group have shown it also. It is a somewhat parallel situation, but it is not clear in the tissue culture experiments that the growth medium has provided the requisite conditions for differentiation. Here you have identified certain factors necessary for differentiation—the nicotinic acid and the illumination—but providing these is not enough, you also have to stop the growth.

PLAUT: Did I understand you correctly that during growth essentially the single cells underwent synchronous divisions?

RUSCH: Yes, there is synchronous mitosis providing the size of the plasmodium does not exceed approximately 5 cm in diameter. When it is larger than this, the time of mitotis varies slightly from one side of the plasmodium to the other. Furthermore, mitosis is not synchronous in pseudopodia that extend away from the main mass of tissue when compared with the main body of the plasmodium.

PLAUT: During differentiation does it form more complex cytoplasmic structures, or does the thing break up into more separate cells?

RUSCH: The spores may be regarded as cellular but the stalks remain acellular.

PLAUT: Do you find any mitotic divisions once you have initiated this process of differentiation?

RUSCH: No, but meiosis occurs during the early stage of spore formation.

WILDE: What is the composition of the material in the stalk?

RUSCH: The exact composition is unknown although the stalks are full of tightly packed pigment granules.

WILDE: Would you like to amplify a bit this subject of nuclei being brought up into mitosis? If there are processes of DNA synthesis and so on, they might have a fixed rate. This is an interesting point and perhaps you have some information about it.

WADDINGTON: Perhaps we could leave this question of the synchrony of cell division until this afternoon when we are discussing mitosis in general. I think perhaps we should stick to the differentiation aspects of this thing at the moment.

POLLOCK: Could you give some idea of the maximum specific growth rate?

RUSCH: Under the most favourable conditions in shaken culture doubling of protein occurs at intervals of approximately 8 hr; however, on surface culture doubling occurs less rapidly, at about every 12 hr. The yield is approximately 0·5 g dry weight per 100 ml of medium containing 1 g glucose and 1 g of tryptone.

PONTECORVO: You mentioned that you sometimes get the cycle without conjugation. What happens then? The gametes grow into what?

RUSCH: The gametes always fuse, and the zygote may or may not undergo syngamy to form the plasmodium.

PONTECORVO: You mean you can have a plasmodium which starts from a single zygote or by fusion of several zygotes?

RUSCH: Yes.

WILDE: Is there any lower limit to the amount of plasmodium that will undergo differentiation?

RUSCH: We have no data on the lower limit of the size of the plasmodium which will sporulate. However, we have noted that several days after sporulation has occurred small areas of plasmodial growth occur away from the main mass of sporulation material. Since no pieces of plasmodia were visible in these areas at the time the main mass sporulated, we assume that the pieces which were not visible to the naked eye at the time of sporulation were already present but in amounts too small to form complete spore structures.

ZWILLING: Have you looked for any difference in staining properties in your aggregates just prior to sporulation?

RUSCH: No.

ZWILLING: This sort of thing has been observed in *Dictyostelium* by Bonner [4]. When to ordinary observation there appears to be no difference, there is a differential staining between the distal part and the main mass.

RUSCH: We hope to examine differences in staining some day but have been unable to get to it thus far.

HOLTZER: Are there any intermediate grades between your negative cultures and your positive cultures? I mean when you have two out of five, or two out of three, do the positives always have the same number of spores?

RUSCH: Yes, there are intermediate grades between complete sporulation and no sporulation. Certain substances added prior to sporulation interfere in various ways. Sometimes sporulation starts and then stops, and occasionally abnormal types of sporulation are observed.

PONTECORVO: Are you doing any genetics on this organism?

RUSCH: No, not at present. But one person in our group plans to do a genetic study as soon as we have completed certain aspects of the nutritional requirements. Dr. Lederberg has also expressed some interest but has not initiated any work thus far to my knowledge.

BEALE: Is this differentiation something that is irreversible? Could you mash them up and then get them to go back to the plasmodium again?

RUSCH: We haven't tried quite this type of experiment, but you will recall that I mentioned certain experiments during my presentation which indicate that, once the process of sporulation is initiated, it is irreversible.

CALLAN: Can you take out individual pieces of cytoplasm with one nucleus and subculture these to form a complete plasmodium?

RUSCH: We have not yet tried to obtain a plasmodium from a tiny piece containing only one nucleus. This should be attempted. However, Dr. Ross, in Professor Raper's department of the University of Wisconsin, has succeeded in culturing the organism from spores. He has noted plasmodia formation both from single zygotes and from varying numbers of zygotes which had previously fused.

CALLAN: And can you take the pieces for the inoculum as uni-nucleate pieces or must they be much bigger than that?

RUSCH: We always use large pieces for carrying our cultures.

WADDINGTON: I think we had better come back to this organism in relation to growth and cell division this afternoon. During the rest of this morning we want to get our last contribution on organisation and differentiation, and I think Berenblum can give us this, and its relation to cancer.

BERENBLUM: We have passed on from cell particulates to whole cells, and then from cells to tissues. When we pass on now to tumours we pass on to a further grade of complexity, a complexity which includes the change from orderly to disorderly types of growth.

The problem of organisation in tumours, forms an intricate part of the wider problem of tumour "autonomy"; and since the latter is a vague and confused concept, I propose to devote the greater part of my remarks to a critical analysis of what precisely is meant by this term, and to examine some of its inherent contradictions.

It should be made clear that autonomy is generally considered in pathology to be one of the basic principles of neoplasia, as is evident from the accepted definition of a tumour as "an autonomous new growth of tissue" [5].

From the viewpoint of the discussion in this symposium, the characteristic feature of neoplasia that calls for attention is the *disorderliness* of its growth and behaviour, in comparison to the orderly patterns of normal tissues. It may be useful, however, to enumerate all the known differences between neoplastic and non-neoplastic processes:

A tumour is composed of a colony of living cells, descendants of a normal cell that has undergone some abnormal type of irreversible transformation. Its growth pattern differs from that of normal proliferation, or of the various pathological hyperplasias, in being *progressive*, i.e. in failing to reach a growth equilibrium. The morphology of a tumour is atypical, involving cellular abnormalities and a defective ability to organise as a tissue. A tumour acquires a disproportionate food allocation from the body, and often induces systemic disturbances. Only in the *malignant* tumour can one discern specific properties that render the growth unmistakably different from non-neoplastic lesions, namely, by its tendency to invade the surrounding tissues and to produce metastases in distant organs.

In general terms, tumour autonomy refers to a relative failure of neoplasms to respond to the controlling influences of the body. The condition has often been figuratively described as one of "anarchy", representing a "defiance" of the laws governing multicellular organisms. The manifestations of tumour autonomy comprise, however, many different types of disturbances—in fact, all the characteristics of neoplasia; and it is my purpose to examine each in turn, and to exclude those that do *not* run counter to biological principles of homeostasis, but which merely constitute imbalances or ineffectual expressions of *normal* processes.

The cellular abnormalities in tumours, known as "anaplasia", comprise variations in the size, shape, and staining properties of the cells and their nuclei, including aberrant forms with giant cells, giant nuclei, distorted mitotic figures, etc., and a derangement in the spatial relationship of the cells to one another, involving a loss of polarity of the cells and a certain deficiency in the ability to organise as a tissue. However, these are not absolute criteria, but tendencies that manifest themselves to varying degrees in different tumours, or in different parts of the same tumour. Benign tumours show little evidence of these cellular abnormalities, and sometimes display a degree of differentiation and organisation that renders them microscopically almost indistinguishable from their parent tissues of origin. On the other hand, the more malignant a tumour, the greater the degree of anaplasia. (This is the basis for the histo-pathological diagnosis of tumours, as a guide to prognosis and therapy.)

It is probable, therefore, that cellular abnormalities are only *secondary* manifestations of extremely rapid growth, degenerative changes, and indirect effects of malignancy. The tendency for a tumour to display deficient organisation as a tissue may have a more fundamental significance than cellular abnormalities (and a better understanding of the principles of organisation *as applied to neoplasia* is, therefore, urgently needed). All the same, deficient organisation cannot be considered as an example of autonomy, if by the latter is meant something contrary to a normal biological process. *A deficiency implies that the process involved is normal, though set at a low level.*

The progressive nature of tumour growth introduces a different principle, in that the factors involved—cell division, cell maturation and cell death—are identical with those of normal proliferation or of the various pathological metaplasias; *yet the end results are absolutely different*. In neoplasia, there is no final limit to the quantity of tissue produced (other than that imposed by the death of the host); in non-neoplastic forms of proliferation, the balance between cell division and cell death invariably reaches an equilibrium. The distinction is a real one, and brings out what is perhaps the most distinctive character of neoplasia. Yet, progressive growth can hardly be described as an example of autonomy, since the underlying process—the disequilibrium between cell division and cell death—is explicable on the basis of a delay in maturation of the (neoplastic) stem cells [6]. It is, therefore, a disturbance in the balance of *normal* processes, not an essential abnormality of the processes themselves.

The disproportionate allocation of foodstuffs in the body towards a tumour is another feature of neoplasia, concerned with its functional behaviour. The phenomenon is demonstrable even in some benign tumours:—A slowly growing lipoma will, for instance, continue to store fat under conditions of extreme emaciation, i.e. when no trace of fat is found elsewhere in the body. In the case of malignant tumours, the phenomenon assumes far greater importance, being responsible for the progressive loss of weight, so characteristic a feature in the clinical course of the disease, and contributing to fatal termination. In terms of nutritional balance, the growth in size of a tumour involves the synthesis of new proteins out of building blocks which, if not provided by the food intake, will be derived from the breakdown of proteins of the normal tissues of the body [7].

Before accepting this as an example of functional autonomy on the part of a tumour, it should be recalled that the same phenomenon applies to the growth of a foetus *in utero* [8], and probably to many normal organs in the body. Yet no one speaks of them as "autonomous".

The allocation of foodstuffs in the body is by no means egalitarian; and during extreme starvation, the different organs lose weight at different rates. Each tissue somehow transmits to the body its minimal requirements, and during nutritional stress, urgent demands by some tissues are satisfied at the expense of others. A tumour does not, therefore, behave autonomously in this respect, but on the contrary, conforms to the biological principle of preferential food allocation according to the respective needs of the various tissues. From the viewpoint of the body as a whole, homeostasis is disturbed; but from the viewpoint of the tumour cells, nutrition operates only too effectively.

Other systemic disturbances resulting from the growth of a tumour are of two kinds: those resulting from excessive hormone secretion, in the case of a tumour of endocrine tissue, and those that develop as a late consequence of a malignant tumour that has invaded extensively and undergone degenerative changes. The latter (known clinically under the name of "cachexia") are clearly end results, and irrelevant to the discussion of autonomy.

With regard to the hormonal disturbances in specific cases of tumours of endocrine tissues, it would indeed be surprising if the progressive increase in the size of the growth were not accompanied by an over-all excessive secretion of the hormones. The situation is actually more complicated, because while the number of tumour cells increases, the amount of hormone secreted per cell is usually lower than that produced by the normal, parent cells of origin; and the more malignant the tumour, the greater the speed of increase of cells, but the lower the amount of hormone production per cell. While it would be incorrect to state that the two tendencies cancel each other out, the fact remains that the degree of hormonal imbalance is often less than one might have expected to occur, and sometimes not discernible at all—thus suggesting that some degree of hormonal homeostasis can operate in neoplasia. There are many nonplastic diseases of endocrine organs in which the hormonal balance in the body is disturbed. One does not call these examples of autonomy because, in such cases, the physiological cause and effect relationship is assumed to be still operative, though set at an abnormal level. There seems no reason to suppose that the same arguments do not apply to neoplasia of endocrine organs.

We come next to examples of "autonomy" concerned with the *local* functional behaviour of tumour cells. It is here that one so often hears about "the uselessness of a tumour in the body economy".

The keratin produced by a tumour of squamous epithelium does not perform its normal function of surface protection; a tumour of muscle tissue rarely exhibits contractile properties, and when it does, the contractions are dissipated in an ineffectual manner; the fat stored by a lipoma is, as already pointed out, not usually available for the rest of the body; while the cartilage and bone produced by chondrosarcomata and osteogenic sarcomata, respectively, rarely contribute to the body's needs for structural support. Many other examples could be quoted.

But here, too, the "autonomous" nature of the process is deceptive. If the keratin of an epithelial tumour displays no effectual function, this is because of its erratic distribution, albeit in excessive amounts. The same applies to the ineffectual contractility of neoplastic muscle fibres, though in this case, there is deficiency of the actual contractile fibrils. Potentially, the specialised products of tumours, be they keratin, fat, cartilage, bone, etc., would function normally but for their situation, pattern of distribution, and the disproportion of the amounts produced in relation to the body's needs. The defects, in other words, are not in the *nature* of the specialised products, but a result of the deficient organisation of the tumour as a functioning tissue—a form of neoplastic disturbance already discussed.

Finally, we come to the specific properties of *malignancy*—invasion and metastasis formation. Since these two properties dominate the clinical picture, being mainly responsible for the damage done by tumours in the body, it is not surprising that they should be considered examples *par excellence* of "autonomy".

In fact, invasiveness, as a biological process, is not unique for malignancy, since the wandering cells of the body—leucocytes, macrophages and lymphocytes—invade many organs and tissue, under particular circumstances, as part of their physiological function, while *destructive* invasion actually represents an essentially physiological function in the case of chorionic epithelium. What is abnormal in malignant cells is the apparent absence of a *cause* for their invasive activity. This is not necessarily autonomy but evidence of lack of knowledge on our part. If we knew the mechanism whereby chorionic epithelium invaded, we might have a better chance of understanding why other tissues, in their neoplastic transformation and the development of malignancy, acquire this specific biological function.

The development of metastases—which represents the most serious attribute of malignant tumours, rendering the growth virtually inoperable —actually depends on factors already discussed: the *scope* for metastasis formation is determined by invasion of the primary growth into blood or lymph spaces, facilitating the development of tumour emboli in various parts of the body. The *growth* of these emboli into metastases is determined by the same factors that disturb the growth equilibrium of the primary tumour and lead to progressive growth. The development of metastases does not, therefore, involve any new principles.

If we were to pause here, to take stock and try to reach some general conclusion, we would find ourselves in the invidious position of having to exclude autonomy from any consideration of neoplasia, without having anything to put in its place. Ewing's definition of a tumour as "an autonomous new growth of tissue" would then have to be changed, for want of anything better, to "a *neoplastic* new growth of tissue". And since we know that a tumour cell can remain in a dormant state, even the term "new *growth*" would have to be eliminated. We would then be left with the tautology that "a tumour is a neoplasm". A glaring example of *reductio ad absurdum*!

The fault lies, of course, in the superficiality of our analysis; for we have merely been considering the *manifestations* of neoplasia.

The deficiency in the power of organising as a tissue, the failure in reaching a growth equilibrium, and the ability to invade the surrounding tissues, may indeed be *normal* biological processes, set at an abnormal level or acting in unexpected circumstances. But the "inner drive" in the neoplastic cell which leads to these disturbances is surely pathological in a very special way, to which the concept of "autonomy" may after all be applicable.

But here we enter the realm of unprofitable speculation because of inadequate data: Is the "inner drive" of the nature of a somatic mutation, an unusual form of "organiser" action, viral action, or due to some other, unknown, mechanism? We simply do not know.

Can we, then, salvage anything from this destructive analysis? I think we can.

Of all the properties of neoplasia which we have discussed, the one that comes closest to a fundamental defect is the failure to reach a growth equilibrium. Though this defect may not conform to autonomy in the strict sense, it may nevertheless be connected with the problem of the defective organisation of tumours.

The possible link between *delayed maturation*—which is considered responsible for the disequilibrium in tumour growth—and *deficient organisation,* seems to me to be a profitable point for starting this discussion.

[Discussion of Berenblum's paper not recorded owing to breakdown of the recording machine, but reconstructed from notes by Selman.]

LEHMANN: Is it possible that tumours have lost something—a protein for instance—which had been the controlling factor?

BERENBLUM: There have been some examples in the recent literature of chemical deficiencies in tumours, without any proof that these are essential features of neoplasia. I am myself not very happy about the data of cancer being caused by a chromosomal deletion. I find it hard to visualise how such deletions could, on the one hand, produce such a wide range of individual differences between one tumour and another, and on the other hand, produce the one common effect of loss of growth equilibrium.

WADDINGTON: I wonder if the attainment of growth equilibrium is the most important criterion of the normality of growth? After all, as I understand it, some fish never attain growth equilibrium, but continue to get larger throughout their whole life, however long that may be.

PONTECORVO: What is the present status of the story that a tumour always emanates from a single cell?

BERENBLUM: The "focal" origin of a tumour, or more specifically, that a tumour is orginally derived from a single normal cell, is strongly supported by the experimental work on the "two-stage" mechanism of carcinogenesis, and particularly on the quantitative analysis of the process.

(Berenblum gave examples with slides.)

When mouse skin is first given brief treatment with a carcinogen (insufficient to induce tumours) and then submitted to repeated treatment with croton oil, tumours appear in large numbers. Reversal of the sequence of the two actions leads to virtual failure of tumours to appear. While croton oil has some "background" carcinogenicity of its own, the two-stage effect cannot be explained on the basis of a summation of two weak carcinogenic stimuli.

RUSCH: At the present time it is not possible, in my opinion, to present a single theory that covers all known facts concerning the mechanism of tumour formation. The problem is a complicated one. Merely stating that viruses induce cancer, or that cancer results from over-stimulation of growth or a lack of restraint is meaningless. The problem must eventually be solved at the molecular level with a clear definition as to which compounds or chemical pathways are altered. It will also be necessary to understand how viruses alter the biochemistry of the cell and to relate disturbances caused by cancer-inducing viruses to the alterations caused by chemicals and physical carcinogens. A good beginning has been made along these lines but considerable work yet remains to be done. Problems that require solution increase at a greater rate than existing ones are solved.

REFERENCES

1. GRAY, W. D. (1939) *Amer. J. Bot.* **26**, 709.
2. DAVIS B. D. (1955) *Amino Acid Metabolism*, pp. 799–811 (Ed. by W. D. McELROY, and B. GLASS.) The Johns Hopkins Press, Baltimore, Md., 1048 pp.
3. GAILLARD, P. J. (1942) *Hormones Regulating Growth and Differentiation in Embryonic Explants*, Hermann, Paris.
4. BONNER, J. T. (1957) *Quart. Rev. Biol.* **32**, 232.
5. EWING, J. (1940) *Neoplastic Diseases*, 4th ed. W. B. Saunders, Philadelphia and London.
6. BERENBLUM, I. (1954) *Cancer Res.* **14**, 471.
7. WHITE, F. R. (1945) *J. Nat. Cancer Inst.* **5**, 265.
8. SEIGERS, W. H. (1937) *Amer. J. Physiol.* **119**, 474.

CHAPTER XI

Cell Division

WADDINGTON: We are now going back to consider an aspect of the behaviour of individual cells, namely, cell division. In this we have, of course, a very highly organised performance of the cell with a number of different components whose operations fit into one another very precisely. We shall probably also get on to the question of growth and the factors which control cell growth. I think that Mitchison is going to begin this discussion.

MITCHISON: I am going to start off by trying to review 50 years' work on the mechanism of cleavage in 10 min, so it will inevitably be a rather summary treatment. I shall be dealing only with cleavage in animal cells and, to begin with, in sea-urchin eggs, because they have been by far the most widely studied type of animal cell. But I will mention at the end some studies on other eggs and other cells. I am going to run through some of the evidence and two or three theories.

The essence of the problem is clear in the sea-urchin egg. You have a sphere; it goes through a dumb-bell stage; and you finish up with two spheres. This involves, for purely geometrical reasons, an increase of 26% in surface area. Now, one thing that simplifies the consideration of cleavage at the present time is that there were a number of earlier theories in which the main mechanism of cleavage was thought to involve the mitotic apparatus inside the egg—the asters and the spindles [1]. But work done in the last ten years or so has made it clear that sea-urchin eggs can divide without the mitotic apparatus inside them. This has been shown both by stirring the eggs [2, 3], by treatment with colchicine [4, 5], and by sucking out the mitotic apparatus [6]; and after all these treatments you still get cleavage. We are only left now, I think, with theories of cleavage which put the main responsibility for the mechanical process on the outer cortex. Now, this cortical layer in the sea-urchin egg is about $1 \cdot 5$–2μ in thickness [7], but see also [8]. It is gelated material, and there is evidence that the orientation of the molecules in the cortex is predominantly radial [9].

WADDINGTON: Could I interrupt for a minute there and ask at what stage you can suck out the mitotic apparatus and still get cleavage?

MITCHISON: The evidence is that you can do it at about metaphase [6]. But, at any rate, you can suck it out and you will still get cleavage.

WADDINGTON: The point I was getting at is that for the initiation of cleavage, isn't the mitotic spindle required?

MITCHISON: That, I think, is still an open question; but for the actual mechanism of the cleavage it is probably not essential.

Now, before starting on the theories, it is worth mentioning two or three key observations which seem to be relevant to the various theories. The first experiment, which is still one of the most important pieces of work on cleavage, consisted of measurements made by Professor Dan and his colleagues about twenty years ago [10, 11, 12]. They measured the changes in the dimensions of the surface which took place in cleaving sea-urchin eggs. This was done by putting kaolin particles on the surface and then measuring the movements of these particles relative to each other at different parts of the surface. When you consider only the linear changes that take place, that is, the movements of the particles in profile, what they found was a wave of expansion which started at the poles of the egg at the beginning of cleavage and moved round the surface of the egg towards the furrow. Recently Dan and Ono [13] have recalculated these data to give the changes in area, taking into account not only the linear changes but also the fact that the egg is a solid of revolution. They found a contraction in area in the furrow, but there was, as before, an expansion in other parts of the surface, and there was also a sequence of changes (area expansion) travelling over the surface from the poles towards the furrow. Now, there is evidence rather like this from optical changes—in birefringence and in light scattering [14, 15]. Although they can't be analysed as fully as the particle changes, the main thing they show is that you get the first sign of the changes in the cleaving egg with something that starts at the poles of the egg; it does not start at the furrow region, and also what happens first at the poles happens subsequently at the furrow. So, again, you appear to get evidence of a change spreading over the surface from the poles to the furrow.

Finally, there is evidence of another sort which comes from measurements that Professor Swann and I did on the mechanical properties of the surface [16–19]. The only thing to mention here which is relevant to theories of cleavage is that the egg rather surprisingly shows a great increase in the stiffness of its cortex just prior to cleavage. The elastic modulus increases by a factor of about 12 during mitosis and the events just preceding cleavage.

In the sea-urchin egg, there are two main theories of cleavage which are tenable today. Both, as I've said before, involve the cortex; one of them puts its emphasis on contraction and the fullest account is given by

Marsland and Landau [20]. In essence, the contraction theory states that there is a ring of contracting material in the region of the furrow. In its simplest form, this theory is difficult to reconcile with the surface changes as seen both from particle movements and from optical changes, where you apparently get something happening at the poles of the egg before it happens at the equator. Recently, however, Marsland [21] has modified his theory to suggest that there may be a "solation" of the cortex at the poles before the furrow starts to contract. This would explain the expansion and the optical changes. Now, my own objections to the contracting ring depend on some pieces of evidence which are circumstantial rather than crucial. One of them is the increase in stiffness which I mentioned earlier. The mechanism that Marsland suggests is a contraction in the furrow, so the rest of the surface is being extended passively by this contracting ring. It is, to say the least of it, odd that the surface should make it twelve times as difficult for this process to happen, by raising its stiffness just at the time that it has to be passively stretched. Secondly, the cleavage furrow will pass unchanged through a micro-dissection needle placed in its path [3]. If there was a contracting ring in the furrow, you would expect it to be broken and deformed by the needle. Thirdly, and this is possibly one of the most important objections, this mechanism is not in any way related to the process of mitosis which has happened just before. You say that there is a contracting ring, but you don't say how it started. Yet it seems fairly clear that cleavage must actually be organised by the mitosis that has happened earlier. Both in time and in position, these two processes are very closely related.

The other theory of cleavage in sea-urchin eggs is one that Professor Swann and I suggested some years ago and have discussed recently in a review [1]. We believe that the main active force in producing cleavage is not a contraction of the membrane but an expansion. The theory started with two lines of work; one on birefringence changes [20, 21, 22] and the other on membrane structure [9]. Swann measured the birefringence in the asters and found that a wave of disorientiation travels outwards from the astral centre. It reaches the polar surface of the egg before the equatorial surface for simple geometrical reasons—the centre of the aster is nearer to the poles than to the equator. Our theory suggests that whatever substance causes the disorientation in the asters also causes a disorientation in the proteins of the cortex. With a predominantly radial molecular structure in the cortex, the effect of this will be a diminution in thickness of the cortex and an expansion in area. Now, the disorientation starts at the poles of the egg, so you get an expansion there leading to the first phase of the cleavage with the nipping-in of the egg surface to form the furrow. The simplest way to explain the formation of the furrow is to say that there is a certain amount of residual tension normally present at the egg surface. The tension is let off at the poles and, since the egg is a three-dimensional figure, you will begin to get a furrow. Then you have to continue the process. We suppose that the membrane expansion continues around the surface of the egg, spreading from the poles towards the equator. This forces the furrow region further inwards. In the form in which we originally suggested this theory we thought that as the furrow went inwards, it would meet increasing concentrations of the disorientating substance and it would also expand [9]. Dan and Ono [13], however, have shown this view is no longer tenable. What appears to be happening is an expansion of the furrow surface in the linear dimension at right angles to the plane of the furrow, counter-balanced by a contraction in the direction parallel to the plane of the furrow. There is a change in shape of the furrow material and, since there is often no wrinkling in the furrow, this material looks as if it were behaving plastically. We have, therefore, modified our original "expanding membrane" theory, and, in our latest account [1], we suggest the furrow behaves passively in the later stages of cleavage and is pushed inwards by active expansion of the rest of the surface.

Now, there are clearly a number of objections to this theory. Whether it will in fact work mechanically is not absolutely certain. One of the difficulties here is that you cannot test the theory with a model system because you cannot make a substance which behaves like the cortex. However, the theory does fit the experimental facts. It explains the surface changes, both from particle measurements and optical observations. It suggests a possible explanation of the increase in stiffness since a membrane has to be stiff in order to push round the surface of a sphere. Finally, it links up the process of cleavage to the process of mitosis that goes before. There are two other theories of cleavage which apply to rather different cells. One is Dr. Selman and Prof. Waddington's theory about cleavage in amphibian eggs [23]. It seems clear from their work that you are getting a somewhat different type of mechanism in these eggs. They have shown that the furrow moves inwards by a process of growth. In the cleaving amphibian egg, there is a differentiated region in the cytoplasm ahead of the furrow and they think that the furrow forms by, as it were, differentiating out of the cytoplasm. Now, they emphasise growth as a major factor in cleavage and of course growth must also happen in the case of the sea-urchin egg. We think that the membrane expands but at some point the egg must also generate new cortical material. It may well be that it does this at a different stage in the cycle in the sea-urchin egg from what it does in the amphibian egg. Personally, I suspect that the mechanism in amphibian eggs is a somewhat unusual one, concerned perhaps with the mechanical difficulty of cleaving a very large egg. There doesn't appear to be evidence at the moment of a differentiated region ahead of the furrow in other cells. As far as it applies to sea-urchin eggs, I don't think that sort of mechanism can give a very convincing explanation of the surface changes.

Finally, most people will say that these theories may be all right for eggs but do they apply to any other kind of cell? One other theory put forward by Chalkley [24, 25] some 20 years ago is, very simply, that the later stages of cleavage in *Amoeba proteus* are controlled by the presence of the two daughter nuclei near the poles of the cell. These nuclei stimulate amoeboid movement at the poles and the cell cleaves by pulling itself apart. This is not unlike the expanding membrane theory. In both theories, the daughter nuclei influence the cell surface in their neighbourhood causing either an expansion or amoeboid movement. Something similar also happens in tissue culture cells where you get a bubbling of the surface at cleavage. This starts at the poles of a dividing cell and it gradually moves over the surface towards the equator [2], in a way very like the surface changes which you get in sea-urchin eggs.

WADDINGTON: Lehmann, would you like to draw any parallels between the sea-urchin phenomena and those in *Tubifex*?

LEHMANN: I should like to mention first some characteristic differences between the spirally cleaving egg of *Tubifex* and the equally dividing sea-urchin eggs. The first type presents intracellular determination events whereas the latter one is acting with supercellular fields. Certainly, a mitosis that happens before onset of spiral cleavage must be very important when all the intracellular segregation processes begin. There is little known about the factors inducing prophase and metaphase. The onset of anaphase can be inhibited by quinones (Lehmann [26], Huber [27]). The egg remains stopped in metaphase and no attempt at further cleavage is made. The transformation of metaphasic to anaphasic state, discussed by Dr. Mitchison, does not even start. We can infer from our observations that as soon as anaphase movements begin, this process seems to be induced and thereafter becomes more and more independent of the spindle apparatus. Some of the inducing influences seem to arise in the spindle region and to pass to the cortex just above the astral zone, where they bring about a loosening and spreading of the plasma coat. This process is much inhibited by naphthoquinone. There is very little bubbling on the surface and there is only a small cell formed. This means responsiveness of cortex inhibited by the quinone. In the first period of anaphase inducing materials from the mitotic apparatus may reach the cortical regions closest to the asters. In the later periods these activated zones may continue with their movements, even when the spindle is entirely disintegrated. So far I share the opinion of Dr. Mitchison about factors of mitosis.

And then I want to submit an idea concerning expansion of cytoplasmic coat which I have got looking at the pictures of pinocytosis of Holtzer [28] and Bennett [29]. Amoebae are capable of incorporating food particles by forming large infoldings and of taking in liquid droplets by pinocytosis. Both processes of infolding require localised expansion of plasmalemma. So far there is some relation between vacuole formation and cleavage processes. I wonder whether there is a mechanism in common behind these two types of cellular surface expansion.

The mitotic poisons or antimitotic substances which have been used in *Tubifex* affect different parts of the mitotic process. In most of our numerous experiments we have tested the same stage, namely, the metaphase of the first cleavage division.

There are several substances which block the mitotic mechanism so effectively that these eggs may live in the undivided state one, two or even up to ten days without cleaving. From this we may conclude that it is possible to suppress some mechanisms inside the cell without abolishing entirely the general maintenance factors but only injuring those factors that are responsible for the cleavage. So here is a dissociation of several biological functions. This term was introduced by Needham [30] some years ago (*loc. cit.* p. 505). Here you have a disengagement of structural maintenance from mitotic activity and progressive differentiation. This survival condition may be useful for further developmental analysis. Our experimental conditions have enabled us to determine how much quinone is required for the inhibition of one cell [31]. One egg has a weight of 50 μg. It is blocked by 2.5×10^{-3} μg quinone. That means that the blocking concentration of quinone is 5×10^{-5} μg per 1 μg egg substance. The blocking concentration of colchicine is about 2×10^{-7} μg per 1 μg egg substance. These figures indicate that some especially active elements of low concentration, probably enzymes, must have been damaged by the antimitotic substance.

Colchicine differs in its type of action considerably from the lower quinones [32]. It has little influence on the motility of the cortex but will induce disappearance of mitotic apparatus in the prophase of the second cleavage cycle. Colchicine treated eggs may also live for many days and never show again a mitotic apparatus. Colchicine suppresses aster formation during the prophase of the second cleavage. The asters disappear for ever, the nuclear membrane is dissolved and the chromosomes become distinct, then they become invisible, too, at least with the ordinary microscope. Later on there appear in increasing number Feulgen-positive bodies but no signs of spindles, asters or chromosomes. One may ask whether the centrosome mechanism is not a cell organoid [33] which is selectively destroyed by the action of colchicine.

However, it must be added that in the case of plants there is not such selective reaction of the mitotic apparatus to colchicine. It is easy to produce x-ploids by successive suppression of mitotic divisions because the spindle apparatus can reappear again, but in animal cells the spindle apparatus in many cases disappears irreversibly and the blocked cells cytolyse later on [34].

The action of colchicine provides us again with a good example of dissociation of several cellular activities. Whereas the mitotic apparatus is unable to function any longer and to induce complete cleavage furrows, the rhythmical change between surface movements and resting surface continues in the same rhythm as in the controls.

In general our experiments with antimitotic substances have shown that it is possible to dissect in a rather selective way the mitotic mechanism but unfortunately for our studies at that time refined methods of electron microscopy and cytochemistry did not exist. They were just developing. So we dropped work with antimitotic substances and started with studies on fine structure [35] and cytochemistry [37] of the *Tubifex* cell. With the aid of a new fixative containing acetone, formaline, some acetic acid, osmium tetroxide and chromic acid we have been able to obtain rather clear fibrous and reticular structures inside the cell. These structures are partly dissolved when we use the orthodox neutral osmium tetroxide (see also [36, 38]). With the aid of the new fixative the mitotic apparatus can easily be visualised in the electron microscope. [The photographs shown at the symposium are now published in [36].] The asters contain in their centre a three-dimensional reticulum of gel-like character from which long straight fibres run in radial directions. There are no mitochondria in the centres but between the radial fibres mitochondria are situated which follow the general direction of astral fibres. The fibres of the spindle are partly tubular. The lateral parts seem to be fibrous, the central region contains small vesicles and granules. The question is how these fibres are composed? I refer here to the experimental work of Mazia [39] on spindle fibres of the mitotic apparatus in the sea-urchin egg and to the studies of H. H. Weber and Hoffman-Berling [40] in Heidelberg. In the formation of astral and spindle structures the sol–gel mechanisms are also involved. *Amoeba* shows formation of an undirected three-dimensional gel-like reticulum which arises from the sol-like cytoplasmic fluid or enchylema by aggregation of individual particulates [41]. An analogous mechanism of strictly oriented aggregation of particulates may be invoked for the formation of astral and spindle fibres. Bajer [42] has found in early prophase an accumulation of enchylema close to or in the nucleus. Mazia finds in colchinised sea-urchin eggs that this mass of enchylema is incapable of forming oriented fibrous structures, probably because the orienting influence of the centrospheres has been somehow abolished by the action of colchicine.

From these preliminary results we can see that electron microscopy will facilitate a more detailed analysis of the formation of the mitotic apparatus. That is, of course, only one way of approach which has to be supplemented by further work with antimitotic substances, and biochemical and cyto-chemical methods applied to mitosis [43].

BERENBLUM: I should like to ask Dr. Mitchison what is the mechanism of the separation of the daughter cells in the case of a cell division which is not globular, but which is elongated so that when the astral bodies separate they certainly don't reach the polar regions? What is the mechanism there?

MITCHISON: I think you might well have the same sort of mechanism. If you take an elongated cell, the disorienting substance will reach the sides of the cell before it reaches the poles, but you will still get an expansion towards the furrow which will tend to push it in (Fig. 11.1). Is that what you were meaning?

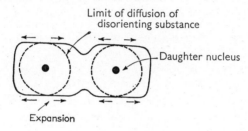

Limit of diffusion of
disorienting substance

Daughter nucleus

Expansion

FIG. 11.1.

BERENBLUM: Well, I was thinking of the really long cell, a fibroblast or even a muscle cell where the poles are really far apart.

MITCHISON: Yes, but don't a large number of elongated cells in fact round up before they divide? Fibroblasts certainly do.

WADDINGTON: When the cell is very elongated or very large, it may be impossible for the stuff coming off the asters to get to the poles, but it would get to two places, one on each side of the future furrow.

MITCHISON: I think you might well have expansion starting in that region; but I am not at all certain that the mechanism can operate in a cell as big as an amphibian egg, and that may be the reason why you get a different type of mechanism operating.

WADDINGTON: Before we go on to the questions about the spindle, which I think Dan is going to talk about, there are some questions I would like to ask Lehmann, or perhaps Lehmann and Mitchison together. One point that Lehmann mentioned was that having destroyed his spindle with colchicine he continued to get periodic changes of the surface. Now, according to Mitchison those changes in the surface would be initiated by something which comes off the anaphase groups of chromosomes and which first breaks down the asters and then reaches the surface. On that theory, what is supposed to be happening in these cells in which the spindle apparatus has been destroyed? Are you getting rhythmic changes in the total mass of chromosome material?

MITCHISON: Yes, I think so. You get this effect if you treat sea-urchin eggs with colchicine early on; then you don't get a spindle formed and you don't get separation of the chromosomes or cleavage, but you *do* get rhythmic changes both in the chromosomes [44] and in the surface [5, 15].

WADDINGTON: Aren't I right in thinking that you can get such rhythmic changes in things which have no nuclear material in them at all? For instance, separated polar lobes of *Ilyanassa*, which Morgan worked on a long time ago? There was some evidence of an autonomy of the surface changes independently of any nucleus.

LEHMANN: Yes. I have seen that myself in *Ilyanassa*. There are very clear rhythmical changes to be observed. You have the same in enucleated eggs of *Tubifex*. It has also been observed by Pasteels [45] on monastral *Chaetopterus* eggs. For instance, with suitable treatment some eggs may stay in the one-nucleated stage but undergo some differentiation, and there you see the characteristic movements of plasmatic regions in relation to the surface independent of the nucleus.

CALLAN: There are two or three nice cases of blastulae in amphibia being formed without the cell nuclei at all. So I think one has to keep the chromosomes out of this particular story.

WILDE: The particular story they are talking about is the sea-urchin one. The Briggs people, in the frog, have found that the cleavage, so called, is very irregular, so that it may be some non-orderly process that is compartmenting the cytoplasm. But in the Harvey story—the parthenogenetic merogony—the little spheres are quite equal in size and certainly mimic the formation of a blastula.

MITCHISON: I think that is a perfectly valid criticism and is probably a difficult one to overcome—the story of these activated enucleated halves in sea-urchin eggs. There are two ways of getting out of it. One is to say that there is a lot of DNA present in the egg cytoplasm, though that doesn't explain why you get something rather like a normal cleavage. The other thing to say is that this cleavage is irregular and very much delayed [22]. I think one has to admit a certain degree of autonomy of the surface, but it is certainly not as well organised as it is when under a nuclear influence. One case, for instance, is the amoeba, which ceases to have organised pseudopodial movement when you enucleate it, but you do get a certain amount of activity of the surface still continuing.

WADDINGTON: I think my view of a process like cleavage would be that it comprises a number of different factors which interact with one another, and normal cleavage requires the organisation and co-ordination of the whole set of components; but each of the components can do something on its own. You can, for instance, have the mitotic apparatus operating without co-operation with the surface, although it can of course be considerably influenced by the surface if the situation is right. One can see that by going back to Morgan's old work on polar body formation [46]; he got quite equal-ended spindles if the apparatus was forced down into the middle of the egg, but asymmetric spindles when it got up near the region of the cortex which was ready to form polar bodies. Similarly, Lehmann's centrifuging of spindles into abnormal locations has, I think, shown considerable interaction between the spindle and the cell surface. And these cases of at least a moderately good imitation of cleavage going on without any spindle apparatus again suggest that the surface can do quite a lot on its own, although it never does it properly unless it has the spindle to co-operate with it.

LEHMANN: If you think about mitosis, even there two different processes are in action; stretching and contracting, which have been discussed recently by H. H. Weber and by Hoffman-Berling [40]. I have seen a beautiful film of glycerol-treated tissue culture cells, which are still able to divide if you add ATP. That looks very convincing. At the same time you see in that film a type of expansion of the surface of these cell models. This is also a very important process in cell division which is also related to ATP. It must be some sort of "Weichmacher effect".

WADDINGTON: What sort of effect is that ? A kind of plasticising?

LEHMANN: Yes, plasticising; that's the word!

MITCHISON: My own feeling is that if you look through the literature, for every one case you get of autonomous surface movements occurring independently of the nucleus, you get five other cases in which the surface movements do appear to be influenced by the proximity of nuclear material. The evidence is not entirely one way, but on balance it is in favour of nuclear influences.

CALLAN: Nuclear or asters?

MITCHISON: I think nuclear. For instance, there is the case of amoeboid movement [47], and there is also evidence that bubbling is related to the nearness of the nucleus to the surface [2].

BRACHET: We should not think only in terms of the actual asters and spindles, because one thing which occurs and which must play a role is the formation of jellified regions of cytoplasm at long distances around the spindles and asters. I noticed this a long time ago when I was studying the effects of certain substances on the metabolism of the frog egg [48]. These substances were, for instance, of the type of urethane or phenylurethane. In that case, you get complete stoppage of the cleavage, but actually the nuclei continue to divide quite well. What you can see in sections is a perfectly normal mitotic apparatus, which divides normally. But around the asters, at telophase especially, you can see that the cytoplasm is affected. It has a different texture from what it has elsewhere. In that case the surface is absolutely smooth and looks normal. Obviously this factor must be, in the case of large eggs at any rate, an important one, which should not be considered as part of the asters themselves, but as something which is happening around them.

WADDINGTON: I think perhaps the time has come now for Dan to tell us his story about asters.

DAN: Mitchison has brought up various theories of cell division. However, I happen to belong to the other school which emphasises the importance of the asters and the spindle in the process of cell division. There was once a rather grave difference between the experimental bases on which the two theories rested. Some years ago I performed so-called perforation experiments [49]. A pipette of rather large bore is pushed against a flattened sea-urchin egg in a shallow hanging drop and a hole is made through the cytoplasm. When the egg cleaved with the perforation, only the perforation is pulled in as a furrow, leaving the cell periphery distal to the perforation inert (Fig. 11.2a and b). However, since a normal furrow is formed on the other side of the spindle where no hole is made, this normal furrow and the substitute furrow fuse eventually and a heart-shaped two-cell stage results (Fig. 11.2c). This result gave me the impression that the force of cleavage is probably coming from the inside, most likely from the mitotic apparatus, and the quiescence of the operated side is the result of blocking the transmission of the force by the presence of the hole. This experiment was really one of the crucial experiments which led me to the internal activity theory [50].

BRENNER: May I ask one question? Does one go right through to the other side?

DAN: Yes.

BRENNER: Only on one face?

DAN: No, all through. A doughnut of a cell. I may add that if two holes are made along a line bisecting the spindle, only the innermost changes into a furrow, leaving the outer hole and the cell periphery of that side quiescent.

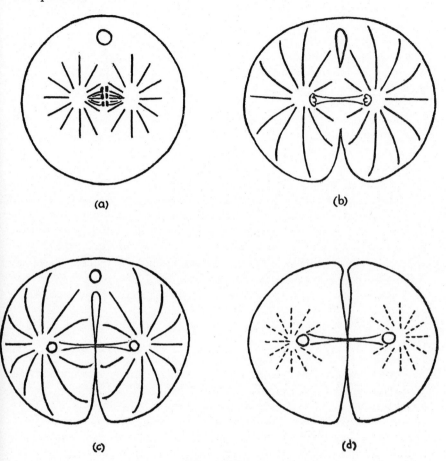

(a) (b)

(c) (d)

FIG. 11.2.

Recently, Professor Swann and Dr. Mitchison proposed the idea of the expanding cortex. They think the polar surface begins to expand under the influence of a substance (structural agent) diffusing out from the separating chromosome sets [9, 22]. In another place they say that some message comes from inside the cell at the metaphase and once the message is received by the cortex, the cortex acquires autonomy to pinch itself into two. Their proposal led me to reconsider my old perforation experiments and I came to realise that when I did this experiment, I tried, for technical reasons, to perforate at as early a stage as possible, so as to have time between the operation and the beginning of the observation. So I think it very likely that I made a hole before metaphase, before the message was sent off in the Swann–Mitchison sense. This expectation has turned out to be true, because if an ample time is allowed before operation, the cortex distal to a hole can also cleave (Fig. 11.2d).

Therefore, although this is a lost point for me, I am happy for the fact that now the observations are all in agreement, including Professor Waddington's observation on amphibian eggs [23]. He put a piece of cellophane through newt eggs, which corresponds to perforation in separating the cortex from the spindle.

Now, I find myself in the position to wonder what sort of thing Professor Swann's so-called message is. They think of it in terms of the diffusion of some substance or structural agent, which is admittedly a rather vague statement. So I went as far back as to study the function of the aster. This attempt was initiated when Professor Mazia and I isolated the mitotic apparatus [51]. In that study, we found that the structural integrity of the spindle apparatus is maintained by disulphide bonds, for if disulphide is reduced to sulphydryl, the isolated mitotic apparatus becomes very flabby. If detergent solution is given anew, the mitotic apparatus which withstood detergent action before is quickly dissolved.

This led me to reinvestigate the distribution of free sulphydryl groups in the cell. I used the very transparent eggs of *Clypeaster japonicus*, which are particularly suited for testing colour reaction. By applying the nitroprusside test, I found that astral centres are strongly nitroprusside positive. However, since the nitroprusside reaction is rather hard to take record of, I turned to so-called sulphydryl staining. On staining *Clypeaster* eggs fixed by trichloroacetic acid with 1-(4-chloromercuriphenylazo)–naphthol-2 which has been worked out by Professor Bennett [52], I found that the astral centres are stained side by side with the spindle fibres and chromosomes. The astral rays, however, are not stained. In anaphase and telophase, the accumulation of free SH at the astral centres has further increased. The present record is not the first one for such localisation of free SH, as Professor Brachet years ago pointed out the same situation in amphibian eggs [53].

Having found this accumulation or liberation of free SH, I began to think about the late Professor Rapkine's famous work [54]. As is well known, he discovered a fluctuation of free SH in pace with division activity, i.e. unfertilised eggs have a content of free SH which decreases midway between fertilisation and the first cleavage. A maximum which is about of the same height as the unfertilised condition is reached some 10 min before the cleavage (probably around the metaphase) and it decreases again as the egg divides. I repeated his experiments literally, using 25% TCA for fixation but only substituting mortar crushing of eggs by a glass-homogeniser. Iodometric titration of the supernate gave me the same SH curve as Professor Rapkine's, which I extended to the end of the second cleavage. The SH change is really a cyclic one repeating itself with division cycles.

However, it soon became clear that the free SH which is fluctuating in the 25% TCA supernate is not glutathione as Professor Rapkine originally predicted. The supernate still contains some proteins, contrary to Professor Rapkine's expectation that 25% TCA would precipitate all the proteins, for by saturating the supernate with NH_4SO_4 the remaining proteins come down. Reducing substances contained in the second supernate are ascorbic acid and reduced glutathione, the latter of which remains unchanged all through the cleavage cycle. In other words, the substance which carries the fluctuating free SH is a protein fraction which was not precipitated by 25% TCA. I also measured S:N ratios in this fraction and found that when the quantity of SH increases the ratio also increases, indicating that some S–S bridges are broken and more free SH radicals are exposed. At any rate, from the above fact, theories of cell division in which glutathione is instrumental may not be valid.

Well, just leaving quantitative estimation of SH for a short while, we go back to stained sections. The nucleus at an early stage—say, at the pronucleus stage—does not take up the SH stain at all. After the fusion of the pronuclei, the synkaryon begins to be stained a little and it continues to take up more stain until the end of the prophase. During mitosis, as has already been said, chromosomes and the spindle fibres are stained together with astral centres. However, after cleavage, the two daughter nuclei lose stainability again and then they begin to pick up the stain as the second division approaches. What I want to say is, here again we come across a cyclic change of stainability in the nucleus. Superficially, nuclear SH stainability precedes the liberation of free SH in the general cytoplasm, but the real nature of the correlation is not fully understood yet.

Going back to the living eggs, I centrifuged them. Making the story as short as possible, the main point is like this. If the *Clypeaster* egg which I mentioned earlier is centrifuged, the hyaline zone, which is positive for the nitroprusside test, appears fairly low down toward the centrifugal side. Granules filling more than half the volume of the egg lying centripetally to the hyaline zone are yolk, I believe, and mitochondria (as identified by Janus Green staining) are thrown down into a fairly small centrifugal portion of the egg. Usually when the egg is centrifuged at metaphase, the mitotic apparatus is thrown down into the hyaline zone rich in SH and the asters continue to grow. However, as they grow, they tend to take up a more central position in the cell and they heave themselves up, so to speak, from the SH-rich hyaline zone into the lighter yolk portion which is nitroprusside-negative. As they do so, a very striking thing is how often one sees two trails of nitroprusside colour following the two astral centres extending out from the hyaline SH zone into the SH-free yolk zone. Naturally from this kind of picture alone, we cannot say whether the streamers of SH are coming out of the astral centres or are being drawn up toward the astral centres.

There is another interesting fact. When you centrifuge eggs, sometimes one of the asters is stuck to the cortex (?) and left in the SH-free yolk zone, while the other aster is thrown into the hyaline SH zone. Applying the nitroprusside test, the former does not pick up the stain at all but the latter acquires a typical SH pool at the astral centre. Furthermore, the latter can begin to grow immediately while the former can do so only after a certain period which is obviously necessary for the diffusion of SH (protein?) from the hyaline zone to where it lies. Putting the above two sets of facts together, it looks as if the aster is pumping up SH substance which is a raw material for growth, and when it is severed from the SH zone, it cannot grow unless a supply line is re-established.

All these things made me think that some protein component labelled with free SH radicals is sucked into the astral centre and in some way taken into the astral rays. In order to be more certain about this "suction" by the aster, I resorted to another kind of eggs. The eggs used were those of *Spisula saghalensis*, a bivalve, and the phenomenon observed was the movement of ordinary cytoplasmic granules and not that of SH. By centrifuging at 3000 rev/min for 10 min, these eggs are easily stratified into three layers, a dark brown coloured light granular layer, the hyaline matrix and a slate-grey coloured heavy granular layer. Now, a unique feature of the *Spisula* egg lies in the fact that once the egg content is stratified, it remains stratified for an hour or more with no obvious back-diffusion. (Fig. 11.3a.)

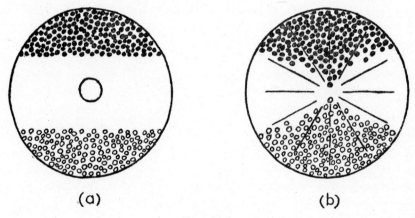

(a)   (b)

FIG. 11.3.

But as soon as the asters begin to form—I will draw only one aster for the sake of simplicity—the two border lines between the hyaline zone and the granular zones on the two sides begin to protrude toward the astral centres and when the asters are fully formed, the protrusions go sharply and accurately to the centres.

We all know that special substances are localised at the astral centre, for example, alkaline phosphatase [55], polysaccharide [56], etc. Although it is not known whether these substances are similarly collected as SH, this may be taken as an indication that it is a centre of some activity. As a result, it is not unjustifiable to think that SH-protein may be spun into S–S fibres of the astral rays by oxidation. Mazia has expressed a similar idea but on fairly vague grounds, and naturally more supporting evidences are desired. As one of them, I would like to draw attention to the fact that the elongation of astral rays is brought about by the addition of new elements at the base of the rays.

This observation was made long ago by a friend of mine, Dr. T. T. Iida [57] and I repeated it with confirmatory results. If we stain sea-urchin eggs of a transparent type with neutral red, using a proper concentration and selecting the right stage, the cytoplasm is dotted with small red vacuoles, yet the cells undergo several cleavage cycles. If we examine these red vacuoles under oil immersion with the microscope diaphragm wide open to make the colour stand out clearly, the majority of the vacuoles are in Brownian movement. However, if we look more carefully we can invariably find a few or several vacuoles which are not in motion and remain fixed. Every time there are stationary vacuoles, by closing the diaphragm an astral ray is found passing very close to it, as far as can be made out microscopically, so that it is tempting to think that such stationary vacuoles are stuck to the ray which is a gel. There is a further support for this conclusion. If this observation is made at a stage when the aster is growing, and a stationary vacuole is watched for a few minutes, we can see it suddenly move. But when it moves, it always moves toward the cell periphery along the axis of the ray to which it is supposed to be struck. When the aster is fading the jerky motion is along the same straight line but in the opposite direction. I think this indicates that when astral rays lengthen or shorten, the material is added to or taken away from the ray only at the base so that the oldest part is always at the tip of the ray.

Consequently, the facts I have so far described make me visualise such a pattern of organisation within the cell that there is an inflow- and out-flow-circulation of materials, the raw material being transported from the cytoplasm toward the astral centre and the finished product (astral ray) being pushed out from the centre towards the periphery.

This is as far as I can get, which still may not be adequate to answer the question I raised at the beginning concerning the nature of Professor Swann's so-called message between the nucleus and the cortex. But at least a possibility can be seen that such circulatory movement as described above could be a means for transmitting an influence to the cortex which gives the latter an autonomy for cleavage.

Have I talked too much?

WADDINGTON: Not at all. If you've got some more, please go on.

DAN: Here I should like to call your attention to unequal cleavage. Figure 11.4 shows an isolated spindle of an unequal cleavage. In the case

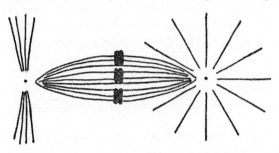

FIG. 11.4.

of sea-urchin eggs of the cleavage stage, if the isolation technique is used with the fertilisation membrane intact, since the membrane is not attacked by the detergent, a complete set of isolated spindles can be obtained enclosed within the swollen membrane. If I try this procedure for the resting stage of 8-cell stage, eight nuclei are scattered randomly within the membrane. At the late prophase of the following division, these eight nuclei are provided with two small asters of equal size. But by the time anaphase or telophase is reached, while four of the eight spindles have well developed radiate asters of equal size, the remaining four spindles have unequal asters (Fig. 11.5). One of the unequal asters is a radiate sphere of the normal shape and size; the smaller one is flat-looking, as if the distal half of the normal aster is cut off [58]. This means that in unequal cleavage the activity of the centrosomes or astral centres is somehow modified so that one side gives rise to a spherical aster, while the other spins out the astral rays not in a three-dimensional way but more or less in a two-dimensional fashion. It is quite surprisingly that in the first cleavage of *Spisula saghalensis*, exactly the same situation is found, indicating that the same mechanism is used for unequal division in such different cells.

LEHMANN: May I ask a question about that diagram? I have shown that during the cleavage *Tubifex* cytoplasm is filled with rod-shaped

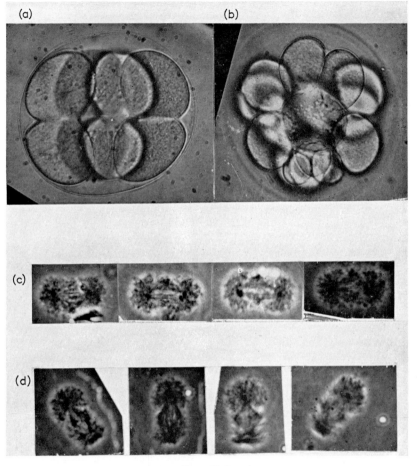

Fig. 11.5.
(a) Eight-cell stage of *Clypeaster japonicus*.
(b) Sixteen-cell stage of the same.
(c) and (d) Eight mitotic apparatuses of *Hemicentrotus pulcherrimus*-
isolated at the transitional stage between the 8- and
16-cell stages (by the courtesy of Kagaku).

elements. In *Amoeba* one can see these elements in the light microscope, and they disperse or aggregate under various conditions, and they are connected together and move in a more or less solated cytoplasm. When it comes to gelation, there must be some further connections formed, and this produces a jelly. In *Tubifex* this material looks just the same in the electron microscope. In the electron micrographs we also found the source material for these rods, which are composed by units which can aggregate very rapidly one after another; after mitosis they probably disaggregate also very fast. This may be a mechanism which is very important. I have been told that the mitochondria during mitosis are more or less inhibited —perhaps even inactivated—but at any rate they seem to show an absolutely different behaviour during mitosis. It seems therefore as though the oxidative metabolism was changed at that stage.

Another point is that if one looks at the spindle and the central asters in *Tubifex* you will find many mitochondria within the spindle, but within the astral centres there are none. So that is also an indication that they must be metabolically different, which would add to your argument.

WADDINGTON: I am very sorry we haven't got Swann here to talk about SH because I know he's been doing a lot of work recently on it. I don't know if Mitchison is close enough to this work to give us the gist of what Swann has been doing.

MITCHISON: Yes, would you like it about that only or would you like it about the whole cleavage mechanism as well?

WADDINGTON: Do talk about the whole mechanism.

MITCHISON: I shall have to take the Conference back to the border line between cell biology and molecular biology. In fact, I want to start by mentioning protein synthesis again. I have the feeling that molecular biologists like Dr. Brenner and his colleagues will probably give us the answer in a few years about the general mechanism by which information is passed on to proteins.

BRENNER: You will probably give us the answer before our ideas clear up.

MITCHISON: No. I think the "central dogma"* may well become a biological law, but there still remains a problem, at a slightly higher level, on the question of control mechanism. How does a growing cell control its rhythm of synthesis of proteins and nucleic acid? I probably part company with the biochemists because I am a cell biologist and believe in the cell theory. I certainly think that you want to tackle this problem by asking the question of the individual cell. Now the sort of question that you should put to the cell is how, in chemical terms, does it control its rate of synthesis;

* That once "information" has passed into protein it cannot get out again.

and perhaps in biological terms you can ask how it grows and also how it goes through the other fundamental process in a growing cell—how it divides and what is the stimulus to division. If you are going to try and answer these questions during a cell's life cycle (from one division to the next), there are considerable restrictions on the type of system you can use. You can measure individual cells by microscopic means but the information that comes out is limited. You can't, as yet, do much in the way of chemistry. If you want to do chemical analysis on changes during the cell life cycle you have to work with synchronous cultures in which all the cells are dividing at the same time. One possibility is to use artificially synchronised cultures, which have become popular in the last few years. Personally, I have doubts about the validity of results from artificially synchronised cultures—in particular, I don't believe that the growth of cells in a heated-shock culture is the same as that in a normal unsynchronous culture. There are, of course, a number of naturally synchronous cells of which the best known are fertilised eggs. But the trouble with them is that they do not grow. However, we have heard this morning of a very elegant system of Dr. Rusch. His slime mould offers considerable possibilities of biochemical analysis on a naturally synchronous system.

These are general points and I now want to go on to describe two sets of experiments on control mechanisms. One of them is the work of Professor Swann on the control of division in sea-urchin eggs [59, 60, 61]. Some years ago he did a series of experiments with inhibitory blocks put on to developing sea-urchin eggs by carbon monoxide. The first division of the sea-urchin egg he was using took place an hour after fertilisation, but the subsequent divisions happened at half-hour intervals. If he applied the block in the first half hour after fertilisation, he found that it delayed the first division for the length of time of the block. If, however, he did it in the second half hour it did not delay the first division but it did delay the second division. He interpreted this rather surprising result in terms of an "energy reservoir". This would fill up for the first half of the cell cycle—up to the beginning of mitosis. It would then discharge either at once (Fig. 11.6a) or gradually throughout mitosis (Fig. 11.6b); but in either case it would start to refill at the original rate. The discharge would be the stimulus to mitosis and division. This scheme would explain why an inhibitory block early in the cycle would delay the build-up of the reservoir for the coming division, whereas a block later in the cycle would not affect the mitosis already under way but would delay the subsequent division. Having postulated a reservoir which rises and falls in this way, he has been spending some time in doing analyses on sea-urchin eggs and other synchronous systems in order to find the chemical nature of the reservoir. He looked initially for changes in nucleic acids and phosphates, but did not find them. So he then moved on to another idea—that the energy reservoir might consist of activated acyl compounds. This looks much more promising. Recently, he has found that there are in fact fluctuations in the amount of acyl compounds during the cell cycle; and these fluctuations agree fairly well with the hypothesis of an energy reservoir. The situation, however, is somewhat complicated since there appear to be two systems. One is more stable than the other, and their cycles are out of phase. It may be that the emptying and filling of the reservoir represents a change of material between the two systems. But we shall know more about this when his experiments are finished.

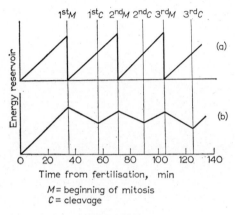

FIG. 11.6.

This is a possible control mechanism for division. The other thing I want to talk about is a possible control mechanism operating on cell growth. For the last two or three years, I have been working with a fission yeast, *Schizosaccharomyces pombe*, which is a convenient cell for growth measurements. It is a cylinder with rounded ends about 3.5 μ in diameter and up to 15 μ in length. It grows only in length, and it divides in two by forming a cell plate across the middle. This yeast has all the conveniences of a micro-organism in rapid growth on sterile media, but it is considerably larger than a bacterium and it has a more respectable method of division than a budding yeast. What I've been doing is measuring the growth of single cells [62]. The growth in volume is quite easy to measure from photographs. But if you measure volume growth only, there is always the possibility that you are merely measuring an increase in water content. Dr. Passano, Mr. Smith and I therefore developed a method of measuring the total dry mass of the cell with an interference microscope [63]. Dry mass increase is a better measure of synthesis than volume increase, though it is not of course a completely adequate measure of protein synthesis. Very briefly, the result that comes out of the growth measurement is this. If you plot against time, the growth curve of volume of a single cell is an ascending curve and then a plateau (Fig. 11.7). The cell plate becomes visible about one third of the way

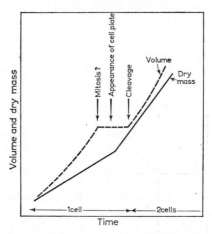

FIG. 11.7. Diagrammatic growth curves of *Schizosaccharomyces pombe*.

through the plateau and cleavage happens at the end of the plateau. Mitosis probably happens at the beginning of the plateau. I have put a question mark because the nuclear arrangements in yeasts are rather uncertain. Now the most interesting aspect of this work is that when you measure dry mass you do not find this type of curve. In fact, you find a straight line. When you take the two cells together after mitosis, each of the cells almost certainly grows along a straight line at the same rate as their mother. So the two of them together will grow at twice the rate. You get, therefore, a discontinuous growth curve composed of two straight lines. Incidentally, a budding yeast also shows the same type of dry mass growth [64]. Now I think the interesting implications here concern the question of control mechanisms. You might think initially that when a cell grows, the rate of growth would be proportional to the amount of material there—the amount of cytoplasm. The cell doubles its size during its life cycle so you might expect an exponential curve that would double its rate as the cytoplasm doubles. This is what would happen with a general autocatalytic theory of growth and it would give a smooth curve of growth going upwards without any discontinuity at division. But you don't get that—in fact, you get a series of straight lines. Therefore, you have to think of some form of control mechanism which is going to stay unaltered in its effect during the cell life cycle. Once growth has started it continues at that rate until the cell divides.

Now Dr. Zeuthen, who found a somewhat similar effect in *Tetrahymena* (measuring rate of respiration rather than dry mass), suggested that synthesis is controlled by a number of active particles or centres in the cell and that these remain unaltered in number until the cell divides [65]. I would also suggest that as one of the possible explanations, and, if one is thinking about particles, one might perhaps go one stage further and suggest microsomal particles. This would mean that the number of microsomal particles would remain constant in the cell until division when they would double and so cause a doubling of the rate of protein synthesis. If all the cellular RNA was in the microsomal particles, this would give a stepwise synthesis curve for RNA (Fig. 11.8a). But one can make a more

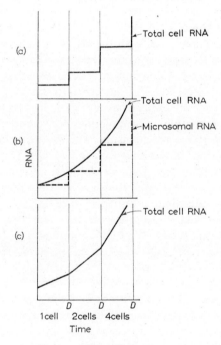

Fig. 11.8.

plausible scheme by taking the soluble non-microsomal RNA into account (Fig. 11.8b). Here I would suppose that the soluble RNA is synthesised continuously through the life cycle (either exponentially as drawn, or linearly) but that it only condenses to form new microsomal particles at division. The total cell RNA would then increase continuously, but the microsomal RNA would only increase at division. We should be able to decide between these two alternatives if we knew how the total RNA

21

increases over the cell life cycle.* So far, I've been tacitly assuming that
the rate of protein synthesis is proportional to the amount of RNA but it
might be that the rate of protein synthesis was proportional to the rate of
RNA synthesis. If so, the RNA synthesis curve should be very similar to
the curves of dry mass increase—a series of straight lines (Fig. 11.8c).
Finally, there is one other possibility, that the rate of synthesis is controlled
by the nucleus—or perhaps by the DNA if it doubled sharply just before
division. I think that nuclear control is unlikely because, if it happened,
you would expect to get a flattening or discontinuity in the dry mass
growth during the drastic nuclear reorganisation at mitosis.

BRENNER: I think that this sort of work is extremely important from the
point of view of the chemical kinetics of the system. I haven't before
drawn attention to the kinetic consequences of the schemes that I put
forward earlier on, as compared with the chemical kinetics put forward by
Hinshelwood and other workers in the field. You can see that this gives a
different picture of what is going on inside a cell from that derived from the
application of the general ideas of autocatalytic systems to an individual
cell. The point about the general autocatalytic system is that it applies
only to a statistical ensemble. The equations are statistical laws and throw
no light on the underlying mechanisms. We can have one substance in a
cell that is, so to speak, functioning autocatalytically, while the remainder
grows linearly until this one material doubles. Furthermore, it is also
possible to see that even this one substance need not obey the exponential
law of increase. It could double discontinuously.

Suppose, for the sake of discussion, that the DNA performs two
functions which require two different configurations and are mutually
exclusive. Either the DNA can act as an information template for making
new DNA, or the DNA can act as an information template for making more
RNA. We would then expect something like this: If we assume that the
rate of protein synthesis, given saturation of the system by precursors, is
a function of how much RNA is present, then as more RNA is made the
rate of protein synthesis will increase, and the protein accumulation in the
cell would in fact be exponential. Mitchison finds, on the contrary, that
the protein increases linearly, which is consistent not with a continuous
increase of RNA but with a single burst of synthesis. During each cycle,
the DNA doubles. The interesting question is, will its increase be exponential? That is, if you measure the increase of DNA in a single cell,
what sort of curve would it follow? The autocatalytic hypothesis would

* After the Conference, measurements were made of RNA synthesis in *Schizosaccharomyces pombe* [66]. These showed a continuous synthesis of total cell
RNA during the life cycle, but the methods were not sufficiently accurate to decide
between linear or exponential curves.

state that the rate of synthesis of the DNA would depend on the amount of DNA present. Since, in fact, the DNA acts as a template, this cannot be true because the DNA in a partly replicated daughter chain does not itself function as a template for the rest of the chain and is kinetically useless. Only the parental duplex is significant and its concentration is constant. The essential point is that the mechanism of growth in a single cell must be studied directly and not deduced from laws which apply only to statistical ensembles.

DEAN: But that is Hinshelwood's theory, the one you've just given.

BRENNER: Yes, but now what mechanisms of cell growth did you deduce?

DEAN: When you get a certain concentration of a key substance, the cell divides, which is in essence what you've just said.

BRENNER: Hinshelwood's theory would state that as the mass increases— if the Hinshelwood theory applied to individual cells—then the rate of synthesis of new mass should increase because the whole ensemble is autocatalytic. Well, it does not. The rate of synthesis remains constant while they are piling up new mass, showing that as far as catalytic synthesis is concerned new mass is inactive. That is the essential point.

DEAN: No, no! I don't see that at all.

MITCHISON: There is one point, since Dr. Brenner has raised the question of DNA synthesis. As far as the evidence goes a number of cells, particularly the cells of mammals, appear to do a sudden burst of DNA synthesis towards the end of their cycle. This, according to our measurements, happens in the macro- and micro-nucleus of *Paramecium*. There is a somewhat curious exception in the macro-nucleus of *Tetrahymena*. There it appears to be linear. There are possible explanations of this, and I believe Dr. Rusch has got some information about this in the slime mould. One other point, according to Maruyama's work [67] on bacteria, you get some increase in DNA in *E. coli* just at the end of their life-cycle, rather like the mammalian situation.

WADDINGTON: I don't see that it makes a great deal of difference whether DNA is synthesised autocatalytically or linearly. It is not the DNA that is controlling the protein synthesis during cell growth. The straight lines that Mitchison showed were the increase in dry mass, and this was presumably mainly an increase in protein, which seems to involve a control by a constant amount of RNA. The DNA presumably only comes in at the end of each cycle, by making some more RNA, but whether it doubles itself by the straight line or exponentially seems to me a secondary problem.

MITCHISON: I agree.

WADDINGTON: Could I ask a question about this? One natural assumption from your results would be that the linearity of the rate of synthesis is dependent on some constant amount of a catalyst or other form of active agent, which doubles when the cell doubles. Therefore, one naturally thinks of the amount of the protein-forming mechanism as being eventually controlled by the DNA. But you have this gap between the time of cell division and the time when your lines inflect. The lines do not change their slope until a little after the mitosis. Can that be accounted for simply by the reconstitution of the anaphase groups into a respectable nucleus? Might it be that the chromosomes do not produce more RNA until they have been unwound and formed a normal type of nucleus?

MITCHISON: Yes, I think that's quite feasible. The point I wanted to raise about DNA synthesis related to Dr. Brenner's theory. If you say that DNA cannot make RNA when it is making more of itself, and if it makes itself in a sudden burst, then it should stop making RNA during that time; if the rate of production of protein is proportional to the rate of production of RNA, then you should get a step in the mass curve.

WADDINGTON: Surely, with your particular mass curve, the DNA cannot go on making RNA all through the cell's cycle. If it was making more and more RNA, then you would get an exponential rise in your rate of protein formation. If the rate of formation of protein is proportional to the amount of RNA, then the amount of RNA must remain stationary.

MITCHISON: That's right. But the rate of production of protein might be proportional not to the amount of RNA but to the rate of production of RNA: that is, one new RNA molecule for one new protein molecule.

BRENNER: But then it would have to be inactivated afterwards.

MITCHISON: Yes.

WADDINGTON: Isn't that making it very complex?

BRENNER: Well, you could make a theory. All you are saying is that the amount of active RNA—the stuff that's doing the work—must remain constant.

MITCHISON: Yes

BRENNER: It could be continually synthesised and inactivated, or in some way turned over, but the steady state of the RNA that is making the protein must be a constant. Otherwise, you would not get a linear curve.

MITCHISON: Yes.

PLAUT: There is one small point I wanted to add with reference to your question whether the DNA synthesis is linear or not. In most systems the time required for DNA synthesis is extremely short and I think it would be technically rather difficult to establish a curve.

MITCHISON: Well, it has been done, as you know, by analysis of random samples of a culture. You measure 200 nuclei and you get a curve. I think the sharpest one was got on *Paramecium* and that is pretty sharp [68]. DNA synthesis may take a very short time, though it does appear to vary. In some of the tissue culture cells it takes quite a bit more but there are a lot of inaccuracies in this method of constructing synthesis curves.

WADDINGTON: One is dealing with a structured system here. In a sense you've already got in the cell one representative of all the different types of DNA molecule that you are going to want eventually. You are therefore dealing rather with the replication of a structure than with the synthesis of a free substance. You have got a DNA chain, which means that you have in effect a template with a certain number of holes in it, and the holes have to be filled. Once all the holes are filled the process comes to an end. I don't see that it is of very great importance whether the holes tend to get filled up faster later on in the process, or whether they are filled up at an even rate all the way through.

BRENNER: It is a secondary problem, but it is an interesting one.

WADDINGTON: If the DNA synthesis depends on the DNA which is already there as a template, plus a hole-filling mechanism—which might be something to do with activated amino acids or precursor nucleotides— then if what I have called the hole-filling mechanism were itself being synthesised, it seems to me you might expect to get an exponential increase in the DNA; but if you are simply dealing with a template with a lot of holes which get filled in by molecular groupings moving at random, then I don't see why the DNA synthesis shouldn't be linear.

BRENNER: Well, I think one would like it to be linear, for the simple reason that one thinks that the process should start at one end and it should have some directionality and go on until it is finished and not just stop in odd areas. The difficulty is that if you had made all the DNA except for one hole, and there was no orientation, you might have to wait quite a long time before collisions found that hole.

WADDINGTON: If you had that sort of system I should expect one end of any very large chromosome to be particularly liable to exhibit mutation. With a zipper mechanism you would finish up with one end of the chromosome having to get the last few nucleotides, and I should expect that end to go wrong more often.

BRENNER: That is if you assume a limited supply of nucleotides.

PLAUT: The ends seem to be more or less protected against disturbance, because we don't find many clusters of active loci at the ends. We find rather the other way.

POLLOCK: Incidentally, isn't there some information on rates of formation of nucleic acids in synchronised bacterial cultures? I seem to remember that some workers found that in synchronised bacteria there was a phase of DNA synthesis to correspond with cell division but that RNA synthesis was more continuous.

BRENNER: The results are contradictory. Maaløe at Copenhagen gets bursts of RNA—well, he gets a sort of negative burst in the sense that he gets RNA being made and then when DNA is made the RNA stops [69]. Cohen got completely different results [70] and Maruyama [67] found an actual step in the RNA synthesis.

MITCHISON: Maruyama gets a step in the DNA, followed by a step in the RNA, followed by a step in the protein.

BRENNER: There you have got all three mechanisms with similar systems but one must wait for clearer experiments. One may add that all three systems were synchronised in different ways. Maaløe's system was synchronised by temperature. Cohen's was synchronised by thymine starvation and Maruyama's system was synchronised by filtration.

MITCHISON: I think technically the latter is by far the best if you can get it to work, because in all the synchronised cultures induced by physiological shock there is evidence that the cells are unusual or abnormal. In the case of heat shock cultures the evidence is very striking. For instance, in *Tetrahymena* the cells are abnormally large and have more DNA than normal *Tetrahymena*. There is also very significant evidence of Zeuthen's about respiration rates. He measured the respiration rate in single cell cultures and found a linear increase very like the dry mass curves in the fission yeast except for a plateau before division, but in synchronous cultures there was a quite different picture [65, 68]. That certainly makes me suspect synchronous cultures.

RUSCH: In *Physarium* the DNA is synthesised in a period of approximately 90 min right after mitosis. So far as the RNA is concerned, this was measured by uptake of labelled orotic acid—that may perhaps be a turnover. I expected a straight line and it was not and this bothered me and we put the results aside, because I wanted to do the work on differentiation which I reported this morning. So that work has been set aside and when I get back I'll have to go over those data and see when these bursts occur. We also have recently initiated studies on total RNA, but I don't have here the results of that.

WADDINGTON: I should like to ask a question of the mathematicians before we go one step further. This straight line of Mitchison's is a straight line of a global quantity—total dry mass or let us call it total proteins. Now, how far could it conceal the competition between different rates of formation of different individual proteins? This is going back to Brenner's point, that none of the autocatalytic mechanisms can apply on an intracellular basis. I am asking whether that is really absolutely the case, since the straight line is only demonstrated for a global quantity. For instance, is it conceivable that the straight line is controlled by some mechanism which is activating the amino acids which are getting ready to pop into place in the proteins? I understand that the amino acids will not line up in the polypeptides unless something special is done to them—I don't know quite what. But is it possible that the control is something of that kind, so that there might still be, within this global quantity, an auto-catalytic process of synthesis of protein B, and so on, the whole thing being squeezed together into this straight line curve only because you sum up the overall total.

POLLOCK: There is one piece of evidence which might throw a light on that. It concerns some unpublished work on induced penicillinase synthesis in *B. cereus*, which might support your suggestion that there is another possible way of looking at the whole question. In induced penicillinase synthesis, as I made clear yesterday, the rate of formation of this

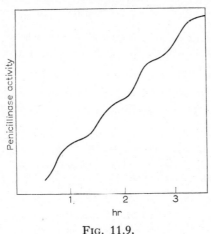

FIG. 11.9.

single protein is linear, even in an exponentially growing culture. Therefore, however we look at the template or catalytic mechanism necessary for the formation of this single protein you would have to assume that it is constant in quantity. If it is an RNA, that particular RNA at any rate is not increasing in function. Now, H. V. Rickenberg succeeded (or at least we think he succeeded; it was difficult to obtain proof) in partially synchronising cell division in *B. cereus*—never mind the details at the moment—and found that in such "phased" cultures there was a stepwise production of the enzyme (Fig. 11.9). Whereas normally, after a short lag (i.e. in "unphased" cultures: see Fig. 7.4), you get a pretty good straight line.

WADDINGTON: Is that on a log plot?

POLLOCK: No, this is an ordinary arithmetic plot. The cells are growing exponentially but the protein linearly. You see the external inducer has been removed and the idea is that you've got a constant amount of some enzyme-forming apparatus, which is stable. In "phased" cells (at least we believe they were phased; and certainly they were treated under conditions under which you might expect them to be at least partially phased) you do not get this strict linear formation of penicillinase. You get jerky rises at intervals which more or less correspond with the mean division time of the organism. Now the point about this is that here is a situation where it was not apparently the hypothetical RNA template concerned which was produced in bursts, because the apparatus for forming the enzyme, you might say, was there all the time. Therefore, it would seem possible that there is a case for some other fluctuations occurring—for instance (as Waddington suggested) in the rate of activation of the amino acids—something connected more distantly with the phase of the growth cycle and nothing to do with RNA.

MITCHISON: You have still got the linear plot in those phased cycles, if I understood this right.

POLLOCK: Yes—in the sense that the mean rate was the same, whether cell divisions were "phased" or not.

MITCHISON: That is rather interesting because Dr. P. D. Mitchell and I did some measurements of dry mass increase in synchronous cultures of temperature-shocked fission yeast (*S. pombe*). They were not very synchronous so the results were difficult to interpret. What we found was a continuous exponential increase in dry mass in the synchronous culture. But if the cells in the synchronous culture were behaving in the same way as normal ones you should get a succession of straight lines as in the single cell measurements [62]—not an exponential curve. There are two possible explanations. One of them is that the type of growth is quite different from that in an asynchronous culture. The other is that what you are doing is synchronising division but not synchronising growth. Once you have got a series of discontinuous steps in your growth curve, you can talk about growth being out of phase with division.

POLLOCK: There's another possibilty there, isn't there; that you aren't making all the different types of protein at the same time?

MITCHISON: That, certainly, is a possibility. There's one interesting thing that I didn't mention that came out of the measurements on budding yeast [64]. Normally, the discontinuity in the mass growth curve happens about 20 min after budding. But in two cells this discontinuity occurred at a different point in the budding cycle. It looked as though the two timing clocks had been put out of phase, the one for growth and one for division. Perhaps as a result of this, both cells died soon after.

CALLAN: Is it worth enquiring about what it is that is accounting for the difference between the volume curves and the weight curves? Clearly, if some osmotically active material is increasing exponentially, that must be subtracted from the dry weight curves if you are looking at the osmotically inactive materials. Is it worthwhile thinking of that at all?

MITCHISON: I think it is likely that the difference between the mass and volume growth in the fission yeast is due to the formation of a cell plate before division. If the cell has only a limited capacity to make new cell wall and this capacity is being fully employed in generating the cell plate, then there can be no increase in volume. This would account for the constant volume stage before cleavage. Since the increase in dry mass continues during this stage, there is an increase in the total concentration of solids in the cell. But the concentration falls again after cleavage when the volume increases faster than the mass.

At this point I shall let a cat out of the bag. If we take into account the formation of the cell plate, then the curve of growth in area of the cell wall is roughly exponential. Now the cell wall accounts for a substantial fraction (about 25%) of the total dry mass. So, if the cell wall growth is subtracted from the linear mass growth curve for the whole cell, it might give a mass growth curve for the cytoplasm which was a convex curve rather than a straight line. However, the uncertain point in this argument is the shape of the curve of dry mass increase of the cell wall. It will only follow the exponential curve of area increase if the cell wall remains constant in thickness and concentration throughout the cycle—and it may well do neither.

CALLAN: That's what I was getting at and the cell wall is largely carbohydrate while the inside is largely protein. It rather looks as though you've got linear total synthesis but that may not be all protein synthesis.

The difficulty about it is I am not quite certain whether it would tilt those curves significantly downwards.

BRENNER: One important fact is that the protoplasts of bacteria will grow arithmetically. In *B. megaterium* protoplasts cannot be transformed back into cells. If you plot the increase of the dry weight, for example, that is arithmetical.

WADDINGTON: That is the dry weight of the culture.

BRENNER: Yes, of the culture.

MITCHISON: And those cells are not dividing?

BRENNER: No, although you can sometimes see dumb-bell objects. If a culture of *B. megaterium* which is growing exponentially is divided into two parts, and one part is protoplasted and the other not, then the cells continue to grow exponentially, but the protoplasts continue at an arithmetic rate. It's not exactly the same rate at which they left off because you can't really aerate them properly. If you shake them they tend to disrupt. Linear growth would be caused by anything which supplies an essential metabolite at a constant rate so there can be an enormous number of different causes for it.

WADDINGTON: Well, can I ask anyone to summarise this discussion? [Laughter.]

DEAN: Certainly not. What I wanted to say was, is there any mathematical background for these theories? I should like to see a complete kinetic interpretation of them, formalised properly, before one considers them seriously.

BRENNER: I think that a mathematical interpretation of this could be made relatively easily. The point I should like to emphasise is this. The "autocatalytic schemes", unless they apply to single cells, cannot provide an explanation of adaptation. If the schemes apply to population changes, this is an entirely different question.

WADDINGTON: You mean that you cannot get competition between chemical systems—that is, competition depending on autocatalysis—you cannot get that, unless it applies on a single cell basis? Is that right?

BRENNER: Yes.

WADDINGTON: Well, I think I should be prepared to accept this as quite plausible at first sight; but that was why I was raising this point of whether you can't in fact reconcile autocatalysis with your straight line over-all curve of total dry weight, and I still think you probably can. Your over-all straight line curve is merely showing that *something* is being provided at a constant rate.

POLLOCK: Surely you don't mean that you never get reciprocal auto-catalysis or competitive effects between two different cells? In fact we can show it by using symbiotic micro-organisms.

BRENNER: I agree. But the essential point is that these are all special cases in which you have to specify what the x's and y's and z's are in the equations. I do not disagree with the principle, and can see how the equations apply in the case you mentioned.

DEAN: Yes, but aren't you making the same fallacy by considering one component—DNA or RNA or something—instead of the growth of the cell?

BRENNER: I am not considering one component. One has put forward a postulate here which I think is amenable to experimental investigation. That's the point. I am not saying it's true. It may all be phospho-lipid in the end. [Laughter.]

BRACHET: I should like to ask what is the experimental evidence for the view that DNA makes RNA. We would very much like it to be like that but . . .

BRENNER: There is *no* experimental evidence. [Laughter.]

DEAN: Isn't there one thing that is hard to explain? With cells in the stationary phase you get no cell growth, but you get an increase in cell number; that is, the cells go on dividing without any increase in mass. Well, if you assume that DNA triggers off the division mechanism, DNA must be formed from the RNA.

BRACHET: Yes, but that is an assumption because . . .

DEAN: Yes, I know, there isn't any evidence.

BRACHET: And I think even the data that Dr. Rusch gave in his summary here was rather against it.

DEAN: Well, the only evidence that I would put up for it is that the DNA content of the bacterial cell is reasonably constant under conditions where the growth rate varies considerably, but the RNA varies widely.

RUSCH: Doesn't the experiment that Dr. Plaut explained the other day, that he did with Stich, doesn't this indicate that DNA forms RNA, if I understood that correctly?

PLAUT: No; the only interpretation, but it's by no means proved, was that there was a specific RNA which was nuclear in origin and necessary for the functioning of the cytoplasmic protein synthesis mechanism.

BRACHET: If we are studying the Feulgen reaction in *Acetabularia*, I would say that we have to conclude that there is no DNA in *Acetabularia*. We cannot believe that, but at the same time one cannot get the slightest sign of a positive Feulgen reaction in *Acetabularia*. The nucleus is very big, and we suppose that there is no endomitosis or anything like that in the life cycle. In the gamete, you can spot DNA, but you can't see it any more after the zygote starts growing. We have to assume, of course, that there is just enough DNA to make something like thirteen chromosomes, but that we cannot see them when they are scattered in the huge nucleus.

BRENNER: May I make one comment? Of course, one is always talking about the transfer of information and information can't be seen under the microscope and can't be labelled with a tracer. Until we learn more about how information is organised in big molecules, for instance, by studying amino acid sequences in relation to nucleotide sequences, I doubt whether we can give the final proof. However, we know that RNA can carry information for the synthesis of proteins. This is the work on the infectivity of RNA in tobacco mosaic virus.

WADDINGTON: I think that the important point which has come out this afternoon is that the most fundamental problem is this matter of the conveying of information as between DNA, RNA and protein. Although Brenner has given us a lot of reasons for thinking that RNA can carry information for protein synthesis, we have really much more, though indirect, evidence that DNA carries information. The genetic evidence, although it is indirect, is pretty convincing. But even in this most fundamental field, just dealing with those three things and asking whether they provide information for each other, we have still got our feet as it were only toes on the ground. Although we can discuss it a great deal, there is still a very large amount of basic information which we have to assume; of course, we think we are assuming right, but we are not 100% certain of it. I am sure we could go on discussing it for a very great deal longer, but possibly this would be the time for a cup of tea.

LEHMANN: May I just say a few words? I think this is the last session. I have been asked by several of my colleagues to say some words of thanks to Professor Waddington. Unfortunately, Professor Weiss left before the end of this meeting. I should have liked very much to leave him this task because he is such a brilliant speaker and is much more used to this sort of thing than I am, but now, unfortunately for me, he has left and I should really like to take the chance because we all feel that this has been a very concentrated and at the same time well organised conference. Now to me this conference looks in some ways like a very attractive model of a cell, a sort of cell on the sociological level. There has been a considerable degree of self-organisation and there was also some pattern of growth of information. There was also this structural substrate which has even provided some sort of mechanism which has acted as a sort of memory. Now, Waddington I think has acted as a very expert inducer and at the same time I think he was a very good organiser—I dare say Waddington doesn't like this word, but I still think it's a useful one. He has very broad interests, as we have all seen, and I think he was really very well suited to have the direction of this whole conference in his hands. There has been—and he himself has provided the word which I think is very acceptable in that way—a well-defined "creode" which has run through the whole of this Congress and he has successfully canalised the integration of all the different contributions of the speakers, and he has also supplied the means to keep down all sorts of excess questions by the speakers. The result has been not, as Professor Berenblum showed us, a disorderly growth, but rather an orderly growth. Now, as you have also heard in this conference, successful integration between living individuals is only possible if there exist good contacts between the different partners, and I must say that Professor Waddington has taken great care to create an environment for these contacts to be very well realised. It was a great privilege for us to enjoy all these special occasions he has made for us, and I should like to mention particularly the lunches in the canteen. I think we all realise how important these general social contacts have been. We should like to congratulate Professor Waddington very much and hope that he will convey our thanks to Mrs. Waddington and to all his collaborators who have helped him.

WADDINGTON: Thank you very much indeed, Dr. Lehmann. It is certainly true that I have got quite a large staff who have been assisting behind the scenes and they have made a great difference to the running of the whole of this conference.

REFERENCES

1. SWANN, M. M. and J. M. MITCHISON (1958) *Biol. Rev.* **33**, 103.
2. CHAMBERS, R. (1938) *J. Cell Comp. Physiol.* **12**, 149.
3. MITCHISON, J. M. (1953) *J. Exp. Biol.* **30**, 515.
4. BEAMS, H. W. and T. C. EVANS (1940) *Biol. Bull.* **79**, 188.
5. SWANN, M. M. and J. M. MITCHISON (1953) *J. Exp. Biol.* **30**, 506.
6. HIRAMOTO, Y. (1956) *Exp. Cell Res.* **11**, 630.
7. MITCHISON, J. M. (1956) *Quart. J. Microscop. Sci.* **97**, 109.
8. HIRAMOTO, Y. (1957) *Embryologia* **3**, 361.
9. MITCHISON, J. M. (1952) *Symp. Soc. Exp. Biol.* **6**, 105.

10. DAN, K. and J. C. DAN (1942) *Cytologia* **12**, 246.
11. DAN, K., J. C. DAN and F. YANAGITA (1938) *Cytologia* **8**, 521.
12. DAN, K., T. YANAGITA and M. SUGIYAMA (1937) *Protoplasma* **28**, 68.
13. DAN, K. and T. ONO (1954) *Embryologia* **2**, 87.
14. MITCHISON, J. M. and M. M. SWANN (1952) *J. Exp. Biol.* **29**, 357.
15. MONROY, A. and G. MONTALENTI (1947) *Biol. Bull.* **92**, 151.
16. MITCHISON, J. M. (1956) *J. Exp. Biol.* **33**, 524.
17. MITCHISON, J. M. and M. M. SWANN (1954) *J. Exp. Biol.* **31**, 443.
18. MITCHISON, J. M. and M. M. SWANN (1954) *J. Exp. Biol.* **31**, 461.
19. MITCHISON, J. M. and M. M. SWANN (1955) *J. Exp. Biol.* **32**, 734.
20. MARSLAND, D. A. and J. V. LANDAU (1954) *J. Exp. Zool.* **125**, 507.
20. SWANN, M. M. (1951) *J. Exp. Biol.* **28**, 417.
21. MARSLAND, D. A. (1956) *Int. Rev. Cytol.* **5**, 199.
21a. SWANN, M. M. (1951) *J. Exp. Biol.* **28**, 434.
22. SWANN, M. M. (1952) *Symp. Soc. Exp. Biol.* **6**, 89.
23. WADDINGTON, C. H. (1952) *J. Exp. Biol.* **29**, 484. SELMAN, G. G. and C. H. WADDINGTON (1955) *J. Exp. Biol.* **32**, 700.
24. CHALKLEY, H. W. (1935) *Protoplasma* **24**, 607.
25. CHALKLEY, H. W. (1951) *Ann. N.Y. Acad. Sci.* **51**, 1303.
26. LEHMANN, F. E. (1951) *Schweiz. Z. allg. Path. u. Bakt.* **14**, 487–508.
27. HUBER, W. (1947) *Rev. Suisse Zool.* **54**, 54–154.
28. HOLTZER, H. and J. M. MARSHALL (1954) *C.R. Lab. Carlsberg. Ser. Chim.* **29**, 7–26.
29. BENNETT, S. (1956) *J. Biophys. Biochem. Cytol.* **2**, Suppl. 99, 1956.
30. NEEDHAM, J. (1942) *Biochemistry and Morphogenesis*, Cambridge.
31. LEHMANN, F. E. and H. HADORN (1946) *Helv. Physiol. Acta* **4**, 11–42.
32. WOKER, M. (1944) *Rev. Suisse Zool.* **51**, 109–171.
33. DE HARVEN, E. and W. BERNHARD (1956) *Z. Zellforsch.* **45**, 378–398.
34. LÜSCHER, M. (1946) *Rev. Suisse Zool.* **53**, 683–734.
35. LEHMANN, F. E. and V. MANCUSO (1957) *Exp. Cell Res.* **13**, 161–164.
36. LEHMANN, F. E. and V. MANCUSO (1958) *Arch. Klaus. Stift.* **32**. In press.
37. WEBER, R. (1956) *Rev. Suisse Zool.* **63**, 277–288; *Roux Archiv.* **150**. In press.
38. WIGGLESWORTH, V. B. (1957) *Proc. Roy. Soc.* **B147**, 185–199.
39. MAZIA, D. (1955) *Symp. Soc. Exp. Biol.* **9**, 335–357.
40. WEBER, H. H. (1955) *Symp. Soc. Exp. Biol.* **9**.
41. LEHMANN, F. E. (1955) *Klin. Wschr.* **33**, 294–300.
42. BAJER, A. (1957) *Exp. Cell Res.* **13**, 493–502.
43. BIESELE, J. J. (1958) *Mitotic Poisons and the Cancer Problem*, London.
44. ZEUTHEN, E. (1951) *Pubbl. Staz. Zool. Napoli* **23**, Suppl. 47.
45. PASTEELS, J. (1934) *Arch. Anat. Microscop.* **30**, 161–197.
46. MORGAN, T. H. (1933) *J. Exp. Zool.* **64**, 433.
47. CHAMBERS, R. (1933) *Anat. Rec.* **57**, Suppl. 1, 93.
48. BRACHET, J. (1943) *Arch. Biol.* (*Liége*) **45**, 611.
49. DAN, K. (1943) *J. Fac. Sci. Imp. Tokyo Univ.* sec. 4, **6**, 297.
50. DAN, K. (1943) *J. Fac. Sci. Imp. Tokyo Univ.* sec. 4, **6**, 323.
51. MAZIA, D. and K. DAN *Proc. Nat. Acad. Sci., Wash.* **38**, 825.
52. BENNETT, H. S. (1951) *Anat. Rec.* **110**, 231.
53. BRACHET, J. (1940) *Arch. Biol.* (*Liége*) **51**, 167.
54. RAPKINE, L. (1931) *Ann. Physiol. Physicochim. Biol.* **7**, 382.
55. DANIELLI, J. F. (1953) *Cytochemistry*, New York.
56. IMMERS, J. (1957) *Exp. Cell Res.* **12**, 145.

57. IIDA, T. T. (1942) *Zool. Mag.* **54**, 364. (In Japanese.)
58. DAN, K. and T. NAKAJIMA (1956) *Embryologia* **3**, 187.
59. SWANN, M. M. (1952 *Quart. J. Microscop. Sci.* **94**, 369.
60. SWANN, M. M. (1954) *Exp. Cell Res.* **7**, 505.
61. SWANN, M. M. (1957) *Cancer Res.* **17**, 727.
62. MITCHISON, J. M. (1957) *Exp. Cell Res.* **13**, 244.
63. MITCHISON, J. M., L. M. PASSANO and F. H. SMITH (1956) *Quart. J. Microscop. Sci.* **97**, 287.
64. MITCHISON, J. M. (1958) *Exp. Cell Res.* In press.
65. ZEUTHEN, E. (1953) *J. Embryol. Exp. Morphol.* **1**, 239.
66. MITCHISON, J. M. and P. M. B. WALKER (1958) *Exp. Cell Res.* In press.
67. MARUYAMA, Y. (1956) *J. Bact.* **72**, 821.
68. WALKER, P. M. B. and J. M. MITCHISON (1957) *Exp. Cell. Res.* **13**, 167; ZEUTHEN, E. and O. SCHERBAUM (1954) in *Recent Developments in Cell Physiology* (ed. by KITCHING) p. 141. Academic Press, New York.
69. LARK, K. G. and O. MAALØE (1956) *Biochim. Biophys. Acta* **21**, 448.
70. BARNER, H. and S. S. COHEN (1955) *Fed. Proc.* **14**, 177.

Index of Speakers

Major contributions are listed first; other participation in discussion thereafter

AUERBACH, C.
54.

BEALE, G. H.
136–139.
140, 141, 274.

BEERMANN, W.
61–70.
24, 53, 54, 56, 60, 81, 83, 85, 96.

BERENBLUM, I.
275–280.
200, 272, 289.

BRACHET, J.
226–229.
35, 36, 37, 38, 93, 94, 99, 103, 104, 105,
129, 142, 145, 146, 156, 157, 198, 199,
225, 230, 258, 292, 313, 314,

BRENNER, S.
24–41.
45, 49, 51, 55, 56, 57, 80, 83, 84, 86, 98,
99, 131, 133, 141, 148, 158, 159, 188,
189, 190, 191, 200, 201, 202, 211, 223,
224, 232, 234, 259, 292, 299, 304, 305,
306, 307, 308, 312, 313, 314.

CALLAN, H. G.
42–55.
60, 85, 94, 105, 146, 151, 152, 155, 156,
174, 224, 244, 257, 274, 290, 291, 311.

DAN, K.
292–298.
233.

DEAN, A. C. R.
167–169.
170, 182, 183, 184, 185, 305, 312, 313.

GALL, J.
45, 46, 51, 53, 54, 55, 80, 93, 95, 103.

GAY, H.
112–114, 115–117.
115, 125, 126, 127, 128, 129.

GUSTAFSON, J.
152–155.
131, 156, 157, 158, 159, 174.

HOLTZER, H.
142–145, 253–254.
145, 146, 147, 148, 149, 150, 151, 152,
187, 188, 245, 257, 274.

LEHMANN, F. E.
16–19, 286–288.
60, 93, 103, 123, 125, 127, 154, 155, 156,
159, 166, 175, 185, 210, 211, 230, 234,
235, 242, 243, 245, 246, 251, 257, 258,
272, 280, 290, 291 298, 314.

MITCHISON, J. M.
282–286, 298–304.
53, 55, 57, 82, 104, 289, 290, 291, 299,
305, 306, 308, 310, 311, 312.

NIEUWKOOP, P. D.
202–203, 212–217, 259–262.
20, 201, 219, 220, 230, 232, 241, 244,
248, 258.

PAVAN, C.
72–79.
82, 83, 84, 115.

PLAUT, W.
100–103.
23, 24, 30, 31, 34, 37, 38, 54, 56, 57, 59,
60, 79, 80, 81, 82, 104, 105, 126, 128,
149, 224, 272, 307, 308, 314.

318

POLLOCK, M. R.
176–182.
81, 150, 157, 158, 170, 175, 183, 184,
185, 186, 187, 191, 199, 200, 211, 223,
224, 252, 258, 273, 308, 309, 310, 311,
313.

PONTECORVO, G.
22, 23, 24, 29, 30, 38, 39, 46, 53, 54, 55,
56, 82, 85, 128, 140, 141, 232, 241,
246, 247, 248, 251, 273, 274, 280,

RIS, P.
50, 51, 54, 57, 82, 98, 115, 133.

RUSCH, H. P.
263–271.
272, 273, 280, 308, 313.

SIRLIN, J. L.
97.

SJÖSTRAND, F. S.
117–123.
126, 129, 130, 133.

TOIVENEN, S.
203–210.
126, 219.

WADDINGTON, C. H.
1–3, 88–93, 110–117, 161–166, 221–223,
254–256.

4, 5, 16, 18, 19, 20, 21, 22, 23, 24, 25,
27, 32, 33, 35, 37, 38, 39, 40, 41, 42,
46, 47, 49, 50, 53, 54, 55, 57, 60, 67,
70, 71, 75, 78, 79, 80, 81, 82, 83, 85,
86, 94, 96, 97, 98, 99, 100, 103, 105,
108, 117, 123, 124, 126, 127, 128, 129,
130, 131, 133, 139, 140, 141, 142, 143,
148, 149, 150, 151, 152, 155, 156, 158,
167, 170, 175, 182, 183, 184, 185, 186,
187, 188, 189, 190, 191, 193, 199, 200,
201, 202, 203, 211, 212, 217, 224, 226,
231, 232, 233, 234, 235, 238, 241, 242,
243, 244, 245, 247, 249, 251, 253, 258,
259, 263, 271, 273, 274, 280, 282, 283,
286, 289, 290, 291, 292, 298, 299, 305,
307, 309, 310, 312, 314, 315.

WEISS, P.
3–16, 105–108, 170–174.
20, 22, 23, 24, 29, 53, 55, 56, 59, 60, 70,
94, 98, 99, 115, 125, 126, 127, 129,
130, 142, 147, 148, 150, 151, 152, 155,
156, 167, 175, 176, 184, 186, 187, 188,
224, 231, 232, 233, 234, 235.

WILDE, C. E.
193–202.
38, 48, 61, 71, 128, 141, 142, 190, 232,
233, 243, 245, 247, 256, 259, 272, 273,
290.

ZWILLING, E.
238–241, 249–251.
148, 235, 242, 243, 244, 245, 246, 247,
248, 249, 253, 259, 273, 274.

Index of Subjects

Acetabularia, xiii, 100–105, 314
Acricotopus, 65–66
active transport, 233
Activating enzymes, 36, 309, 310
Activation, 213–217, 219, 249
of nuclei, 88
Adaptor hypothesis, 37
Algae, blue-green, 33
Allelic differences, visible, xii, 46, 47, 49, 67, 68, 84
Alternative pathways, xvi, 84, 161–170, 182, 190, 193, 194, 203, 217, 220, 253, 271
Amino acid pool, 99
Amoeba 56, 100–104, 123, 142, 287, 290, 299
Amphibia, cleavage, 285, 294
electron microscopy, 126, 154
prosencephalon, 260
Analogues, 195–201, 229, 265–268
Antibodies, fluorescent, 137, 142–152
Arbacia, 155, 156
Ascaris, xv
Ascites cells, 132
Aspergillus, 39, 55
Asters, 282, 284, 286, 287, 288, 291, 292, 294
asymmetric, 298
growth, 296, 297
Asymmetry, 20
of cell division, 290, 298
Autocatalysis, 302, 304, 309, 312
Autoradiographs, 35, 37, 38, 57–59, 77–80, 82, 88–93, 228, 233
and induction, 221–223, 225, 233
interpretation, 95, 97, 104
resolution, 98
Axon growth, 105–108

Bacteria, adaptation, 167–169, 175–191
ghosts, 133
cytoplasmic particles, 132
nuclei, 33
protoplasts, 312

Balbiani rings, 62–71
Basement lamella, 7, 10, 11, 13, 129, 130, 231
Blastoderm, disaggregated, 249, 250
metabolic patterns, 251
Blood, 174, 175
Blood islands, 9
Bombinator, 234
Brain extracts, 174, 175

Cancer, 203–209, 263, 275–281
Carcinogenesis, xviii, 208, 280
Carcinogens, 185, 186
Cartilage, induction, 210
vertebral, 245, 253, 254
Cell division, 282–314
amphibian, 285, 294
and synthesis, 302–314
energy, 300, 301
synchronised, 122, 264, 272, 300, 308, 301
Swann--Mitchison theory, 283–285, 289, 293, 294, 298
Tubifex, 286–288
without nuclei, 290
Central dogma, 34, 299
Centrifuged eggs, 155, 156, 291, 295
Chaetopterus, 290
Chemical kinetics, 161–170, 202, 257, 304, 312
Chimaeric aggregates, 234
Chironomus, 61–71, 96, 127
Chlamydamonas, 33
Cholesterol, 15, 212
Choline esterase, 186, 193, 194
Chromocentres, 61
Chromosomes, 42, 44, 46, 47, 50, 41
axis, 42, 51, 52, 55
and cell division, 290
duplication, 37, 38, 57–59, 307
end-to-end pairing, 67
importance, of 33, 34
lampbrush, 42–57

multi-stranded, 38, 52–59, 115
salivary, xii, 24, 60–86
Cis-trans test, xii, 28, 39, 40
Cistrons, xii, 28–30, 39
Clypeaster, 294
Coccids, 54
Coding problem, 25, 27, 31, 32
Coenzyme A, 153, 157
Colchicine, 282, 287, 290
Collagen, 9, 13, 20, 60, 151
Competence, 203, 210, 217
and genes, 234, 235
Complexity, 5
Conjugation, 232
Contact guidance, 13, 15
Co-operation of loci, 85
Creode, 163, 164, 166
Crepis, 37, 38, 57–59
Crossing over, 22, 52, 53
Cyclopia, 19
Cytochrome oxidase, 157
Cytomembranes, xiv, 118, 119,
Cytoplasmic structures, xiv, 117–134
Cytoplasmic, determinants, xv, 136, 141
transfer, 231, 232
uptake, 100–105, 228

Dictyostelium, 274
Differentiation and size, 273, 274
Digital condensations, xvii, 238, 242,
251, 252
Disaggregated, blastoderms, 249, 250
cells, xvii, 232, 234, 240, 247, 257,
260
DNA, dimensions, 31, 55, 57
diploid amount, 43
duplication, 34, 37, 307
molecular weight, 56
non-chromosomal, 81
overproduction, 80–82, 86
synthesis and cell division, 304, 305
surplus, 81, 86, 141
DNAse, 53, 55
Drosophila 61, 72, 85, 93, 110–117,
124–129

Ears, 234, 235
Electron microscopy, xiv, 7, 11, 33, 42,
52, 59, 63, 70, 98, 103, 110–134,
139, 154, 230, 231, 299
Endoplasmic reticulum, 120, 123, 124

Enucleated cytoplasm, 100–105
and cell division, 290
Enzymes, competition, xvi, 183, 187,
309, 310, 312
number of, 86
Enzyme induction, 158, 176–191, 202,
251, 252, 309, 310
mammals, 177, 185, 186
Ergastoplasm, 110, 113, 115, 116
Evocation, xvii, 18, 20, 202
Evolution, xvi, 17, 163, 164

Feathers, 12, 14
Feed-back, xvi, 17, 64, 117, 172
Femur, 244, 246
Fibres, lateral register, 8, 59
Fish, 12, 280
Fixation for E.M., 122, 123, 287
Freeze drying, 122

Gene, activation of, xiii, 61–86, 137–139
contiguous, xii, 28–30
co-operating, 85,
definition, xi, 23, 24
duplication, 25, 80–83
extended/contracted, 83, 84
inactivation, xiii, 166
size of, 22
splitting of, 30, 40
Gene-string, stability, 23
Genetic maps, 54
Genetic material, length, 45, 52
Genetic mechanisms, 33, 52
Gills, 245, 247
Golgi apparatus, 119, 120, 121, 129
Growth, bacteria, 168, 169, 184, 185,
305, 308, 309, 312, 313
and differentiation, 263–265, 271, 272
equilibrium 279, 280
mass and volume, 311
single cell, 301–312
tissue specific, 170–175

Haemoglobin, 26, 27, 30, 36, 40, 174
Hair, 12
Heart, 147, 150
HeLa cells, 208–210
Heterochromatin, 50, 61, 82, 111, 116
Heterozygous loci, 46, 47, 49, 67, 68, 84
Histogenetic key substances, 164, 199
Hormones in tumours, 277

Hybrids, lethal, 142, 229
Hybrid molecules, 40
Hydroids, 3, 67, 96, 175, 243

Ilyanassa, 290
Incorporation, rate of, 92
Indeterminacy, 5
Individuation, xvii, 18, 202, 218
Induced enzyme synthesis, 158, 176–191, 251, 252, 309, 310
Inducers, 184, 188
  and gradient systems, 227–229
  heterologous, xvii, 18, 203–209, 222
  ribonucleoprotein, 210, 222, 225–227
Induction, embryonic, xvi, 14–16, 188, 194–235
  autoradiography, 221–224, 225, 233
  cartilage, 210, 233, 253, 254
  cell contact, 224, 230, 231, 233
  and enzyme induction, 252
  feathers, 247
  immediate effects, 216
  kidney, 224, 235
  lens, 222, 224, 225, 231
  limb, 231, 246
  membranes, 223, 225, 235
  mesoderm, 217
  neural, 202–235
  phases, 213–217, 219, 220
  regional, xvi, 18, 20, 203–221, 249
  relay mechanism, 226, 234
  and sera, 208
  techniques, 212
  time relations, 214–217, 220, 221, 232
  two inducers, 220
Inhibitors, specific, 172–175
Insulin, 26, 28, 30
Intergenic material, 24

Kaolin particles, 283
Keratin, 188, 278
Keys, in Finland, 209
Kidney, 15, 224, 235
Killer system, 136, 138, 139, 141
Kinetic principles, 168

Lambrush chromosomes, 42–57, 71, 83, 85, 94
  breakage, 47
  elasticity, 49, 70
  size, 45, 49, 50

Leukaemia, 204–209
Limbs, 14, 19, 231, 233, 238–242, 246
  amphibian, 241
  asymmetry, 239, 246
  disaggregated, 240
Linear order, 22, 23, 29

Malpighians, 61–71, 96, 128
Mate-killers, 138–140
Melanin, 194–201
Membranes, porous, 15, 223, 225, 235
Mesoderm, induction, 217
Metabolic antagonists, 166
  sinks, 190, 202
Metaplasia, 188, 199
Microbodies, 131
Microsomal particles, 36, 70, 98, 99, 103, 118, 123, 129, 131–133, 153, 165, 185, 303
Mitochondria, 110, 118, 119, 123, 132, 153, 156, 157, 165, 230, 229
  fusion, 158
  origin, 130, 131, 154, 155
Mitotic apparatus, isolated, 294, 298
  gradients, 153
Modulation, 165
Molecular configurations, 195, 200
Molecular organisations, 8
Muscle cells, 9, 89, 90, 128, 142–152, 164, 194, 198, 199, 201, 256, 278, 289
Mutation, 27, 28, 30, 32, 38, 56, 67, 68
  random, 164
  somatic, 279
Myosin, 60, 142–152, 164, 190, 199, 201
  precursors, 149, 150
Mytilus, xiii
Myxomycetes, 263–274, 300, 308

Nerve fibres, 105–108
Neural crest, 194–201
  induction of, 201, 217
Neurospora, 252
Nuclear differentiation, 65, 88, 228
Nuclear membrane, 70, 89, 110–117, 122, 125
  and ergastoplasm, 125–127
Nuclear movements, 125, 128
  sap, 53, 60, 95
  transplantation, xiii, 166, 228

Nucleo–cytoplasmic transfer, xiii, 102, 110–117, 122
Nucleoli, 69, 89–92, 96–98, 105
    absence of, 97
    extrusion, 128
    isolated, 100
    and microsomal particles, 98, 99
    organiser, 96, 97
Nucleus and cytoplasmic membrane, 142

Oocytes, tracers, 90, 94, 95
Optic bud, 124, 125
Organisation, concept of, 1–6, 17
    induction of, 18, 20
    origin, 3, 7–16
    temporal, 6, 20
Organisers, xvii, 16

Paramecium, xiv, xv, 136–141, 305, 307
Parthenogenetic merogony, 290
PAS reaction, 112, 129
Pattern, origin of, xvii, xviii, 251, 254, 255
    reduction, 242, 243
    size, 19, 243, 244
    somites, 254, 255, 258
    transformation, 254
Penicillinase, 176–191, 309
Periodicity, 3, 6, 163, 258
Phage, 23, 28, 29, 33, 38, 57, 224
Phenylalanine, 194–197
Physarum, 263–274, 300, 308
Pigment cells, 194–201
Pinocytosis, 233, 287
Plasma membrane, 118, 142
Plasmagenes, 136–141, 152
Platycnemis, xv
Polar expansion, 283, 284, 289, 293, 294, 298
Polar lobes, 290
Polydactyly, xvii, 239, 241, 245, 247, 248
Polysaccharides, 25, 112, 129
Position effect, xii
Proteins, active sites, 28
    interconversion 211
    precursors, 99, 149, 150, 189, 190
    structure, 25, 26, 28
Protein synthesis, activation energy, 35
    and cell division, 298–306

embryonic cells, 88–95, 99
    neurones, 105–108
    and RNA, 25, 33, 34, 38, 95, 101, 102, 189, 229
Protoplasts, 312
Puffing, 62–86, 114
Puff, autoradiographs, 77–80, 93
    regression, 76, 80, 83
    secretion, 69

Quinones, 286–288

Recombination, 22, 29, 50
Regeneration, 147, 151, 166, 246, 248, 249
Register, lateral, 59
Reorganisation, time for, 241–243
Reversibility, 165, 169, 182, 187, 188
Rhynchosciara, 62, 63, 72–86
Ribonuclease, 25, 69, 102, 105
Rickettsia, 141
RNA, structure, 35
    templates, 33, 35–37, 40, 81, 189

Salivary chromosomes, xii, 24, 60–86
    autoradiographs, 77–80, 82, 89, 92, 93
    electron microscopy, 113–117
    proteins, 82, 92
    staining, 69, 74, 75
Salivary gland secretion, 66, 83, 112
Scales, 12, 13
Sciara, 61
Sea-urchin eggs, 152–159, 282–314
    gradients, 257, 258
Self-organisation, 8, 9, 13, 19–21, 218, 219, 249, 259, 260
Self-reproducing cycles, 181, 182
Sequence hypothesis, 27
Sequential induction, 179–182, 253
Specificity, wing-leg, xviii, 239, 240, 246, 247
Spisula, 116, 296, 298
Stability of differentiation, 165, 182, 187

Stochastic processes, 2
Strongylocentrotus, 157
Sub-genes, 22–34
Substrates, for cell growth, 15, 259
Sulphydryl and division, 294–297, 299
Switch mechanisms, 84, 252, 269–270

Synchronised divisions, 122, 264, 272, 300, 308, 310
Symbiosis, 141, 142

Teeth, 234, 235
Tetrahymena, 303, 305, 308
Thymus nuclei, 38, 57
Thyroid, 174, 187
Tissue culture, 14, 15, 128, 130, 188, 194–201, 212, 250, 259, 272, 286, 291
Tobacco mosaic virus, 314
Tracers, intracellular movement, 94, 97, 101
Tradescantia, 50
Transduction, 23, 33
Transformation, genetic, 18, 33
   inductive, 213–217, 219, 249
Trichocladius, 65, 66
Tubifex, 123, 124, 286–288, 298

Tubularia, 175
Tumours, autonomy, 275–281
   induction, xviii, 279, 280
   unicellular origin, 280

Uncertainty principle, 5

Vicia, 58
Vitamin A, 186–188, 199

Wingless, 239, 240
Wounds, 10, 11

Xenopus, 89, 174, 222, 241, 242

Yeast, 33, 301, 302, 310, 311
Yolk utilisation, 93, 97, 154

Zymogen granules, 120

Index of Authors

ABBOT, J.   144, 147, 152.
ACTON, A. B.   68, 76.
AFZELIUS, B. A.   116, 122.
AGRELL, I.   153, 158.
ALFERT, M.   45.
ALLFREY, V. G.   38.
ANDRES, J.   13, 204, 234.
ASTBURY, W. T.   31.

BAHR, G. F.   70.
BAIRATI, A.   103.
BAJER, A.   288.
BAKER, R. F.   122.
BALBIANI, E. G.   64, 68, 69, 70, 71.
BALINSKY, B. I.   231, 246.
BALTUS, E.   100.
BALTZER, F.   234.
BARNER, H.   308.
BAUD, C. A.   147.
BAUER, H.   65, 69.
BAYREUTHER, K.   81.
BEALE, G. H.   137, 138.
BEAMS, H. W.   282.
BEERMANN, W.   60, 61, 62, 64, 65, 66, 67, 68, 69, 70, 71, 73, 99, 114.
BENNETT, S.   287, 294.
BENZER, S.   28, 29.
BERENBLUM, I.   276.
BERGER, C. A.   61.
BERNHARD, W.   131, 287.
BERNSTEIN, M.   57.
BIESELE, J. J.   289.
BODDINGIUS, J.   201.
BOELL, E. J.   155, 193, 194.
BONNER, J. T.   274.
BOTERENBROOD, E. C.   203, 244, 259.
BRACHET, J.   69, 77, 94, 95, 100, 101, 123, 142, 222, 225, 226, 227, 229, 230, 294.
BRAHMA, S. K.   222, 223.
BRENNER, S.   299.
BREUER, M. E.   60, 62, 63, 72, 73, 74, 75, 77.

BROWN, G. L.   95.

CAIRNS, J. M.   239.
CALEF, E.   39.
CALLAN, H. G.   42, 70, 83, 95, 115, 122.
CANTI, R. G.   130, 244.
CASPERSSON, T.   69, 116.
CAVANAUGH, M. W.   107.
CHALKLEY, H. W.   286.
CHAMBERS, R.   282, 286, 291.
CHANTRENNE, H.   100.
COHEN, S. S.   308.
COHN, M.   176, 182.
CHUANG, H. H.   203, 204.
CUNNEY, A. H.   185.
COONS, A. H.   142.
CORI, J. T.   211.
CORLETTE, S. L.   76, 79.
CRICK, F. H. C.   27, 32, 37.

DAN, J. C.   283.
DAN, K.   283, 285, 292, 294, 298.
DAVIS, B. D.   267.
DETWILER, S. R.   255.
DEUCHAR, E. M.   255, 258.
DINICHERT, J.   246.

EAKIN, R. M.   155, 230.
EBERLING,   .   187, 188.
EBERT, J. D.   147, 199.
EVANS, T. C.   282.
EWING, J.   275, 279.

FABER, J.   248.
FELDMAN, M.   99, 248, 251.
FELL, H. B.   188, 199, 244, 245, 272.
FICQ, A.   72, 77, 78, 94, 95, 100, 101, 255.
FINCK, H.   145, 147, 151, 152.
FISCHER, F. G.   277.
FLEMMING, W.   61.
FRAENKEL, G.   113.

FREDERICQ, J. 154.
FRIEDRICH-FRESKA, H. 56.

GAILLARD, P. J. 272.
GALL, J. F. 42, 51, 115.
GALLAND, M. 246.
GALLERA, J. 203, 215.
GAMOW, G. 31, 32.
GASSELING, M. T. 239.
GAY, H. 110, 111, 112, 114, 116, 126.
GERARD, P. 108.
GOLDSTEIN, L. 101.
GOTHIE, S. 227.
GRABAR, P. 223.
GRAY, W. D. 264.
GREEN, D. E. 132.
GRIFFITHS, J. S. 32.
GROBSTEIN, C. 15, 16, 224, 235.
GROSS, J. 132.
GROSS, S. R. 252.
GRÜNEBERG, H. 166.
GUSTAFSON, T. 157, 163.
GUYENOT, E. 246.

HADORN, H. 287.
HÄMMERLING, J. 105.
HANNAH, A. 111.
HANSBOROUGH, L. A. 238, 239.
HANSON, J. 144.
HARRISON, R. G. 246.
HARTWIG, H. 227.
DE HARVEN, E. 287.
HARVEY, E. B. 155, 290.
HEISENBERG, W. 5.
HINSHELWOOD, Sir, C. 167, 168, 187, 305.
HIRAMOTO, Y. 282, 283.
HISCOE, H. B. 105.
HOAGLAND, M. B. 36.
HOFFMAN BERLING, H. 288, 291.
HOLTFRETER, J. 203, 204, 232, 257, 260.
HOLTZER, H. 144, 145, 147, 149, 151, 152, 194, 210, 233, 245, 253, 255, 287.
HOLTZER, S. 253.
HORI, K. 201.
HÖRSTADIUS, S. 194, 257, 258.
HSU, T. C. 128.
HUBER, W. 286.
HUGHES, W. L. 58.
HUGHES–SCHRADER, S. 54.
HUGON DE SCOEUX, F. 225.

HULTON, T. 153.
HUNT, J. A. 27.
HUXLEY, H. 144.
HYDEN, H. 105.

IIDA, T. T. 297.
IMMERS, J. 297.
INGRAM, V. M. 27.

JACOB, F. 33, 232.
JACOBSEN, C. F. 211.
JAMES, R. 14, 152, 187.
JONES, R. 199.
JOHNEN, A. G. 214.
JURAND, A. 139.

KACSER, H. 137.
KAUDEWITZ, F. 56.
KAUFMANN, B. P. 114, 115.
KAVANAU, J. L. 170, 172.
KAY, L. M. 247.
KELLENBERGER, E. 132.
KELLENBERGER, G. 132.
KELLER, E. B. 132.
KELLER, P. J. 211.
KENDREW, J. C. 26.
KIMOTO, Y. 127.
KING, J. J. 166.
KING, T. J. 228.
KLEINFELD, R. 45.
KNIGHT, G. R. 92.
KNOX, W. Y. 177.
KONINGSBERGER, V. V. 36.
KOSSWIG, C. 61, 62.
KREBS, H. A. 182.
KUUSI, T. 227.

LACOUR, L. F. 54.
LANDAUER, W. 172, 284.
LANGMAN, J. 224.
LARK, K. G. 308.
LASH, J. 144, 253.
LEAF, G. 95.
LEDERBERG, G. E. M. 185.
LEDERBERG, J. 30, 185, 274.
LEHMANN, F. E. 17, 18, 103, 123, 124, 155, 166, 226, 230, 241, 243, 286, 287, 288.
LENIQUE, P. 174, 175.
LERNER, A. B. 200.
LEVANDER, G. 204.

LIPMANN, F. 36.
LITTLEFIELD, J. W. 132.
LUSCHER, M. 288.

MAALE, O. 308.
MANCUSO, U. 123, 124, 288.
MANGOLD, H. 196.
MARQUARDT, H. 54.
MARSLAND, D. A. 284.
MARTIN-SMITH, C. A. 39.
MARSHALL, J. 142, 145, 147, 151, 152, 287.
McKEEHAN, M. S. 231.
McDONALD, M. R. 114.
McMURRAY, V. 12.
MARUYAMA, Y. 305, 308.
MAZIA, D. 57, 100, 288, 294.
MECHELKE, F. 60, 65, 67.
MELLANBY, E. 199.
MILLER, E. C. 185.
MILLER, J. H. 185.
MIRSKY, A. E. 38.
MITCHELL, P. D. 310.
MITCHISON, J. M. 282, 283, 284, 285, 290, 293, 301, 302, 304, 307, 308, 310, 311.
MONOD, J. 176, 179.
MONROY, A. 282, 290.
MONTALENTI, G. 283, 290.
MOOKERJEE, S. 255.
MORGAN, T. H. 290, 291.
MOSCONA, A. 14, 15, 24, 188, 234, 247.
MOSCONA, H. 24.
MULHERKAR, L. 223.
MULLER, H. J. 22, 54.
MURRAY, P. D. F. 244, 245.

NAKAJIMA, T. 298.
NEEDHAM, J. 226, 287.
NEUMAN, R. E. 199.
NIEUWKOOP, P. D. 18, 201, 203, 213, 215, 216, 217, 225, 230, 243.
NIGTEVECHT, G. v. 213.

OIKAWA, I. 201.
ONO, T. 283, 285.
ORGEL, L. E. 32.
OSAWA, S. 38, 227.
OSTERGREN, G. 54.
OWCZARZAK, . 82.

PAINTER, T. S. 114.
PALADE, G. E. 70, 78, 118, 120, 131, 132.
PANTELOURIS, E. 90, 97, 223.
PARDEE, A. B. 132.
PASSANO, L. M. 301.
PASTEELS, J. 290.
PATAU, K. 82.
PAVAN, C. 60, 62, 63, 72, 73, 74, 75, 77, 114.
PELC, H. 81.
PENNERS, A. 123.
PERRY, M. M. 99.
PIEPHO, H. 227.
PLAUT, W. 52, 57, 97, 101, 102.
POLLOCK, M. R. 176, 177, 188.
PONTECORVO, G. 24, 29, 30, 86.
PORTER, K. R. 120.
POULSON, D. F. 113.
PREER, J. R. 139.
PRESCOTT, D. M. 100, 101.
PUCK, T. T. 211.

RABINOVITCH, M. 36.
RAPKINE, L. 294, 295.
RAPER, K. B. 274.
REBHUN, L. I. 116, 125.
RHODIN, J. 131.
RICHARDS, F. 30.
RICHARDSON, . 186.
RICHTER, G. 101.
RICKENBERG, H. V. 310.
RIS, H. 50, 52, 115.
ROBERTSON, R. 170.
ROSE, S. M. 174, 175.
ROSS, . 274.
ROUILLER, C. 131.
RUDKIN, G. T. 60, 76, 79.
RUDNICK, D. 246.
RUSCH, H. P. 300, 305.
RUTISHAUSER, A. 54.

SALA, M. 201, 217.
SAUNDERS, Jr., J. W. 238.
SAUNDERS, J. W. 239.
SAXEN, L. 204, 220.
SCHACHMAN, H. K. 132.
SCHERBAUM, E. 307, 308.
SCHERBAUM, O. 307, 308.
SCHMALHAUSEN, I. I. 172.
SCHROEDER, W. A. 247.

SCHULTZ, J. 75, 79, 80, 116, 117.
SEIGERS, W. H. 277.
SELBY, D. 245.
SELMAN, G. G. 285, 294.
SENGÜN, A. 61, 62.
SHAVER, J. R. 153, 157, 159.
SHEN, S. C. 193, 194.
SIEGEL, R. W. 138, 139.
SIEKEVITZ, P. 118, 131, 132.
SIRLIN, J. L. 82, 89, 92, 222, 223, 225.
SJÖSTRAND, F. S. 122.
SKREB, . 101.
SLIZYNSKI, B. M. 62.
SMITH, F. G. 144, 155, 156.
SMITH, F. H. 301.
SONNEBORN, T. M. 137, 138.
SONNEBLICK, B. P. 113.
SPEMANN, H. 19, 196.
SPIEGELMAN, S. 157, 183.
SPRATT, Jr., N. T., 233, 251.
STANIER, R. Y. 132, 180.
STARK, P. S. 139.
STICH, H. 102.
STONE, L. S. 188.
STOTZ, E. 156.
SUGIYAMA, M. 283.
SWANN, M. M. 282, 283, 285, 290, 293, 294, 298, 299, 300.
SWIFT, H. 45, 116, 125.
SZARARZ, D. 101.
SZENT-GYORGI, A. G. 149.

TAKATA, A. 227.
TARDENT, P. 175.
TATUM, E. L. 252.
TAYLOR, J. H. 38, 52, 58.
TENCER, R. 227, 229.

TOIVONEN, S. 18, 204, 217, 218, 220, 222, 226, 229.
TOMLIN S. G. 122.
TOWNES, P. L. 257, 260.
TSCHUMI, P. 166, 241, 242.
TURING, A. M. 2, 3.

VANDERHAEGHE, F. 100, 101.
VELICK, S. F. 149.
VOGEL, H. J. 175.

WADDINGTON, C. H. 7, 69, 88, 99, 172, 222, 225, 226, 248, 251, 255, 258, 285, 294.
WAELSCH, H. 108.
WAGNER, G. 234.
WAKONIG, G. 54.
WAKONIG, T. 54.
WALKER, P. M. B. 287, 307, 308.
WATSON, M. L. 110.
WEBER, R. 124, 155, 288, 291.
WEISS, P. 7, 14, 105, 152, 165, 172, 187, 199, 221, 230, 245.
WHITE, F. R. 277.
WILDE, C. E. 188, 194, 196, 244, 245, 247, 250.
WILLIAMS, ROBLEY 55.
WOLLMAN, E. I. 33, 232.
WOOD, P. S. 58.

YAMADA, T. 18, 126, 155, 210, 211, 226, 227, 229.
YANAGITA, F. 283.

ZAMECNIK, P. C. 132.
ZEUTHEN, E. 290, 303, 307, 308.
ZUBAY, G. 57.
ZWILLING, E. 19, 233, 238, 239, 240.